Peter Wadhams

THE GREAT OCEAN OF TRUTH

Memories of "Hudson-70", the first circumnavigation of the Americas

Published by

MELROSE BOOKS

An Imprint of Melrose Press Limited
St Thomas Place, Ely
Cambridgeshire
CB7 4GG, UK
www.melrosebooks.com

FIRST EDITION

Copyright © Peter Wadhams 2009

The Author asserts his moral right to
be identified as the author of this work

Cover designed by Matt Stephens
Colour Photography by: Peter Wadhams
Black and White Photography by Peter Wadhams,
    except figs 1, 2, 9, 26-32 taken by Roger Belanger, Bedford Institute of Oceanography

ISBN 978 1 907040 30 6

FSC
Mixed Sources
Product group from well-managed
forests and other controlled sources
Cert no. SGS-COC-2953
www.fsc.org
© 1996 Forest Stewardship Council

Printed and bound in Great Britain by:
CPI Antony Rowe. Chippenham, Wiltshire

In memory of

PETER REYNELL

I do not know what I may appear to the world, but to myself I seem to have been only like a boy playing on the sea-shore, and diverting myself in now and then finding a smoother pebble or a prettier shell than ordinary, whilst the great ocean of truth lay all undiscovered before me.

Isaac Newton

EXPÉDITION HUDSON 70 EXPEDITION

Resolute
Baffin Bay
Mackenzie R.
Vancouver
Halifax
Tahiti
Rio de Janeiro
Valparaiso
Buenos Aires
Puerto Williams
South Georgia
South Shetland Is.

Direction des sciences de la mer
Ministère de l'Énergie. des Mines et des Ressources

Marine Sciences Branch
Department of Energy, Mines and Resources

CONTENTS

Peter Wadhams

ACKNOWLEDGEMENTS

I AM DEEPLY GRATEFUL to my wife Maria Pia for her loving support over the many years that it took me to write this book and bring it out, and for carefully compiling the index. In Halifax, Nova Scotia, I am grateful to Betty Sutherland for proof-reading and constructive suggestions, to Dr Charles Schafer for contributing Appendix B, and to Bedford Institute of Oceanography for permission to reproduce photographs. Many friends and colleagues have read through versions of the manuscript and contributed ideas, corrections and diary entries; they include Roger Smith (Calgary), Prof Eric Mills (Halifax) and the late Prof Peter Wangersky and Dr Dick Brown (Halifax).

CHAPTER 1

BEING IN ALL RESPECTS
READY FOR SEA

*Whenever I find myself growing grim about the mouth;
whenever it is a damp, drizzly November in my soul; whenever I
find myself involuntarily pausing before coffin warehouses, and
bringing up the rear of every funeral I meet ... then, I account it
high time to get to sea as soon as I can.*

Herman Melville.

A**S I GAZED OUT** of the porthole at the ragged sky the ship gave
another enormous lurch and the porthole went under water. For a
few seconds I could look down into the green depths of the North
Atlantic Ocean, while water oozed out around the poorly sealed rim and ran
down the bulkhead onto the deck. I braced myself for the return roll; when
it came it threw my chair and the contents of my desk across to the corner of
the cabin. The cabin door was wrenched open. It was the watchkeeper.

"Come to batten you down," he said, fastening a steel plate over the
porthole with enormous brass screws.

"Time for your watch."

He was a Nova Scotian and a man of few words.

I staggered up two companionways and emerged on the bridge deck.
Passing the door of the radio shack I heard the shipping news "... and a Liberian
tanker has broken in two off Nantucket. The Coast Guard is at the scene."

After many bruising collisions I reached the geophysical console area,
where I was greeted by the beatific smile of William von Arx, one of the
greatest living oceanographers and a man totally at home in this watery
world.

1

"So how do you like oceanography?" he asked with a grin.

"Fine so far," I replied. And vomited.

The voyage which began so violently was "Hudson-70". It was the last of the great oceanographic exploring expeditions, a tradition which started in 1872 with the voyage around the world by HMS *Challenger*. "Hudson-70" lasted one year, and during that time the ship accomplished the first circumnavigation of the Americas, testing her hull against the pack ice of both the Antarctic and the Arctic. I was immensely privileged to be able to sail on the entire voyage. As a lowly scientific assistant I was able to see, and take part in, every aspect of the ship's work, and it was the most wonderful introduction to the science of oceanography and the excitement of visiting the world's distant corners. With this book I hope to share some of the experiences and tell the story of "Hudson-70" from the viewpoint of a young recruit to marine science. If it encourages other young people to take up oceanography, so much the better. It is a wonderful way to spend your life as a scientist.

Opportunities which change your life usually occur by accident, and "Hudson-70" was no exception. In the spring of 1969 I was finishing my degree in physics at Cambridge University and feeling very reluctant to spend the rest of my life in a dusty laboratory. The Cavendish Laboratory, which was still in the Victorian buildings once used by Maxwell and Rutherford, seemed to me to be a dispiriting place to spend my career. I had an adventurous streak and a desire to go to sea, probably inherited from a family tradition of seafaring. One day I went to a lecture by Sir Edward Bullard, a fabled Cambridge figure who had been one of Rutherford's students in the 1930s and who had then built up the Department of Geodesy and Geophysics as a major world centre for the study of the Earth and the forces which have shaped it. His lecture was on seafloor spreading, a theory proposed decades before by Alfred Wegener but only now being accepted as a result of work done at sea. It showed how the continents must have originally formed a single mass 'floating' in the oceanic crust, which had then broken up and separated, driven by immense forces of convection deep in the earth. Bullard began his lecture by reminiscing.

"When I was a research student, Rutherford came up to me one day and said, 'Teddy, it's time you got an honest job!'"

The honest job was to survey India. Sure of his grip on the audience,

Bullard unfolded the fascinating evidence which had caused the new theory of the Earth to be accepted. What is driving the continents apart is the upwelling and sideways spreading of molten rock from the interior of the Earth along the mid-ocean ridges, great underwater mountain chains which run along the centre of every ocean. As the rock solidified it took on the local magnetisation, and as the Earth's magnetic field reverses from time to time this produces strips of rock magnetised in different directions, like a magnetic tape recording which tells us how fast the continents are moving apart. And all this incredibly exciting scientific work, which had revolutionised our view of the earth, was being carried out from ships at sea. This was more like it!

I went to see Bullard and told him of my interest in doing marine research. I asked if he could take me as a research student. Bullard had a reputation for direct speaking.

"Well, we might be able to. But how do you know you'll enjoy the sea? Besides, there are many branches of marine science. There's marine geophysics, which we do here. Then there's physical oceanography, where you look at currents and waves, and marine chemistry and marine biology. Why don't you get a summer job in a marine lab first and see how you like it? Here's a place that takes summer students." He passed me a name and address.

I felt sure that I would enjoy the sea. Both of my grandfathers had been engineers with the Atlantic Transport Line, a company that once ran passenger ships from Tilbury to New York, and my surviving grandfather had captivated my four-year-old mind by reeling off sea stories and shanties as I perched by his sickbed. I had grown up beside the Thames at Grays, on the Essex marshes, and the drabness of the town threw into sharp relief the beauty of the great white P & O liners that sailed from nearby Tilbury to the ports of the Far East. As a child I used to enjoy wandering round Tilbury Docks, sniffing the heady aroma of fresh timber, spices and oily water and gawping at the rust-streaked freighters registered in romantic ports like Takoradi, Lagos, Bombay and Rangoon. As a schoolboy I would spend hours by the river with a telescope and notebook and an equally keen friend, logging the names of all the ships that passed.

I wrote off straight away to the person named by Bullard, Dr Bosco Loncarevic of the Bedford Institute of Oceanography, the Canadian government's largest oceanographic laboratory, in Dartmouth, Nova Scotia. Then I had to forget the ocean and settle down to study for my examinations.

One day in May a letter arrived from Loncarevic. There were no summer jobs. But he enquired diffidently whether I would be interested in spending a whole year at sea as a scientific assistant on a major oceanographic expedition called "Hudson-70". By chance my letter had arrived on his desk at a time when he had a problem. The expedition needed an assistant, preferably of as low a grade as possible, who would remain on board through the entire voyage to ensure that record keeping and procedures were maintained in the same systematic way for each of the legs. But none of the employees at the Institute wanted to spend a year at sea, as they were all married or otherwise committed. They must be crazy, I thought. The ship would sail in November and the route read like an escapist's dream: Rio de Janeiro, Buenos Aires, Cape Horn, Antarctica, Chile, the Pacific and the Northwest Passage. The ship would accomplish the first circumnavigation of the Americas. Would I be prepared to go? the letter asked gravely. Yes! Yes! I screamed, leaping around the room like a kangaroo. The letter didn't mention a salary. I didn't care. Please take me!

The Institute agreed and even offered a salary and the grand-sounding title of 'Assistant to the Senior Scientist'. From then on nothing else was in my thoughts. After much wearisome paperwork I set off from Grays station on September 8 with two brand-new airline suitcases clasped in my hands and a ticket for Halifax, Nova Scotia. My father saw me off and handed me a farewell present, a watch.

"I may not be here when you get back, matey," he said gravely.

I suddenly realised the depths of my own selfishness and that this adventure, which was so exciting for me, meant something different to my parents. My father, whom I loved dearly, was a sick man who had had more than one heart attack. I was an only child. There was a real chance that we would never meet again. He had done everything to encourage me to follow my dreams, and had been as thrilled as I was by this opportunity. Tears welled into my eyes as the train pulled away and I waved farewell to the prematurely grey figure on the platform.

The Air Canada DC-8 bumped down through several thousand feet of solid cloud, and finally emerged over a most unappealing landscape of dark green fir forest. "Welcome to Canada" said the air hostess, who travelled into town in the same taxi. It was my first visit to North America and it was a cultural shock. We passed through miles of rain-soaked scrubby forest interspersed with lakes. The emptiness was overwhelming, the only sign of human habitation being the occasional clapboard cottage by a lake shore. Finally we reached Dartmouth, and entered a half-world of wooden houses, undeveloped lots, pavements of churned mud and an overhead thicket of telephone and power lines. Through this shattered landscape meandered cars as big as tanks, bouncing wildly on their soft springing. I was deposited at the Holiday Inn, where the Bedford Institute had booked me a room, and settled down to watch the pelting rain and the cars stream across the Angus L. Macdonald Bridge from the city of Halifax on the other side of the harbour. I felt very homesick.

Next morning I took a taxi out to the Bedford Institute, a large blue building on a promontory overlooking the Narrows. This is a passage of water that separates Dartmouth from its parent city of Halifax; it opens at its landward end into the large circular Bedford Basin, an assembly area for wartime convoys, and at its seaward end into Halifax Harbour itself. The rain had slackened to a drizzle and a thick morning sea mist had rolled up the Narrows from the Atlantic. As the taxi pulled into the Institute grounds I caught a glimpse of a white ship lying at the pier.

"Is that the *Hudson*?" I asked.

"Yeah, that's her. Jinx ship. That'll be two dollars."

Swathed in the silent mist she seemed like a ghost ship. Her lines were those of a yacht at first glance, but then her high flared bows and full hull showed that she was built to deal with the stern seas of the North Atlantic.

At the Institute I was greeted by the genial Dr Charlie Maunsell, who rapidly introduced me to the members of the Physical Oceanography Group, in which it had been decided I would work. He found me a desk and took me down to the personnel section where I was given a Social Insurance number. Later that day he found time to tell me about the Institute and the history of the "Hudson-70" expedition.

The Bedford Institute of Oceanography (BIO), of which the largest part was known as the Atlantic Oceanographic Laboratory (AOL), was founded in 1960 by the Canadian government to investigate the waters of the North Atlantic and Baffin Bay. Ships of the Institute had already worked in the Arctic seas of Canada, the Denmark Strait between Greenland and Iceland, the North Atlantic out to the mid-Atlantic Ridge, and the warmer waters of the Gulf Stream and the Caribbean. Now they were extending their horizons. Dr Cedric (Ced) Mann, head of the Physical Oceanography Group, had mooted the idea that it would be worthwhile to investigate the great eastward flow of water through the Drake Passage, that constricted strait of mountainous seas that lies between Cape Horn and the Antarctic Peninsula.

The way that this single idea evolved into a one-year circumnavigation plan was told to me later by Dr William (Bill) Ford, the Director of the Institute.

It happened in February 1967 aboard *Hudson* while she was stormbound off the east coast of Greenland. Ced Mann, Bill Ford and the ship's captain were wedged together in the bar. Mann brought out his Drake Passage idea; the Captain topped this by saying that he would like to take *Hudson* through the Northwest Passage. Ford already knew that the marine geophysicists at BIO wanted to work off the Queen Charlotte Islands on the Pacific coast of Canada, where there was thought to be a 'triple point', a place where three of the moving plates which make up the Earth's crust come together. He also knew that there was a need to study the unknown Beaufort Sea in the western Arctic, which was believed to have offshore oil potential. The Beaufort Sea is accessible from the west, round the north of Alaska, early in the summer, while the Northwest Passage is not open until later in the season. Finally, Ford also knew that the fjord oceanographers of the University of British Columbia would love to be able to study the unknown fjords of Chile and compare them with their own waters. Why not combine all of these ideas in one gigantic expedition? Drake Passage – Chilean fjords – Queen Charlotte Islands – Beaufort Sea – Northwest Passage, following the summer around the Americas. It all made sense, as do so many things in the bar of the *Hudson*.

Back in BIO, to their surprise, the idea continued to make sense. The great oceanographer William von Arx of Woods Hole Oceanographic Institution in Massachusetts pointed out how valuable it would be to do a long northward transit of the Pacific recording the gravity and magnetic fields, to serve as a calibration line for an oceanographic satellite due to be launched a few years hence. Firm plans were in place by the autumn of 1968. *Hudson* would take a year to circumnavigate the Americas, working in the southern hemisphere from December to April and then reaching the Arctic for August and September. This would be the greatest single effort that Canada had ever made in oceanography, and the longest oceanographic expedition of modern times.

The cost of the expedition, however, outstripped the resources of BIO. The shortfall was modest by today's standards: a mere $25,000 for extra fuel. Ford had to take the proposal to the Federal Government, in fact to Joe Greene, Minister of Energy, Mines and Resources. Greene had just rejected proposals for a telescope and a linear accelerator, each of which would have cost $100 million, and found the *Hudson* project an attractive and cheap alternative to support. He was due to announce approval for the project in the House of Commons in November 1968, but suffered a heart attack the day before. Planning for "Hudson-70" had to stop until he recovered. The vital speech was made in February 1969 and received enthusiastic support from the opposition parties as being 'the sort of thing that Canada should be doing in the world'. The voyage could proceed.

I soon moved from the expensive Holiday Inn and lodged with a Miss Claire Otto, a wonderful old lady who had been a nurse all her life. She remembered the great Halifax Explosion of December 1917, when a munitions ship blew up in the Narrows, killing 3,000 people and destroying much of Halifax. She called me 'her English boy' and had an endearing habit of referring to England as 'the mother country', something which probably no Canadian would do today. I gradually became more at home in a city which at first seemed strange and raw. I missed the gentle countryside of England and the pubs which were so different from the rugged bars of Halifax. On the other hand I developed a lust for hamburgers, fried chicken and coleslaw, Dairy Queen milk shakes and similar fast-food items which had not then crossed the Atlantic. Halifax's main landmark was Citadel Hill, which had been originally fortified by Governor Edward Cornwallis at the time of the first settlement in 1749 as a bastion against the French and Mi'kmaq Indians. Tradition says that the settlers refused to help with the work, which had to be done by the troops of the garrison. The current Citadel, built in 1856, is now dwarfed by new buildings and Halifax has turned into one of Canada's most attractive cities.

At BIO I plunged into learning as much as I could in a short time. I started with the gravity meter and magnetometer which would be our main geophysical sensing tools at sea. The magnetometer is a towed instrument that measures small changes in the intensity of the Earth's magnetic field, while the gravimeter measures small gravity changes by detecting its varying force on a heavy beam restrained by sensitive springs. I learned to program and run the PDP-8 computer that *Hudson* carried to process data on board ship. This was an advanced item to have aboard an oceanographic ship, but of course by modern standards it was pathetic: it took up half a rack, had lots of switches and flashing lights, was programmed from a teletype console and a paper tape reader, and boasted a mere 8K of memory. The little laptop computer on which I am writing this has several million times as much capacity. I was also appointed Expedition Photographer and was given rapid instruction on four cameras, including a 16 mm Bolex movie camera, that I was to operate. Finally, and most exciting, I was sent down to Washington for a course on the US Navy's new Omega navigation system, which we would be carrying as an experiment and which again I was meant to operate. This was designed to give a position fix by comparing the phases of very low frequency radio signals from a number of transmitting stations distributed over the globe.

My companion on the Washington excursion was Roy Gould, a plump jolly Englishman who was Navigator of *Hudson*. He treated the whole business with great relish. We arrived in Washington to find ourselves in the midst of the October Moratorium, a huge protest against the Vietnam War. We made our way to the Commonwealth Building, one of a set of high-rise blocks that were sprouting in the formerly quiet suburb of Arlington, Virginia, to accommodate an overflow of the military from the Pentagon. The first 18 floors of the building were occupied by design offices for the Safeguard Anti-Ballistic Missile, a short-lived project that was soon cancelled after an agreement between the US and Russia that neither side should be allowed to defend itself. Right at the top of the building was the Omega Project Office. Our first morning's work consisted of lectures on the operation of the system. The lecturer, who was also one of the designers of the system, explained sadly that only four of the eight necessary transmitting stations had been built, because of political difficulties with the host countries. This would restrict Omega coverage to the Northern Hemisphere for the time being, which would make it useless for "Hudson-70". Today, in the era of the Global Positioning System, Omega is obsolete of course.

Our lecturer took us for lunch to the Army and Navy Country Club, whose luxurious buildings were set in vast grounds outside the city. Electric golf carts whined past laden with overweight admirals, while in the bar ribbon-decked generals sipped martinis and legions of black flunkeys flitted from table to table. Alcohol-clouded eyes gazed suspiciously as we mere civilians entered and started to sink martinis. Our host was a leader of the project and entertained us royally, with the result that the afternoon session vanished into an alcoholic haze. That evening I saw another side of America when I went to a rally on Constitution Hill where 100,000 people listened to Coretta King, Martin Luther's widow, as she denounced the Vietnam War. The crowd then marched in silent candlelit procession round the White House, where Richard Nixon was watching TV.

During our visit to Washington Roy and I were officially entertained by the Canadian Defence Liaison Officer, who wore a perpetually worried face.

He lived in the elite suburb of Georgetown, but had recently been mugged in a novel way. He was walking along his street when he was brought to the ground by a pair of well-thrown bolas (the weighted ropes that gauchos use to lasso cattle), which wrapped themselves round his legs. A hand was thrust into his pocket and his wallet disappeared. He advised me not to walk the streets alone at night, especially near the Capitol where some of the worst streets were to be found. I had no trouble, but did find the atmosphere of violence in Washington disturbing. At FBI Headquarters an agent demonstrated to me and a crowd of young children how to empty a sub-machine gun into a target at thirty paces. At the Smithsonian Museum I was interested to see a crowd of clergymen photographing each other against a mock-up of an Atlas ICBM. I really could see a difference between the fabric of life in Canada and in the gun-toting USA, which at first seem so alike.

Back in peaceful Nova Scotia the leaves were turning red and gold and the time drew near for sailing. On November 3 the *Hudson* was sent out on a 'shakedown cruise' to test her equipment and engines. I persuaded a reluctant Ced Mann to let me sail with her so as to find out a little more about my future home.

"You'll find out soon enough when the expedition starts," he observed in tones of deep foreboding.

The *Hudson* was in a state of confusion on the grey morning that I slipped aboard, with technicians tearing out wiring, and engineers rushing around below with pieces of engine. I dumped my gear in a helicopter pilot's cabin near the stern and went on deck as we cast off and sailed out past the ragged skyline of Halifax. Once out of the shelter of the harbour we ran head-on into a mountainous swell. Bracing my feet against the angle of the deck I gazed out across the chaos of sea and sky and felt a fierce joy – a strange stirring of long-buried instincts. This is my element and I have found you at last, I realised thankfully.

The homely feeling soon passed as we turned beam-on to the sea and began shipping green water along the weather deck, while sheets of spray were thrown up by the bow and whipped back along the decks by the wind. The ship took on an alarming roll. She was screwing herself up to full speed to run a measured mile and there was not enough fuel aboard to fill her anti-roll tanks. I prudently withdrew below and tried to make myself inconspicuous, but I was soon trapped by Ted Corbett of the Marine Geophysics Group, who, with a friendly grin, enquired as to my availability for work. I started to help him with running up the gravity meter (gravimeter for short), which was to be calibrated on the BIO gravity range, a stretch of sea just off the edge of the continental shelf where the earth's gravity had been accurately surveyed. The meter is a barrel-shaped object which rolled drunkenly around on a gyroscopic platform in a tiny compartment deep inside the ship. My queasiness got worse, and when Ced came down to assign me to the next watch on the geophysical instruments he also suggested that I got some rest. I retired to my cabin, from which I was later dragged so mercilessly by the seaman.

Having greeted von Arx, the world's greatest oceanographer, with the visible evidence of my sickness, I settled to my watch in the console room. The bank of equipment that met my bleary gaze was known as the 'Cathedral', because its semicircular shape and multiplicity of knobs and switches gave it a distinct resemblance to a cathedral organ. The watchkeeper-cum-organist was enthroned in a rally seat taken out of a Volvo car. To his left was the gravimeter recorder, which charted the reading from the gravimeter down below and also the output of a set of accelerometers which gave the cross-coupling error, the level of uncertainty in the gravity reading due to the motion of the ship. In front of him was a precision echo sounder recorder measuring ocean depth, and hanging from the deckhead were a gyro repeater, giving the ship's course, and two logs to show the vessel's speed. One was an electromagnetic log, which measures the water flow across a small coil, and the other was a 'Sal' log, which measures the water pressure in a tube that is open at one end. On his right was the recorder for the magnetometer, while behind him in long cabinets were the ship's general purpose computer, a satellite navigation receiver, and a paper tape system to record all the data being displayed on the gravimeter and magnetometer charts. This set of equipment made the *Hudson* one of the most advanced oceanographic ships afloat, because even during transits from port to her operating area she could record vital geophysical data in a state-of-the-art way.

Bill von Arx had only one instrument to tend, his brainchild. It was a very simple but accurate vibrating string gravimeter, based on the principle of a weight on the end of a string. As gravity changes, the tension in the string changes and the string vibrates with a slightly different frequency or 'note'. Bill planned to use this on the Pacific leg of "Hudson-70", and this was his chance to test it against the ship's gravimeter and the gravity range. We spent the watch in pleasant conversation about gravity, and then I retired to my bunk, wedged myself in and tried to sleep.

Next day a particularly heavy sea sent the ship over at an angle of 35°, an unofficial record. Once again I was thrown across my cabin, while in the lounge an armchair, normally bolted to the deck, was wrenched free and thrown across the room with its occupant still in it. Terrible sounds of smashing crockery came from below. We were on the edge of the gravity range, some 200 miles out from Halifax, but we were forced to heave-to. Here we sat for three miserable days riding out the gale. I had to keep night watches in the console room, but at least during the day had a chance to explore the ship. Let me explain her layout.

My new home, the CSS (Canadian Scientific Ship) *Hudson*, was then one of the largest and best-equipped oceanographic ships afloat. She is still a valuable vessel today, and still looks smart and graceful at the age of 46, despite having been transferred to the Coast Guard and painted red. She was one of the few vessels designed to operate as effectively in the Arctic as in the Tropics. Below the waterline her hull is cut away in the classic icebreaker shape that enables her to ride up over ice floes and smash through using her full weight. Built in 1963 she displaces 4,660 tons and is 294 feet long with a beam of 50 feet. Before "Hudson-70" she had been employed only in the North Atlantic, Eastern Arctic and Caribbean, and this cruise would be her first into really distant waters.

A quick tour of the ship begins right down at the bottom, just above the bilges. Here are the ship's workshops and storerooms, a laundry, a large forward hold, and the engine room. Four diesels, each of 16 cylinders and producing 8,400 horsepower altogether, drive the ship via four 1,500 kilowatt generators. The control of the engines is highly automated. When I first visited the engine room the Chief Engineer waved at the bank of control instrumentation and exclaimed:

"It shouldn't need all this bloody electronics to drive this pisspot through the water!"

The next deck up is the main deck. Two alleyways run the length of the ship on this deck, with rows of cabins opening on their outboard sides. The seamen's and stewards' cabins were right for'ard, with the sheer of the bow turning their outer bulkheads into sloping wedges. Amidships lived engineers and mechanics, while further aft were technicians and the most junior scientists, including myself. The centreline space between the alleyways contained (moving aft from the bows) the crew's mess, the galley, the gravimeter room, the upper part of the engine room; various toilets (or 'heads'), and a large laboratory for geochemical analysis. Class distinction was the rule in the heads. There was a separate head for each category of person: technicians, engineers, petty officers, seamen, officers and hydrographers. This made life very complicated. Each head had a shower, as the ship's sea water evaporators provided ample fresh water (except when they broke down). On the starboard side near the stern was the Core Store, fitted with long racks to receive the tubes of sediment from the seabed that we planned to obtain with our corer, a long pipe that can be driven by a heavy weight into the ocean bottom. This room was maintained at 40°F to preserve the cores, and was also used to preserve the expedition's beer supply. Right aft is the 'machinery space', a complex set of hydraulics and gearwheels that convert the orders of the ship's wheel into rudder movements.

We go up one more deck and come to the weather deck. The open foredeck is a clutter of anchor chain, winches and cranes, often swept by spray, so we duck into the superstructure. Here there were cosy but very small cabins for more senior scientists, boasting imitation wood panelling and having a real window instead of a porthole. Two of the cabins, intended for the rare occasions when the ship carried women scientists, had private showers. Today, when women scientists go routinely to sea, these arrangements seem impossibly quaint. The Chief Scientist's suite was on this deck, and also the Officers' Mess and pantry, a library doubling as a coffee room, and a chemistry laboratory for'ard. Aft on this deck were a sick bay and the after laboratory, a 'wet lab' from which the low poop was directly accessible for operations over the side.

The next deck up is the boat deck. Besides the two lifeboats and two survey launches, it contains cabins for the navigating officers, the ship's office and, right aft, a helicopter hangar and flight pad. We would be carrying a helicopter in the Arctic for ice reconnaissance. On the starboard side was a small compartment called 'The Chains' and containing two heavy winches from which oceanographic casts were carried out. Stretching the full width of this deck at its for'ard end was the officers' and scientists' lounge and bar. This boasted armchairs with flowery covers, a thick-pile carpet and a luxurious bar, thickly padded to avoid injury to serious drinkers in heavy seas. Liquor was available on an honour basis, with tickets costing 15 cents for a beer and 25 cents for hard liquor. This room was destined to become our home from home, our pub, club and common room rolled into one.

Right at the top of the ship is the bridge deck, the brain of the ship from which all of her actions are controlled. Most important is the wheelhouse itself, carrying radar displays with ranges of up to 48 miles and two remote control panels for the ship's engines as well as the traditional wheel and telegraphs. A flying bridge with a beautiful teak rail (later removed, including the teak) ran the whole width of the ship in front of the wheelhouse, giving the officer of the watch a clear view of activities on the foredeck as well as the whole length of the ship's sides. Aft of the wheelhouse was a small chartroom, then the radio shack, a separate scientific chartroom for planning operations, and an electronics workshop. Behind this was a spacious, airy room containing three large plotting tables, intended for use in hydrographic surveying. Finally, behind this was the console room, my place of suffering on the shakedown cruise.

After three days there was still no sign of a let-up in the weather, so it was decided that we would put back to Halifax since there was still so much work to do on the ship. We had been well and truly 'shaken down'.

The final two weeks of preparation were chaotic. Vital equipment arrived at the quayside until the day before sailing – when a computer turned up – and the ship was always full of swearing, panic-stricken figures. I was making my own preparations. To avoid possible boredom at sea I bought a steel-stringed guitar for nautical sing-songs and a selection of heavy literary works. I drew a foul-weather seakit of parka, oilskins and seaboots from the Institute's stores and took charge of the official camera equipment and a vast stock of film which went into the Core Store to protect it from fungus in the Tropics. A week before sailing, my passport and vaccination certificate disappeared on the way back from having a visa made out in Montreal. The British High Commission in Ottawa sent me an emergency passport which arrived the day before sailing, and I had to have all my vaccinations repeated in a single painful session at the Halifax Seamen's Clinic.

Meanwhile, on November 10, Captain Butler had received his sailing instructions from the Operations Officer at Bedford Institute of Oceanography. They were couched in the standard terminology of BIO, and began with the preamble:-

> *Being in all respects ready for sea and with the survey or research party embarked, you are to depart A.O.L. at 1530 hours on November 19, 1969, to carry out the cruise as requested by the Chief of Party Onboard.*

With this uninspiring official document the adventure began.

The day of sailing was cold and rainy, and the first snow dusted the hills behind Halifax. I bade farewell to Miss Otto and carried my cases, guitar and umbrella aboard the ship; the umbrella caused much ribaldry amongst the Newfoundland crew who considered it both landlubberish and unlucky. I opened the boxes of BIO camera equipment, loaded the Bolex movie camera, the Nikon F 35 mm reflex, the Yashica twin-lens reflex and the Instamatic (the only one about which I was confident) and emerged on deck to film our departure.

A dais had been set up on the Institute pier around which a large crowd of friends, wives, mistresses and colleagues had gathered, braving the weather. Joe Greene, the Minister, was expected at any moment, but in the mean time a Mr. Kenneth Grant, in full Highland dress, marched up and down the quay playing a lament on the pipes with the wind whistling up his kilt. It was a fitting Nova Scotian farewell. At length Greene swept up in a motorcade and made an inspiring speech that was mostly lost to the wind. He was followed by Bill Ford, Captain Butler of the *Hudson*, and Ced Mann, all of whom were equally inaudible. The crowd cheered enthusiastically. The last loved ones were escorted ashore and at 3.24 p.m. the lines were cast off by a crew in immaculate uniforms.

At the next berth lay the *Acadia*, a veteran coal-burning hydrographic ship, retired after 56 years of service and scheduled to be turned into a museum. Painfully she raised steam for the last time in her life and gave us an asthmatic whistle as we sailed past, a tribute from the old to the new age of ocean research. To a fading chorus of cheers and shouts, and the last notes of the pipes, we began a stately progress down the harbour and under the Angus L. Macdonald Bridge. We released sonorous blasts at frequent intervals but were steadily ignored by other shipping, except for the Halifax-Dartmouth ferry which hooted frantically as we crossed her bows. The city of Halifax slipped past and away.

"Hudson-70" was under way.

CHAPTER 2

SAILING DOWN TO RIO

Farewell to Nova Scotia, you sea bound coast,
Let your mountains dark and dreary be;
For when I'm far away on the briny ocean toss'd
Will you ever leave a sigh and a wish for me?

Nova Scotian folk song.

AS THE WOODED COAST of Nova Scotia was swallowed up in the misty gloom I went below and began to stow my gear. For the first time I was able to take stock of the small cubicle that was to be my home for the next eleven months. My cabin, normally occupied by the Decca technicians, was on the port side towards the stern. By an accident of the ship's hull form it came out at roughly eight feet square, making it larger than most others on this deck. The inboard wall (or rather bulkhead, as it is known at sea) was occupied by two bunks, with curtains to allow a little privacy. The rest of the furniture was built into the ship's side: a closet, a chest of four drawers, and a desk top with a lip to prevent (usually unsuccessfully) papers from being ejected onto the deck in a heavy sea. Two large drawers under the bottom bunk completed the storage space, which I succeeded in totally filling with my gear. I knew that my isolation could not last, and I anticipated conditions of extreme overcrowding when I gained a cabin mate, expectations that were to be amply fulfilled. There was a chair for the desk and a washbasin with real hot and cold running water, of the colour and consistency of Brown Windsor Soup on account of rust in the fresh water tanks. The easy chair and scrap of carpet that should have completed this luxurious décor had both been spirited away. The bulkheads were covered with plastic sheeting of a hospital green colour. Ventilation came from a forced draught in the deckhead, supplemented by a small fan, and lighting from the single porthole with its strong brass frame and deadlight for battening down in gales.

The ship was already beginning to roll as she became exposed to the full force of the North Atlantic, and the grey tops of waves periodically slopped across the glass. I levered myself up to gaze across the heaving expanse and bravely decided that everyone should try to follow his dreams; the man who lets himself slip into a boring and monotonous life is letting his soul die by slow stages.

It was now time for dinner, an early meal which was taken between 4:30 and 5:30 p.m. Officers and scientists ate in the Officers' Mess which, unlike the more spartan Crew's Mess down below, boasted tablecloths and plastic imitation leather chairs. The tables were, of course, bolted to the deck and the chairs chained down. The Captain's table was a large ellipse at one end of which presided Captain David Butler, a quiet English emigrant whose previous command had been a research ship on the Great Lakes. On the Old Man's right sat the Chief Mate, Fred Mauger, a Nova Scotian who had spent most of his life on cable ships; his son Don was also aboard as a seaman. On the Old Man's left sat Sam Lambert, the Chief Engineer. Sam was a hard-drinking character, part Huron Indian, who displayed a highly-developed cynical sense of humour when in his cups. Opposite the Captain sat the Chief Scientist flanked by his top scientific minions. The smaller fry distributed themselves amongst the other tables. Every officer had an assigned seat, the scientists taking up the seats that were left. Thus if a group of us went down to dinner together we would often have to spread out amongst several otherwise empty tables. Food came up by dumb waiter from the galley to the pantry and was distributed by stewards. In these early days we were expected to wear a collar and tie, though this was quietly forgotten as soon as we reached warmer climes, and many people took to carrying a knotted tie around in their pockets at all times. During a previous voyage, I was told, a somewhat absent-minded Chief Scientist forgot that he was already wearing a tie and proceeded to slip on a second one at the dinner table.

Everyone was up for the first meal and so I was able to meet some of the inhabitants of this new little world. Some of the scientists I knew already from the Institute: Ced, of course; his stalwart assistant Bruce Carson who did the heavy work of oceanographic sampling; Ted Corbett, a genial veteran of the U.S. Navy who was now in charge of nursing the gravimeter; Al Grant, the computer programmer; and Jan Piechura, a young Pole from the Gdynia Ocean Institute who was spending a postdoctoral year in Canada.

Also from the Institute was Iver Duedall, who would be in charge of the sea water chemistry work all the way to Vancouver. As assistants on this leg he had Bob Cook and Larry Atkinson, two research students from Dalhousie University in Halifax. Professor Watt of Dalhousie was aboard with his Korean research student Chung I Choi; they would be studying phytoplankton (the microscopic plants that drift with the ocean currents) and the way in which they take up the energy of sunlight to produce food.

I found myself sharing a corner table with a large mass that radiated raw good health. This was George Gill of the Defence Research Establishment Atlantic in Dartmouth. As he insisted on telling everyone, he came from Musquodoboit Harbour, which I gathered was a small fishing village near Halifax. Beside him sat Orest Bluy, his boss and a Ukrainian by origin. These two would be setting off charges in the sea and studying the reflection of the sound from fish and plankton. Two others who sat at our table were Dick Beamish, a young biologist who would be collecting deep-sea fish specimens for the Royal Ontario Museum; and Roger Smith, a geology student from Queen's University at Kingston, Ontario, who had taken time off from his studies to sail as a general dogsbody like myself so as to take bottom sediment samples for his professor. Then there was Pete Beamish, a wild and intensely keen whale researcher, who was hoping to record the sounds that whales make underwater.

Among the officers, the rotund Roy Gould I knew already; and on the shakedown cruise I had also met Pete Reynell, the young English Third Mate, with whom I formed an immediate friendship. Finally there was Lew Rustige, the ship's Doctor, a most unusual person. Born in the Dutch West Indies, his life story is obscure, for he presented a differently embroidered version of it on every occasion. He claimed to have been a Dutch Resistance fighter, a tank driver, a frogman and a commando, though by our calculations he was only 18 when the war ended. In his cabin he kept a frightening array of guns, a sign of a bloodlust that was somewhat disconcerting in a doctor. He also had a large Doberman Pinscher dog called Mark, who was highly intelligent but unnaturally docile and cowed. The dog annoyed the stewards intensely by relieving himself from time to time on the lounge carpet.

Assuming that the rough weather on the shakedown cruise had given me my sea legs I ate a hearty dinner, after which we all repaired to the lounge for drinks. As I relaxed in an armchair, choking on a can of Oland's Schooner beer, Ced Mann came towards me with a gleam in his eye and I knew that this meant work. For the first eleven days at sea we would be steaming steadily for a distant point in the ocean – the Equator at 30°W – where we would start our serious oceanographic work. On the way we would be monitoring the ocean bottom profile and the earth's gravity and magnetic fields. A round-the-clock rota of watchkeepers was required to man the instruments, and Ted Corbett, Jan Piechura and I were the first victims. We tossed for watches and I came off with the 4-8, so I retired early to my bunk. Wedging myself in, I was soon lulled asleep by the steady throbbing of the engines.

I was rudely shaken awake by Jan at 3:30 a.m. The ship was now rolling heavily in a full gale, and nausea quickly set in as I made my way up to the console room, colliding with every possible obstacle on the way. I relieved a white-faced Jan and settled at the Cathedral to begin my watch. Once again I faced the bewildering array of instruments. My task was to love and to cherish them, and to mark and change the tapes and charts when necessary, a monotonous task requiring constant vigilance.

The most important recorder was that of the gravimeter. To measure accurately the small local variations in the earth's field the meter must be sensitive to changes of one part in a million in gravitational force, and care-ful precautions are necessary to achieve this. Firstly the sensitive beam of the meter itself (made by the German firm of Askania-Graf) is mounted inside a barrel-shaped jacket within which the temperature is kept constant, in order to avoid expansion of any of the components. This barrel is then mounted on a 'gyrotable', a heavy stabilised platform which keeps itself absolutely horizontal whatever the motion of the ship. To do this it uses a set of electrically-maintained gyroscopes, which detect any slight deviation from the horizontal and send commands to servo-motors on the table's supporting yoke which in turn restore the platform to its proper orientation. To help the gyrotable in its task the system is set up as near as possible to the ship's centre of gravity in a little room on the main deck; the output from the meter is fed from there to the chart recorder in the Cathedral, and to a paper tape punch in a cabinet beside me.

Gravity is measured in gals (named after Galileo); one gal is equal to an acceleration of one centimetre per second, and falling bodies at the earth's surface have an acceleration that varies from 981 gals at the Poles to 978 gals at the Equator. This variation is caused by centrifugal force, strongest at the Equator, which compensates for gravity by trying to throw you off the earth's surface. Knowing the strength of this force, and taking into account the slight flattening of the earth at the Poles, it is possible to calculate the expected values of gravity over the whole surface of the earth. The local deviation of gravity from this ideal value is called the Free Air Anomaly. At sea these local deviations occur when we pass over undersea mountains or areas where the rocks beneath the sea change in composition, so gravity profiling is an invaluable aid to marine geologists in their efforts to understand the seabed.

This first night we were passing over the steep continental slope where the shallow waters of the continental shelf fall off into the 5,000-metre depths of the ocean abyssal plain. The gravity reading decreased rapidly, and the pen of the recorder would often go off the end of the scale. My task was then to stagger down three decks to the gravimeter room and alter the spring settings on the meter. The gyrotable appeared to be rolling wildly in all directions ; in fact it was stationary while the ship and I were doing the rolling.

Another recorder in my care was that of the magnetometer. The instrument itself is towed on a cable 200 metres behind the ship's stern so as to avoid interference from the ship's own magnetic field. The streamlined fibreglass 'fish' at the end of the cable contains a bottle of JP4 aviation fuel, which is rich in hydrogen atoms. An electric current is put through a large coil wrapped round the bottle, and this sets up a strong magnetic field which aligns some of the hydrogen atoms, each of which can be thought of as a tiny magnet. When this current is switched off the aligned hydrogen atoms look for whatever magnetic field is left – in this case only the Earth's field. They begin to precess around the direction of this field, like disturbed spinning tops, and set up a signal which is picked up by a small detector coil and fed to the recorder in front of me. The frequency of the precession is proportional to the intensity of the Earth's magnetic field. Again local variations tell us about the composition of the underlying rocks.

Finally, facing me on the console, there was the big paper roll of the precision echo sounder recorder (PESR). Echo sounders of sorts have been used on ships since the 1920s. The principle is very simple: an acoustic transducer on the bottom of the hull sends out a loud ping every few seconds, and the time taken for the echo to return from the sea bed is measured. When the echo is received it causes a moving electrode to burn a mark on a roll of sensitised chart paper. Not until 1953, however, was an instrument devised that was accurate enough to show the depth correct to the nearest fathom (= 6 feet) even in the deepest parts of the ocean, so our present good knowledge of the topography of the sea bottom comes mainly from the large number of surveys conducted since then. We carried with us Russ Melanson, the Regional Hydrographer for Eastern Canada, who would be transferring depth readings from the sounder roll on to plotting sheets. These sheets would then be sent to the International Hydrographic Bureau in Monaco, to help in the compilation of a new edition of the General Bathymetric Chart of the Oceans (GEBCO). This is a contour map of the entire ocean bottom. The first edition was produced in 1903 by Prince Albert I of Monaco, a pioneer oceanographer who used his royal yacht for extensive worldwide research cruises.

The 4 to 8 is in many ways the worst watch, for the normal patterns of sleeping, waking and eating are completely disrupted. The only compensation is that you can watch the dawn come up each day. On this first morning at sea the early hints of light revealed a leaden sky and an ominous grey sea slipping by. Quite suddenly a garish yellow orb arose, splashing colour over the whitecaps on the waves. At 8 o'clock, by dawn's watery light, I tottered down towards my cabin with aching limbs and a pounding head. I was just passing the deserted Mess when a weather-beaten Newfoundland steward saw me and called out:

"Feel loik some breakfast, b'y?"

The look I gave him merely made him grin and add:

"Seasick, eh? C'm in and set-ye down."

Unwillingly I collapsed at a table, retching at the odour of frying bacon that drifted from the pantry. The steward immediately set a large bowl of steaming porridge before me.

"Am I supposed to eat this?" I asked incredulously.

"Aye, b'y. Eating be the best cure for seasickness."

When I had finished he replaced it with a second bowl after which, to my surprise, I actually felt better. I was even able to ask him a question which had been troubling me for some time.

"By the way, why is *Hudson* called a jinx ship?"

The steward cackled.

"Ah, b'y, that be them papers. On our last trip, y'know, a steward killed hisself falling down the stairs and hitting his head on the water cooler. Then the Doctor died – he musta been more'n seventy and he jist died in his sleep with a heart attack. He used to jog round the deck, y'know. We tried to land the body at Lisbon, but them Pork n'Beans wouldn't accept it. So we had to bury him at sea. The carpenter made a lovely coffin but he didn't put enough weight in, y'see, so it floated. We stood by fer two hours waitin' for it ter sink, then we was jus' gettin' up ter ram it when it went under. Then as soon as we got back to Halifax the Old Man died sudden. That surely was a toim, b'y. But I reckons the ship be over it all now."

I went below, carefully skirting the water cooler, and when I woke up in the afternoon I was as good as cured. From that day I have never suffered from serious seasickness, and whenever a twinge occurs I start eating bland food until it subsides.

After waking up I emerged on deck to a scene of watery desolation. From the low poop the foam-streaked waves looked like mountains sweeping inexorably towards the ship. Each time, when disaster seemed imminent, the ship would rise up and the mountain would pass under us and race off to leeward. The air was filled with spray and the heaving deck was awash from the broken wave crests that spilled over the rail. November is a month of almost continuous gales in the western North Atlantic, and we were not being spared. I espied three bedraggled figures huddling beside a winch. They turned out to be Roger Smith, Orest Bluy and Dick Beamish, looking very green indeed. We greeted each other like long-lost explorers, for we seemed to be the only people alive on the ship. However, the trio had only emerged briefly for air and soon returned to the horizontal position below, while I had to climb up to the console room to resume my vigil at the instruments.

By the next day we were well into the Gulf Stream, the sea had gone down somewhat and the air was warmer and more humid. People were recovering from their misery and becoming active again, so Ced took me off watch-keeping to enable others to be trained at the job. Instead I set to work helping Al Grant to debug the ship's main computer which, like the satnav computer, was a PDP-8. Programs to compute gravity and magnetic anomalies from the daily tape records, process oceanographic data and perform many other tasks, were stored on magnetic tape spools ready to be fed into the memory when required. The machine was attached to an automatic plotter, which could draw graphs in several colours. For all its usefulness our PDP-8 was very temperamental, and at this stage was riddled with faults which needed putting right.

Another of my new tasks was to take navigational fixes on the satellite navigation receiver. As expected, the Omega navigator had lost lock soon after leaving port, and despite all the efforts of Fred Muise, the electronics technician, it could not be made to give a position fix. Luckily, in our satellite receiver we possessed a far more potent and accurate means of determining our position. The idea began in 1958 when scientists at Johns Hopkins University, Maryland, discovered that they could determine their geographical position by measuring the Döppler shift of signals coming from Sputnik I (the Döppler shift is the change in pitch of a note when the object emitting it, such as a train whistle, is coming towards you or receding). The U.S. Navy got interested and set up a navigational system for warships using special 'Transit' satellites in 1960. Since the Transit satellite is also used for spying it took a seven years' battle before the system was released for civilian use. By 1969 scientific and survey ships were using satellite navigation to fix their positions to an accuracy of 200 metres, far better than that obtained with celestial fixes. The cost of the early equipment (over 40,000 dollars) prevented its use in merchant ships, and at this time only research ships had it, except for the biggest liners such as the *Queen Elizabeth 2*.

Taking a fix was still a tedious matter; only satellite passes that were not too high or too low would give good fixes. Therefore if we wanted a very accurate position we had to wait for one of these (perhaps for two hours) then use the PDP-8 to compute the position from the signals received. Soon after "Hudson-70" integrated Satnav receivers were offered to the world's merchant fleet, by which the position is computed automatically and updated between fixes using the ship's log. Today, of course, Satnav itself has been rendered obsolete by the Global Positioning System (GPS), which uses 24 satellites so that there is always one over the horizon and a fix can always be obtained. Combined with its low cost, the ease of use of GPS has now rendered all other kinds of navigation, and the traditional skills of the navigator, obsolete. The concepts of Satnav and of GPS are the same. The satellites transmit information about the shape of their orbit as well as a pure signal at a fixed frequency. This frequency, when picked up by the shipboard receiver, has been Döppler shifted by the satellite's speed, and the shift is measured by comparing it with a reference frequency from an internal crystal oscillator. The receiver in turn (in our case) fed all the information that it was receiving into another PDP-8 computer, to which it was permanently connected. The operator had to type in some parameters concerning the ship: her course, speed, very rough position and the height of the radio antenna. The computer then worked out an accurate position. With GPS this all happens within a small microchip.

By November 22 we were out of the Gulf Stream and in the great flat mill-pond known as the Sargasso Sea. The North Atlantic Ocean is a basin which possesses an enormous clockwise circulation of water; this goes by different names in different places – the Gulf Stream in the north, the Azores Current in the east and the North Equatorial Current in the south. In the middle of this huge eddy is the Sargasso Sea and, just as the froth on a stirred cup of coffee collects at the centre, so the Sargasso Sea attracts the floating detritus from the surrounding currents. This now includes lumps of crude oil – as Thor Heyerdahl found on his *Ra* voyage – but the most famous floating objects are the masses of Gulf-weed, *Sargassum*. These must have been derived originally from the coasts of the Caribbean, but now they live, reproduce and die in the open sea. They are alleged to form great floating islands, but from the *Hudson* we saw only small pieces of weed drift past, like sods of brown grass, with a density of about one piece to every 4-5 square metres of water surface. The weed has little bladders on its fronds to buoy it up, and it provides a floating home for tiny crabs and larvae. When Columbus first saw the weed he thought that he had reached India at last, and wrote excitedly of 'many tufts of very green seaweed which, it appeared, had not been long torn from land'.

The Sargasso Sea is also the breeding ground for all the eels that are found in the rivers of Europe and America. Many years ago the Danish oceanographer Johannes Schmidt recorded the sizes of eel fry all over the Atlantic, and found that as you head towards the Sargasso Sea they decrease in size and age. In the Sargasso Sea is a small creature like a transparent willow leaf, that was thought to be a separate species, *Leptocephalus brevirostris*, until some were kept in an aquarium and turned into elvers, the baby eel. Thus the enigma was solved. River eels somehow find their way thousands of miles back out into the Atlantic to breed; their larvae drift back towards the land, growing bigger until they are large enough to make their own way up a river somewhere. The reason for this tremendous migration is completely unknown.

On November 23 we started to cross the Mid-Atlantic Ridge with the echo sounder trace revealing magnificent peaks towering up 4,000 metres or more from the 6,000-metre depths of the ocean bottom. Every ocean in the world has this stupendous ridge system running through it, a mountain range longer and more rugged than any on land. Scientists now believe that this marks a line where the deep rocks of the Earth's mantle well up and then spread out sideways, pushing the continents apart. We followed the Ridge all the way to the Equator, as it tends eastwards to keep midway between

Africa and South America. Our gravimeter was showing huge anomalies and needed constant adjustment.

During the evening of November 24 we crossed the Tropic of Cancer, and next morning the first flying fish appeared. Off our bow a wave crest erupted as five black blobs with filmy wings leapt from the water and skimmed across the surface for about 20 yards before plopping back in again. They seemed to be 'bouncing' over the higher waves, working their tail fins to get back up to take-off speed. One fish, who managed to soar a little with the wind, kept aloft for over 100 metres. Soon the sight of a dozen or more, leaping together from our bow waves and scudding away, became common.

That day we also saw our first tropical squall. It appeared on the horizon; a massive and very localised accumulation of cumulus cloud. Between the cloud and the sea was an obscurity of dark grey, marking the region through which torrential rain was falling. Apart from this one tiny area the rest of the sky was perfectly clear. From that day on there were usually two or three squalls constantly in sight, and, if the sun was in the right place, small rainbow arcs could be seen within them, ending in the sea on both sides. Sometimes a squall would sweep over us, drenching us with rain for a few minutes and whipping the sea up before leaving us in peaceful sunshine again; the decks would then steam for an hour or so.

The next few days, the last days of peace before the real work began, were idyllic. Cruising through the tropical seas we spent our off-duty hours sunbathing on the upper deck, where I delved into Sir Alister Hardy's superb book *The World of Plankton* and became fired with his enthusiasm for these strange and marvellous creatures. The sky was of azure and the clear calm ocean was of deepest blue – a sign of the sparseness of plankton. Not a breath of wind ruffled the oily calm of the waters. These are the Doldrums, loathed by the masters of the old sailing ships because of the days or weeks of delay that they caused. But to us they were sheer delight. Apart from occasional squalls the only discomfort was the incredible humidity; the air was warm and wet during the day, and, in the evening when the temperature dropped, a mist of water droplets hung in the air and deposited itself over the ship as a heavy dew.

Each sunset was magnificent, a daily spectacle that brought everyone to the rail. The splendour of its colours cannot be described, but just as lovely was the fragile afterglow when the sun had disappeared and the high cirrus clouds were streaked in delicate pink and orange. In the evening the helicopter flight pad was used as an open-air auditorium for film shows, the pictures being projected on to the hangar door. The ship was equipped with 50 old Hollywood movies, all of the most turgid quality, but the nightly show was a communal activity in which everyone took great delight, cheering the hero and shouting encouragement and advice to the participants in love scenes. Later at night, when the ship was darkened down, I would sometimes go up to the crow's nest and look out over a sea that was ablaze with millions of tiny orange sparks. Each spark comes from a wavecrest where the turbulence stimulates thousands of tiny dinoflagellate organisms to emit simultaneous flashes of light.

The Chief Engineer had not succeeded in making the air conditioning system work, and the cabins down below were stifling. Conditions were particularly bad in the Chief Steward's cabin, and since the Chief Steward is a very important person he was allowed to commandeer Roger Smith's cabin. Ced Mann moved Roger in with me, the beginning of a partnership that lasted until the end of the voyage, and a friendship that has continued for a lifetime. A ship is a tight community in which you are continually forced to rub shoulders with the same people. Every person needs a private place to take his thoughts when this permanent intimacy becomes abrasive, and so your cabin is an important refuge. If you have to share a cabin it is vital that you get along well with your cabin mate; depression, brawls, knifings and murder have been known when these conditions have been denied. Roger and I were lucky in getting along well from the start – or rather, we quickly learned to tolerate each other's bad habits. On the first day I watched in horror as my formerly tidy cabin was converted into a Wild West general store with mounds of assorted detritus, crowned by a stove-in ukulele with only three strings, for which Rog had an unreasoning attachment.

The cabin was so stifling that we decided to try sleeping on deck, so we carried our bedclothes to the upper deck and arranged ourselves on camp cots, joining several other sufferers. The tropical night was unbelievably lovely. A full moon, surrounded by a ghostly ring, lit up the sky and slashed a silver path across the sea. The vault of heaven was set with strange constellations that glittered like jewels in the clear air. I was lulled to sleep by the firmament swinging above me and the gentlest of breezes sighing through the rigging. During the night we entered the belt of North-East Trade Winds, and I awoke to find my bedclothes blown off me and my shivering body soaked in dew. I did not repeat the experiment.

Such a sybaritic existence could not last, and on November 29, as we neared the Equator, Ced called a meeting to tell us of his plan for the oceanographic stations. Each station would start at dawn and take about twelve hours, encompassing a full range of sampling activities. We would then sail overnight the 150 miles to the next day's station. The eleven stations stretched at 2 1/2° intervals along the 30°W meridian of longitude from the Equator down to 25°S. Duties were parcelled out, and I found that I was to help Bruce Carson with the bottle casts as well as supervising the launching of bathythermographs on passage during the night. Bruce took me down to the after laboratory to explain the working of the latter instrument.

The expendable bathythermograph (or XBT) is a device that measures the temperature profile of the upper waters while the ship is on passage, thus enabling you to sample conditions between stations. It consists of a platinum resistance coil mounted on a lead weight and attached to 800 metres of fine copper wire. The weight, shaped like a bomb so that it falls at a known speed, is stored ready for action inside a plastic cartridge together with a reel on which the wire is wound. The disposable cartridge is loaded into the breech of a launching tube at the stern, and the copper wire makes contact via the breech with the electronics of a chart recorder in the after lab. A holding pin is withdrawn, launching the 'bomb' into the sea. As the bomb falls the chart recorder plots out the increase in depth while recording the change in temperature as shown by the change in the coil's resistance. At 800 metres the wire breaks and the bomb and wire are lost to the depths. This seems a waste, especially as each 'shot' cost $7; however any method which involves recovery of the sampling device would need the ship to be stopped, a manoeuvre which costs far more in terms of time and fuel. We carried 500 XBTs, and on passage between stations we would launch one at midnight and one at 4 a.m.; fortunately I was only required to deal with the midnight launch.

Meanwhile, in the console room, the magnetometer record had been going haywire, so at noon we hauled up the magnetometer 'fish' and found to our surprise that it had been chewn to pieces by an unknown agent. Normally it is a stout cylinder, 6 feet long, with fins to maintain its stability, but now the fins and the whole after part had disappeared and the rest was jagged and torn, with long marks scored in the casing. We were debating whether the villain was a shark or something larger when a sudden cry came from the lookout on the bridge wing: "Whales-oh!"

Everyone rushed to the rail, or down below for their cameras. At first there was not much to be seen. About a mile away, on the starboard quarter, came a small puff of vapour which hung in the air for several seconds before dispersing. A whale was blowing. Then came another close to it, and a third. Then came a sudden flash of black as a huge body arched out of the water, showing a triangular dorsal fin. Pete Beamish was almost speechless with excitement. Whilst snapping away with a gigantic telephoto lens he revealed that they were sperm whales because their blow was directed forwards at an angle, whereas the blows of other whales are vertical. The ship's engines and major auxiliary motors were now stopped while Pete lowered a hydrophone into the water and recorded the whales' sounds on magnetic tape. After half an hour, when the tape was exhausted, we resumed the pursuit and soon came up with another family on the port bow. I shall never forget my first close sight of a whale's glistening black back as it unexpectedly slid out of the water near the ship. After this the whales seemed wary and kept their distance, although they were blowing on all sides. After nearly two hours of this exciting chase we had to give up and resume course.

When he had recovered his composure Pete came to the conclusion that we had seen three or four families of young, small sperm whales, though one enormous blow of 30-40 feet in the far distance may have been a rare blue whale. The sperm whale, who grows to 60 feet, is the largest and most formidable of the Odontoceti, or toothed whales. He is armed with a powerful underhung jaw which is long and narrow and can thus exert tremendous leverage. The peg-like teeth are designed for crunching, and were a favourite souvenir of whalermen who carved intricate designs called scrimshaw into them. The huge squared-off head is filled with spermaceti, a strange liquid wax that can be rendered down into a very fine and valuable oil. For this reason the sperm whale was hunted mercilessly by the sailing whalers of Nantucket and Dundee, and sometimes it fought back – Moby Dick was an albino sperm whale. Their chief food is squid, shown by the squid beaks that are found in their stomachs and the sucker marks on hides that speak of combats with giant specimens: perhaps our poor magnetometer fish had been mistaken for a squid. Sperm whales breed in the Southern Ocean and migrate up to tropical seas in the southern summer, so the families which we saw were at the end of a long journey.

Pete had succeeded in obtaining some superb recordings, and later in the day he played them back for us. The whales' sounds came as a series of high-pitched clicks. On playing the tape very slowly (1/64 of the recording speed) each click resolved itself into a short burst of pulses, resembling a rapidly ticking clock. It had been known for some time that whales, like dolphins, use sonar – they emit pulses of sound, but not until recently had it been discovered, using improved hydrophones, that most of this sound occurs in the ultrasonic region, above the range of human hearing. It is thought that plankton-eating whales use sonar primarily to detect the presence of shoals of plankton by echo-location, but it is also certain that they, and more especially the intelligent toothed whales, use sonar to speak to one another in a very definite language. The nature of sound propagation in water is quite unusual; except near the Poles the velocity of sound decreases with increasing depth until it reaches a minimum value at a few hundred metres, whereupon it starts to increase again. This layer of minimum sound velocity acts as a 'sound channel'; if a whale swims down to that layer to speak his sound can carry horizontally for hundreds of miles, because sound waves which would otherwise disperse above and below are refocused. In this way sounds have been recorded off Nova Scotia which are thought to come from whales swimming near Bermuda. The humpback whale seems to communicate by distinct, melodious 'songs' but the sperm whale, judging from Pete's recordings, uses a complex code of click patterns to convey information to his fellows. If this is truly a language, and if we could decode it, the consequences for our view of the world would be incalculable. For the first time ever, humans would be in a position to communicate with another species as intelligent as ourselves. Apart from the immense amount that we could learn about the mental world of the whale, the effect on mankind's overwhelming arrogance would be extremely beneficial.

Late in the evening we reached the Equator and hove-to, but thanks to the whale-hunting episode and the unnatural absence of engine noise I found it difficult to sleep that night. To my disappointment I learned that there would be no time for the traditional Crossing The Line ceremony, for early in the morning we had to begin the stern business of the first oceanographic station.

CHAPTER 3

SAMPLING THE DEEP

Beyond the shadow of the ship,
I watched the water-snakes:
They moved in tracks of shining white,
And when they rear'd, the elfish light
Fell off in hoary flakes.

Samuel Taylor Coleridge.

I SHALL ALWAYS REMEMBER the excitement of that first day of oceano-graphic work. We were probing the abyss in a place where no ship had sampled before, so that the information which we gained furnished an entirely new piece in the slowly-growing jigsaw of Man's knowledge of the ocean. To me, accustomed to arid and lifeless laboratories, it was a new experience to be doing original scientific work that actually consisted of sheer manual labour out on the open sea under the glorious heat of an equatorial sun. And there was also a new and heady feeling of oneness with Nature; acknowledging her authority in this watery domain we were humbly asking her for knowledge instead of bludgeoning her into insensibility as Man normally does these days. It was small wonder that by the end of the day I felt that a new career and life had opened up for me.

Because this first oceanographic station set the pattern for all of those to follow I shall describe what went on in some detail.

The first piece of work woke me up in the morning; the dull thump of exploding TNT revealed that Orest Bluy and George Gill were in action. They used one-pound charges fitted with a lead azide detonator and a fuse which burns underwater. The fuse is lit and the charge, attached to a red balloon float, is lobbed over the stern. The sound produced by the explosion is recorded on two sets of hydrophones. One records sound from all directions and just hangs underwater from a surface float. The other is a directional receiver, so it has to be kept upright and stationary in the water. To achieve this it is mounted on a large, heavy 'cone', a big steel weight six feet in diameter suspended by a manila spring rope so that its inertia tends to keep it stationary in the water against the motion of the ship. This imposes a tremendous strain on the rope and makes the work very dangerous in heavy seas.

When the intensity of the received sound is plotted against time there is first a big peak, occurring almost immediately; this is the noise of the explosion transmitted directly through the water. Then comes a steadily diminishing echo from sound waves which have started out in other directions only to be scattered back again by the sea surface. Finally there comes another peak from sound reflected from the ocean bottom. All this is expected; what is unexpected is a big bump in the trace, which must come from something in the water itself. This is the mysterious Deep Scattering Layer, the object of Orest's interest.

The Deep Scattering Layer (DSL) is the name given to a phenomenon that was observed when echo sounders were first used at sea. Scientists noticed that they were getting diffuse reflections from a kind of layer, some 100 metres thick, at mid-water depths. They thought at first that this was some curious property of sea water, but then they found that the layer rose towards the surface at night and sank deeper after daybreak. It is now known that these reflections come from the swim bladders of certain deep-sea fish – swim bladders are little air sacs which bony fish use to help them balance in the water. These fish feed on plankton and, as the plankton layers move towards the surface at night, the fish follow them. It was found by experiments in tanks that it only needs one fish in every 30 cubic metres of water to produce enough scattered sound to account for the DSL. The fish are exposed by the sound waves in the same way as the dancing dust particles in the air of a room are lit up by a shaft of sunlight.

When Orest and George were finished the ship got under way slowly and the Isaacs-Kidd mid-water trawl was streamed from the A-frame on the starboard side of the foredeck. This huge net, with a mouth four metres across, is designed to trawl at up to 600 metres depth and catch the strange fish that dwell in the abyss and are the cause of the Deep Scattering Layer. After an hour of towing at three knots the big foredeck winch began to rumble and the net was slowly hauled in. There was an air of great expectancy as the spreader bar, which keeps the mouth of the net open, broke surface. Many of the deck crew used to be coastal fishermen, and they felt a professional interest in what might emerge. When the cod-end of the net finally came into sight it was filled with a pink shapeless mass. This was emptied into a galvanised bath and found to consist of large numbers of extraordinary gelatinous cylinders, about three inches long and of the shape and consistency of monster jelly babies. A baffled crowd gathered round the bath, and even Dick Beamish, whose task was to collect and preserve the fish from these trawls, had no idea of the nature of these creatures. As soon as I had a chance to examine one I realised, as a result of my recent devotions to Sir Alister Hardy's wonderful book *The World of Plankton*, that this was none other than a colony of *Pyrosoma*, a luminescent polyp. *Pyrosoma* (Greek for fire body) is an amazing little creature that assembles itself into cylinders, closed at one end so as to enjoy the advantage of jet propulsion. The individuals, embedded in the jelly of the cylinder, rhythmically draw in water from the outside, pass it through their bodies to extract any nourishing material, then expel it into the inside of the cylinder. The excess water comes out of the open end and the reaction drives the colony along. Colonies up to eight feet long have been known, and they are a major source of luminescence in tropical seas.

My burst of erudition was received with amazement and it was immediately assumed that I was a biologist. In vain did I point out that I had only read one book on marine biology in my life and that I had reached the vital page on the previous day.

Among the other creatures in the net were lantern fish and hatchet fish, true representatives of the dark deep ocean's population. The lantern fish, or myctophid, is a beautiful little creature a few inches long, with silver, blue and black scales. He is given his name because of the rows of photophores, or light-producing cells, which stud his belly. These help to break up his outline when viewed from below in the gloomy waters, and so protect him from predators. The hatchet fish is a grotesque little animal, foreshortened and as flat as a coin, with an enormous mouth and bulging eyes gazing ever upwards. The unkind force of evolution has made him so ugly because he must rely for sustenance on gulping lumps of detritus which sink down from the more productive surface waters. The fish all had grossly distended bellies, caused by expansion of their air bladders when the pressure of the deep water is removed. Finally there was one little *Leptocephalus* eel larva in the net, transparent and about four inches long, with chevron markings along its sides.

While we were all gathered round the bath Roger Smith was up in the winch-house lowering his vertical plankton net. This is a long narrow net of fine nylon mesh, with about 100 strands to the inch, designed to catch the tiny microplankton (the nets caught both zooplankton and phytoplankton, so microplankton is probably the best term to use) that inhabit the surface waters, drifting with the ocean currents. A little propeller in the net's mouth, attached to a counter, records the amount of water filtered by the net as it is slowly hauled to the surface from some 300 metres down. At its bottom end is a collecting bottle and this accumulates a thick sediment of pinkish flakes, composed of thousands of these microscopic plants, each too small to be seen with the naked eye. Amongst them may be a few struggling shrimps or darting copepods – a tiny crustacean with two long antennae which is probably the most abundant animal in the world's oceans. Roger washed the plankton down into a bottle which is topped up with formalin and sealed. Much later, back in Canada, a laborious worker with a microscope would sort out these tiny organisms and thereby estimate the concentration of each species in this part of the ocean.

The next act in the day's performance was the lowering of the Bathysonde, a device which automatically records the temperature and salinity of the water column as it descends. It was designed to replace the use of cumbersome water bottles and thermometers, but the model in use in 1969 was not yet accurate enough to take over from the traditional techniques. Also, its pressure casing could withstand a depth of only 2,500 metres, half the typical depth of the ocean. Today its more efficient descendants are known as CTDs, conductivity-temperature-depth probes, and have completely replaced bottles for oceanographic casts. Bruce Carson was in charge as the buoy-shaped instrument disappeared from view and a mile and a half of wire began to rattle out. Three probes protrude from the instrument casing, measuring water pressure by means of a Bourdon gauge, the electrical conductivity of the water (a measure of its salinity) using a pair of coils, and the temperature by a platinum resistance thermometer. The three measurements are used to alter the frequencies of three oscillators, and the three frequency signals are then transmitted up the supporting wire to be interpreted by a receiver at the surface. This cast took about an hour, after which it was time for the bottle cast, an opportunity for me to make my contribution.

Let's go to the winch-house as we prepare to do an old-fashioned bottle cast. Most of the space inside the tiny deckhouse on the starboard side of the boat deck is taken up by the drums of two enormous hydraulic winches, at one of which is perched Old Stan, the quiet and dependable winch-man. Two sally-ports at the side of the house give on to small wooden platforms overhanging the ship's sides, known ominously as 'The Chains'. Bruce is checking our equipment – twenty-six of the famous Knudsen reversing bottles. This is a strong cylinder of stainless steel, about eighteen inches long, with spring-loaded stopcocks at both ends. To its outside is attached a frame containing three reversing thermometers. These are the Rolls-Royces of the thermometer world. Hand-made by Richter and Weise in Germany they are extremely costly but are accurate to one-hundredth of a degree Centigrade. Such a thermometer is free to come to equilibrium when it is right way up, but when it is quickly turned over the mercury column breaks and the thermometer stays fixed at its current reading. Two of these thermometers are used for greater accuracy, and the third is an unprotected thermometer, i.e. its mercury reservoir is subjected to the pressure of the sea. This drives the reading higher, and the difference between the readings of the unprotected and the protected thermometers is used to accurately calculate the depth to which the bottle was sent.

While Bruce is checking the bottles I am shackling a 70 lb weight to the end of the hydrographic wire, which has already been led round a pulley overhanging the Chains. When the Officer of the Watch shouts down from the bridge wing that the ship is on station with her head to the sea, we swing out the weight and lower away until it is just in the water. Bruce now hands me the first bottle and I hang out over the Chains – trying to avoid glancing at the sharks cruising below – and screw the bottle to the wire. I 'cock' it by opening both stopcocks and setting the trip mechanism, then Stan lowers away. The pulley turns a counter which shows the amount of wire paid out, and when this reaches 200 metres we screw on the next bottle. This and all subsequent bottles have a 'messenger' – a grooved lead weight which slides on the wire – attached to them. We carry on until we have loaded 15 bottles and paid out 1,600 metres – about a mile – of wire, so that the bottles are hanging at depths of 5, 50, 100, 200, 300, 400, 500, 600, 700, 800, 900, 1,000, 1,200, 1,400 and 1,600 metres. Throughout this process the ship has to manoeuvre using her bow thrusters so that the wire is kept vertical; if it leans towards the ship a bottle can easily get rubbed off against the hull, while if it leans away the wire cannot be reached from the Chains without the danger of the operator falling into the sea.

We wait for ten minutes to let the bottles reach equilibrium, then send a messenger sliding down the wire. When it hits the first bottle it releases the trip mechanism so that the stopcocks slam shut, enclosing a sample of sea water, and at the same time the top clip is released so that the bottle turns over, reversing the thermometers. The next messenger is also released by this process to carry on down to the next bottle. When the whole chain is tripped we start to haul in. One of us unloads the bottles and carefully sets them in their racks, while the other guides the winch-man, watching for the bottles to break surface, for if a bottle is allowed to slam into the top pulley it can break the hydrographic wire, causing an expensive loss of equipment and a peril to the oceanographer from the snaking wire-end that remains.

Having finished the shallow cast we now set the deep cast, which requires a slightly different technique. Instead of a weight on the end of the wire we use a 'pinger', a battery-operated device that sends out an audible pinging sound. We set our remaining eleven bottles at intervals of roughly 200 metres, then we keep lowering while we follow the pinger's progress on the echo sounder receiver in the winch-house. This displays two echoes; one comes directly from the pinger, and the other is the pinger's sound reflected up from the sea bottom. When these two echoes come together it means that the pinger is resting on the ocean bottom. We try to stop with the pinger a few metres away from the bottom, and send down our messenger as before. As the ocean is often at least 5,000 metres deep it takes the messenger almost half an hour to reach the bottom.

While we are waiting we read the bottles from the shallow cast, using a magnifying glass. While the reversed thermometers have been in the winch-house they have been warming up – the temperature of the deep water is only a few degrees above freezing point – and the glass has expanded, putting the reading slightly in error. To compensate for this each one has an ordinary thermometer attached to it which shows how much warming has occurred, and we must read these as well. We draw off water samples from each bottle for the determination of salinity, and Iver Duedall and his henchmen now appear to draw their own samples which are used to measure the concentrations of dissolved oxygen and of mineral nutrients in the water. Finally we haul up the deep cast, read the bottles, drain and re-set them. Bruce goes off to the laboratory to run the salinity determinations on a salinometer while I go on up to the computer and run our results through it. The computer corrects the temperature readings from each thermometer using correction curves stored in its memory, and calculates the depth to which each bottle was sent using the unprotected thermometer readings. Sometimes a bottle trips accidentally on the way down, and this instant analysis reveals the error while there is still time to repeat the cast if necessary. If all is well we turn our nose southwards and begin the overnight journey of 150 miles to the next day's station.

Thus passed the first station, and the ten more that followed. After the day's work an exhausted band of oceanographers would make for the bar and celebrate their achievements in liquid fashion. Usually we would be held spellbound while Bruce unreeled part of his huge stock of dirty jokes, made more hilarious by the innocent, surprised voice in which he told them. Meanwhile the ship trembled to the steady throb of engines as we pounded through the peaceful tropical night. Soon I fell into a routine and lost count of time, content to drift through the limitless ocean for ever.

Sometimes, if the station went quickly, we would have time to slow down about midnight so that Dick Beamish could do a surface trawl to catch the creatures that rise up from the deeper water at night. He used a Neuston net, a close-meshed tow-net slung from a boom at the stern. I was always up in the after laboratory clutching my Hardy when the net was emptied, and the little zinc bath was a wonderland for me. Tiny transparent squid studded with luminous photophores; little medusae, minute and perfect umbrella-shaped jellyfish only a millimetre across; red annelid worms, with the bristles of each segment adapted into paddles; the treacherous *Sagitta*, or arrow-worm, which darts forward in a sudden spurt to envelop fish larvae in its jaws; this new world of life filled me with excitement. Eventually Dick took pity on me and gave me some formalin to preserve my own specimens. My prize find was a most remarkable creature which looks like a huge glass spider. Fortunately Hardy had a plate of it; it was the phyllosoma (sleep-loving!) larval stage of the crayfish *Palinurus*. It has an absolutely flat body, as hard and transparent as glass and as thin as a piece of paper, with skeletal jointed legs projecting from it. It was impossible to believe that any organs could function inside such a body; its purpose, apparently, is to provide a high frictional resistance to the water and so support the animal while it drifts with the plankton. After a while Roger became infected with my enthusiasm and began his own collection, resulting in much unscientific bickering over the rarest specimens.

As the stations progressed we all became quicker and more efficient, so the midnight trawl was extended into a short stopover for Roger to do an extra vertical plankton tow. This gave George Gill a chance to demonstrate his skill with the Mexican casting net, a circular throw-net with lead weights round the periphery. While we were hove-to searchlights were turned on the water near the stern and as soon as a fish swam into the pool of light George would try a cast from the quarter-deck. In one memorable evening he began by catching a large orange oceanic squid from among a group which suddenly appeared, jetting along in spurts. Objecting to being hauled aboard the creature emitted a cloud of ink, and tried very hard to achieve a jet take-off from the bucket in which he was placed. On being transferred from an orange to a yellow bucket he changed colour from red to yellow-brown; squid have a network of pigment cells, or chromatophores, over their skin which enables them to change colour at will. A squid is a surprisingly advanced animal; it has a complex nervous system, a brain that can learn easily from experience and an eye which is very similar to the human eye. George now caught a magnificent but unwary flying fish, a foot long, with superb royal blue upper scales, large liquid eyes, iridescent wings and a silvery belly. We pegged him out for stuffing, but the exquisite colours immediately began to fade. Finally George caught a strange dagger-like fish which was two feet long but only an inch across, with a row of spines along the back and a sharply pointed mouth with fearsome teeth. This was identified as a *Gempylus*, or snake mackerel, a rare species the first specimen of which was caught on the *Kon-Tiki* expedition.

During the daily station the favourite hobby for off-duty sailors was shark-catching. The first shark had appeared at the equator, a streamlined chocolate-brown shape which nosed inquisitively round the hydrographic wire, his yellow-tipped dorsal fin just breaking the surface. From then on, sharks were our constant companions; they were attracted by the vast quantity of garbage with which we polluted the sea – after a day of being hove-to the water around us would be covered with beer cans, cigarette packets, food scraps and waste oil from the cooling loop of the engines. From the stern the crew would set steel hooks baited with meat, and when an unwary shark took the bait the bloodthirsty ship's Doctor was always on hand with his revolver to pump bullets into the poor creature. I was present when the first shark was hauled aboard, bleeding from several wounds but still struggling and twisting. He was landed on the deck where he writhed for several minutes, spouting blood in all directions, before lying still. George Gill immediately moved in to cut off the jaw for a souvenir and to hack away some edible meat from near the tail. The shark was a fine dark-green specimen, about six feet long, with a yellow underbelly. Pete Beamish performed an autopsy; the first things that came out were a long flat liver and a pair of immensely long testicles. On slitting open the stomach a stream of brown gastric juices poured out and then the contents were revealed: several large sheets of bacon rind; a hambone; cigarette packets; a partially digested squid; and, miraculously, part of a letter which one of the scientists remembered throwing overboard at least two days earlier. The hide of the shark was made up of short bristles which gave it a file-like surface. This explains why sharks sometimes attack swimmers: they are normally not aggressive unless they taste blood, but a shark nosing round a swimmer may accidentally brush against him, and the hide can inflict a graze. If several sharks together smell blood a 'feeding frenzy' may result in which the fish go mad and tear at everything within reach, including each other. Despite its habits a shark has as much right to life as any other creature, and after a while this daily spectacle of gore on the after-deck began to disgust me.

There are two interesting animals which live off the earnings of a shark. One is the pilot fish, *Naucrates ductor*, which is about ten inches long and has vertical blue bands along its body. This swims with the shark, and is supposed to guide it to prey in return for a share in the meal. From my vantage point in the Chains I could sometimes see one or two of these fish swimming a little way ahead of a shark, but whenever a shark was hooked they deserted their erstwhile protector and made off. Not so the bizarre sucker fish, *Remora remora*, which has the dorsal fin on top of its head modified into a large sucker by which it attaches itself to the shark's hide to hitch a lift. This sticks remorselessly to the end, and the first shark to be hauled aboard had two Remorae fixed to it, one of which I procured for preservation.

Other odd creatures occasionally appeared to break the monotony of the work. While we were hove-to one day, a Portuguese Man O'War jellyfish, *Physalia physalis*, drifted past, was netted and put in a tank on deck. Its air bladder was a beautiful iridescent blue, changing to pink along the puckered crest which acts as a sail. Below this float hangs a tangle of blue tentacles which extend down into the water to catch prey. Each tentacle is studded with stinging cells, called nematocysts, which stun or kill any small fish unfortunate enough to brush against them. The victim is pulled up into the sheaf of smaller tentacles just under the bladder, where there are other specialised cells called gastrozoids which fasten themselves round the fish, forming a stomach which digests the victim. The Man O'War is fascinating because the stinging and digesting cells are themselves individuals, each capable of existing in isolation, yet they come together to form this distinct animal in which they have complementary functions. Can we say that the Man O'War is an individual, or should we say that it is something like an ant colony?

And then of course there were the whales. One day Roger ran into the cabin screaming "Whales!" and pointing a frantic finger out of the porthole. I just had time to see a fin flash closely by, and then I rushed up on deck. Two whales, each about thirty feet long, were cruising past the ship. The nearer sailed majestically along without apparent bodily effort with his back a few inches below the surface but his small triangular dorsal fin exposed. The other was more frisky, arching his back out of the sea and rolling from side to side. They were minke whales, also known as the lesser rorqual, a scaled down version of the giant fin whale. Their small size has enabled them to survive Man's holocaust, for until recently they were spurned by whalers. Isolated minke whales subsequently paid us several visits, as if to keep an eye on this metallic intruder. Each sighting drove Pete Beamish into spasms of ecstasy and massive expenditure of film.

On December 8 we sighted land for the first time, after nineteen days at sea. It was the island of Trindade, a tiny blotch on the horizon more than 30 miles away. This little isolated rock, rising to 2,000 feet above sea level, is owned by Brazil but is uninhabited. It remained tantalisingly in sight all day as we did our station, bringing thoughts of our coming landfall. Two days later we were preparing for our eleventh and final station at 25°S, beyond the Tropic of Capricorn.

By way of farewell Nature sent us our first real storm. All morning the sky and sea had been iron grey, with an ominous black band across the horizon and a heavy stillness in the air. The first sign of the storm was a williwaw, a small waterspout consisting of a wide vortex of spray about five feet high which came scudding towards us at 25 knots. This was closely followed by a solid wall of wind and rain which lashed the sea surface into striated rivulets of foam. We started our hydrocast at lunchtime in the teeth of the gale, and only with the greatest difficulty could the ship's head be kept to the sea. The lifeboat had been sent off in the morning, with Chung aboard to do his phytoplankton work, and we were now wondering where it had got to, for the driving rain had reduced visibility to less than a hundred yards. Suddenly the boat appeared, hanging on the crest of a huge wave. We immediately stopped the hydrocast so that the boat could be recovered; Chung staggered aboard, green and almost unconscious from continuous vomiting. Not so the coxswain, Frank Durnford, who nonchalantly stepped on board as if he had just been for a row on a pond in his native Newfoundland; he and his brother Merle were undoubtedly two of the best seamen on the ship. I finished the cast stripped down to swimming trunks and completely drenched.

Next morning we set course for Rio. In eleven days I had screwed and unscrewed 286 Knudsen bottles, acquiring a pair of sea legs and a deep tan. The crew were suddenly galvanised into frantic activity, painting and tarting up our scruffy, rust-streaked home in preparation for the arrival. They strung rows of fairy lights over the upper deck, round radio aerials and across our recumbent bodies as we lay memorising the Portuguese phrases required to chat-up girls. The tatty Canadian ensign flying from the stern was replaced by a brand-new one of double the size. December 13 was our last day at sea. The wind was blowing off the land, carrying faint odours of pollen and trees. After 24 days at sea I had become used to a simple ordered world three hundred feet by fifty with only eighty-four inhabitants, and the thought of the immense new continent lying over the horizon produced a certain trepidation as well as anticipation.

That night, in time-honoured fashion, the crew got roaring drunk and, being Newfoundlanders, took to their favourite pastime of fighting. To escape these combats, which were spreading down the alleyways aft from the Crew's Mess, I emerged on deck to be greeted by one of the most awe-inspiring natural spectacles that I have ever seen – a massive electrical storm over the coast of Brazil. The ship was hove-to about six miles offshore, and continuous sheet lightning lit up the panorama of coast ahead of us in lurid blue. Each flash revealed huge accumulations of cloud and silhouetted a long coast of low dark hills. Towns showed as occasional nests of light and Cabo Frio, a promontory just north of Rio, loomed ahead as a black hump capped by its lighthouse. Three strange lights on the starboard quarter turned into a freighter in the artificial glare. After a few minutes forked lightning began to develop, with powerful bolts flashing into the sea ahead of us, yet the air was absolutely still, the sound of the thunder was faint and the sea was unnaturally calm. I was joined on the upper deck by Hugh Henderson (the ship's technician) and Bruce Carson, equipped with beer supplies so that the spectacle could be enjoyed in greater comfort. By midnight the storm had decided to head out to sea towards us; heavy gobs of rain began to fall, then the wind rose to gale force quite suddenly. Bruce, who was now somewhat inebriated, clung to the radar mast and announced his intention of dying a spectacular lightning-frazzled death, but we prised him free and went down to the shelter of the winch-house. From here, as if from a private balcony in hell, we could hear the wind actually howling (as in Hollywood sea films) and see solid masses of rain sluicing down over the sea. The beam of Cabo Frio light was picked out by the walls of water as glistening silver sheets. More inebriated colleagues arrived, and I judged this a good moment to retire, so as to be ready to film our arrival in the morning.

CHAPTER 4

BRAZIL

The land is one great wild, untidy,
luxuriant hothouse, made by Nature
for herself, but taken possession of
by man.

Charles Darwin.

ROSE WITH THE sun to find us passing Ilha Rasa, the first of a chain of hummocky wooded islands guarding the approach to Guanabara Bay. After a quick breakfast I draped myself with camera equipment and began to film the mountainous vista of the coastline. On our port bow great masses of granite and greenery swept down to a long pencil line of white beach backed by the uneven gleaming teeth of apartment blocks. These are the famous beach resorts of Copacabana, Ipanema and Leblon, facing five miles of surf along the Atlantic coast. Behind the luxury apartments there rose conglomerations of festering shacks, the *favelas* or squatter settlements, creeping like skin cancer up the wooded hillsides. Beyond Copacabana loomed the phallic massif of Sugarloaf Mountain, or Pão do Açucar, some 1,200 feet in height. This marks the narrow entrance to Guanabara Bay, where we paused to await a pilot. We could see the Sugarloaf cable lift swaying crazily in space, and wondered whether the car would be plucked from its wire by the airliners which grazed the rock as they took off from Santos Dumont Airport.

No pilot boat appeared so, braving the gun emplacements on Flagstone Island in the centre of the Narrows, we proceeded slowly into the widening bay. Immediately the full magnificent panorama of Rio de Janeiro was opened to us. The city swept round in dazzling whiteness from Sugarloaf, past the sheltered cove Enseada da Botafogo with its anchored yachts and flesh-laden beach, past the busy coastal motorway, beyond the airport and the business section and into the mountainous inner reaches of the Bay. Far off to the right of the Bay I could see the ragged skyline of Niteroi, a city in its own right and capital of Rio de Janeiro State. The very centre of Rio is surrounded and infiltrated by glorious jungle-covered mountains. The greatest of these is Corcovado (The Hunchback), rising 2,300 feet above us and dominated by a gigantic concrete statue of Christ the Redeemer, who appeared fleetingly with outstretched arms through the clouds.

The first boat that came to meet us was a cabin cruiser with a girl in a bikini draped across her foredeck. We had not seen such a delightful creature for weeks, and miles of celluloid recorded her charms. The roadstead was crowded with vessels, from freighters to small open fishing boats, and at length a launch detached itself from the throng and came alongside. It transferred a pilot and two customs inspectors, the latter with large briefcases. Later we found that they demanded, and obtained, substantial bribes of liquor. A more ancient launch brought the ship's agents, a shifty-eyed bunch led by a dissipated Englishman. We threaded our way through the shipping, past the naval base on the Ilha das Cobras (Isle of Snakes) where American surplus cruisers and landing craft rotted at their moorings, and finally approached a jetty close to the downtown business section. Dressed overall, and sporting our huge new Canadian flag, we executed a smart docking manoeuvre for the benefit of three stevedores and came to rest in Brazil at 11:30 a.m. In front of us was the freighter *Entre Rios* of Buenos Aires, and beside us lay the Brazilian destroyer *Paraná*, her decks covered with lines of washing.

Lunch was a hushed and solemn meal, since everyone was busy skimming through a vast pile of mail. Then Roger and I, equipped with dictionary and phrasebook, set out on foot to explore South America.

The dock gates gave on to a busy square, the Praça Maua. The first few streets, as in all major seaports, were infested with sleazy bars, night clubs and tawdry souvenir shops, but at length we found ourselves in Avenida Presidente Vargas, an immensely wide boulevard lined with banks and hotels. Here we spied Mike Crimp, a huge but gentle and noble Nova Scotian who had taken a year off agricultural college to work as a seaman on the *Hudson*. We joined forces and tried to get our bearings, lost in the unaccustomed cacophony of a city environment. Dust flew, garish colours assaulted us, traffic roared past at breakneck speed and people scurried by with preoccupied faces. Seeing the magic name Copacabana on a bus that was fortuitously stopped in a traffic jam, we leapt aboard. The driver sent the vehicle hurtling round bends and through tunnels, throwing the occupants from one side to the other. At length we were deposited, more dead than alive, at the famous beach, having seen nothing of the route that we had followed.

Copacabana is a long arc of beach, curving round from Sugarloaf at one end to a spit of land, the Ponta do Arpoador, at the other. The beaches of Ipanema and Leblon stretch further beyond the spit. The resort is hemmed in from behind by mountains, and extends back only four blocks from the beach. Its apartments and hotels stand in closely packed ranks which looked impressive from a distance. From closer up they showed signs of neglect and peeling paintwork, and I felt as if I were in an abandoned film set for a Hollywood musical of the 1930s. We crossed the tessellated promenade and wandered down the wide beach, against which Atlantic breakers thundered. It was a cloudy afternoon and the international jet set appeared to be elsewhere, for the beach was occupied by modest locals who were surfing, fishing from the beach, or playing irregular games of football or volleyball. The gleaming white sand was well littered with paper and was infested with extremely large ants. In two places pipes came down to the beach, disgorging what looked like raw sewage.

Quite accidentally we began talking with a trio of bikini-clad girls. Their colours ranged from white (i.e. pink) to dark brown. There is little racial prejudice in Brazil because there is no racial separation. When the Portuguese colonised the country in the 16th century they brought Negro slaves from West Africa to work the plantations, but intermarried freely with them and with the native Indians, resulting in a complete racial amalgam. Our conversation progressed famously with the aid of the phrasebook and the language of the eyes, but unfortunately our gringo-like appearance attracted a large crowd of friendly Cariocas, who started questioning us closely about football. This prevented us from carrying out our intention of propositioning the young ladies, so after an exhaustive discussion of Manchester United we wandered on. Twilight was now approaching, and in a quiet square families were taking their evening walks, children were playing on swings and lovers were making assignations. It was all very human and normal, and quite unlike the fabulous visions that the word 'Copacabana' conjures up.

We ate in an inexpensive Italian restaurant, paying with great handfuls of the grubby and almost worthless cruzeiro bills that I had obtained from the ship's agents. Brazil was suffering from massive inflation and the paper money lagged far behind; the highest bank note in circulation, a ten thousand cruzeiro denomination, was at this time worth two dollars. After we had taken a bus to Avenida Vargas it was still quite early in the evening and so, hearing strains of rock music coming from a subterranean haunt called the 'Subway', we descended in search of ethnic entertainment. It proved to be a night club where the intentions of the inmates were nothing if not explicit. We were immediately grabbed by three of the attractive young girls who had been gyrating on the dance floor, and were invited to dance, drink and exchange intimate conversation with a view to further naughtiness. Everything was going well, and already my escort Marcia appeared through my misted eyes to be the innocent girl of my dreams, when suddenly an ancient fat woman, representing the management, began to lambast Roger.

"You are naked!" she exclaimed.

"No, I'm not," laughed Roger, after giving a quick glance downwards for reassurance.

Roger, in fact, was naked only as far as his knees, since he was wearing a perfectly respectable pair of shorts. The fat woman brought reinforcements in the form of her equally fat, bald and perspiring husband.

"Sir, it is not permitted to expose knees in our establishment," he explained with grave courtesy. "You would please to leave?"

Outside we enquired if Roger was often thrown out of whorehouses for being improperly dressed. He was not amused, and was further discomfited on the way back to the ship when a highly decrepit young lady leapt from the shadows of a railway wagon and threw her arms around his neck. It appeared that earlier in the day the ship had been swarming with these ladies, who found in the crew a ready source of foreign aid. They had finally been thrown off, but were to cause much work for the Doctor in the weeks ahead.

The next morning was hot and sunny, and the scientists embarked on a bus tour of the city laid on by the Brazilian Hydrographic Service. First we passed through a dirty industrial area where the grey concrete walls were plastered with political slogans. Then we entered a rich suburb of luxury villas, beyond which we gained our first close view of a favela. Every big city in South America has its shanty settlements - in Lima they are called *barrios*– where impoverished peasants have moved from serfdom on the land in the hope of a job of sorts and a better life. In Rio the squatters, some 800,000 in a city of four million, appropriated the steep lower slopes of the mountains, the only land that was empty. Here they built shacks of corrugated iron and packing cases, one on top of the other up the side of the hill, with no heat, light or sanitation. In times of heavy rain a whole favela may be washed down the hillside by floods.

Beyond the favela the road plunged into a double tunnel of parabolic cross-section that carried it for nearly two miles below Corcovado. We emerged on the shores of an inland lagoon, the Lagoa Roderigo de Freitas, lined with new apartments, the racetrack and the botanical gardens. This, the swankiest area of Rio, is overlooked by another favela, which boasted its own 'shopping centre' of corrugated iron stalls along the roadside. After a tour of the beach areas, the war memorial (Brazil sent a small contingent to the Italian front in 1944) and the pink stucco buildings of the University of Brazil, we drove through the naval base on the Ilha das Cobras and thence by a causeway to what looked like an icing-sugar castle on a tiny island.

The green Gothic apparition was Ilha Fiscal, headquarters of the Hydrographic Service. The driver got down and conversed by vigorous gesticulations with the armed sailors manning the gate. It appeared that a tour of the place had been planned, but that the Hydrographic Service had not been informed through the proper channels, therefore we would please to return tomorrow.

After lunch Roger and I caught a taxi to the funicular station at the base of Corcovado. We waited for an hour, and then a tiny bright red diesel locomotive chugged into view, pulling a single wooden charabanc. A large crowd jumped aboard and the engine began a laborious ascent, driving itself by a cogwheel which engaged with a continuous rack between the rails. The journey was incredibly beautiful, through a world of fleshy trees hung with lianas, of giant fern fronds, strange fruits, carpets of red flowers, huge orchids and weird fungus growths. Lizards darted over rocks, and termite nests clung like red gourds to the tree trunks. Occasionally the leaves parted to reveal a clearing with a shack full of young children, or a distant view of Rio. After an hour's climb we reached the top and a viewing platform beneath the great statue of Christ. He is floodlit at night and down his left side runs a lightning conductor. He looks down in blessing on a breathtaking view. The great sweep of the city sparkled and danced in the heat, while hawks effortlessly swooped and hovered in the upcurrents and swifts made quick sallies from the mountainside. Range upon range of coastal mountains spread in a green procession to the horizon, where they merged with the hazy blue of the Atlantic.

On the journey down we began talking to a young girl and her brother who were sitting beside us. They explained to us in careful English about the *giacca* fruit, a brown fleshy globe which grew in profusion beside the railway line. This is used to catch birds, they said. The fruit secretes a sweet, sticky juice which is spread out on the top of a wall. Songbirds are attracted by the smell and perch on the wall, where they become stuck and are easily captured. Then the children sell them to songbird dealers.

Later in the evening we took the cable car up Sugarloaf Mountain. The ascent is in two stages. The first swung us perilously to the top of Morro da Urca, a smaller peak in front of Sugarloaf. The slopes of this crag are completely naked, but a couple of enterprising squatters had succeeded in building shacks on the almost vertical rock face. The summit had trees and a souvenir shop, where I encountered the most tasteless object that I had ever seen: a plastic model TV set featuring Christ on Corcovado, who flashes on and off when plugged in. I wondered who might appreciate this as a gift, but the second cable car was waiting. At the top of Sugarloaf a huge shed houses the antiquated cable apparatus, looking like the engine room of the *Great Eastern*. We were surrounded by an ocean of lights, lapping the sides of the black mountains. Botafogo Cove shone like liquid gold in reflections from the coastal highway, and even the favelas sent forth a few flickering lights from lanterns. Like many cities, Rio is at its most magnificent when seen from high mountains or from the sea. Back at the foot of the mountain we began to walk home along the deserted oil-streaked beach of Botafogo. We noticed that hollows had been scooped in the sand, in which groups of lighted candles had been placed. Mystified, we waited for a while. An ancient black man appeared quietly and, ignoring our presence, scooped a hole and planted some candles, muttering under his breath. Then he slipped away. We found out later that this was a voodoo ritual, or *macumba* as it is known in Brazil. The candles are votive offerings to the gods Oxala and Zambi, for fertility and healing of disease. When the tide covers them the magic takes effect. The macumba religion was brought from Africa by slaves, and is still widespread despite ecclesiastical efforts to stamp it out.

We continued along the side of the coastal highway, but were attacked by an army of giant cockroaches that lurked in the grass. We were forced to trust our lives to an insane taxi driver, and arrived back at the ship gibbering with terror. We found that a party for the ship's agents had taken place in our absence, wherein the agents had got drunk and carried off, as if by right, all movable objects in the lounge. They had also raided the officers' cabins and Pete Reynell caught one who was proudly carrying away his record collection.

Pete Reynell, Roger and I decided to escape and visit Brasilia, the fabulous new capital in the interior. I obtained permission from Ced Mann to disappear for a day or two, and we booked tickets for a long-distance bus which left the next afternoon. Pete and I spent the morning on Ipanema beach, leaving Roger to lay out a display of plankton nets for an open house, then we met up at the bus station. Buses are the main form of transport in a land with few railways and much poverty, and the bus station is a minor metropolis with rows of shops and restaurants. We bought cheese, bread and two bottles of red wine for the journey, then went to find our bus. To our surprise it was a luxury Mercedes coach which featured reclining seats, a loo and free coffee.

The route out of Rio passed through endless industrial suburbs, including the huge oil refinery of Petrobras (Petroleo Brasileiro), the state oil company. Then after a few miles of fields the mountains loomed ahead, part of a great escarpment where the ancient granite massif of the Brazilian Plateau comes down to the sea, leaving a very narrow belt of coastal lowlands along which most of Brazil's population live. The road entered the mountains abruptly and wound crazily upwards between a sheer drop and a jungle-covered wall. Above us rose rounded peaks of darkest green, while streams tumbled down plunging valleys into silent brown lakes. A simple hut would appear in a clearing, with washing laid out to dry on bushes.

In an hour we climbed 4,000 feet and reached the first highland town, Juiz de Fora, whose small adobe houses were lined up along a single street. A tank was on display in the main square, to commemorate the fact that it was here that Brazil's most recent descent into military rule began. In 1964 President Goulart, who in three years of office had introduced land reform and other dangerously radical measures, was unseated by a military revolt which began with the governor of Juiz de Fora. From then on Brazil had been a military dictatorship, with a variety of generals as president. Juiz de Fora was also the home town of Brazil's national hero, Alberto Santos-Dumont, who made a heavier-than-air flight in 1906 and several pioneer airship excursions, including a circumnavigation of the Eiffel Tower.

As the day wore into evening we climbed higher and the jungle turned slowly to grassland. We stopped every three hours for refreshment. The first place was the 'town' of Simão Pereira in Minas Gerais province, which was an isolated restaurant with no habitation in sight. Here Roger bought a bamboo tube of *pinga*, a potent local liquor, and we ate chicken legs covered in fat. The second place was owned by the bus company, and free coffee and biscuits were doled out. At midnight we passed through a blaze of lights – the city of Belo Horizonte with a million inhabitants – and made our final stop at a steak house some way beyond.

During this long evening we made friends with two students, both called Carlo. They spoke fluent English and we talked far into the night about the customs of our respective countries. The Carlos were most interested in sex.

"If a man on his wedding night finds that his wife is not a virgin, when she had previously said that she was," said Carlo-I, "he is legally entitled to an annulment. But here is the catch. There is no divorce in Brazil and an annulment does not permit remarriage. So most husbands put up with what they find."

"Also," said Carlo-II, "if a man lives with a woman for five years she is entitled to the same legal privileges as if she were his wife. That includes a share of his property. So there is a four-and-a-half-year trade-in period for mistresses among the rich!"

The Carlos were on their way to Brasilia to take the entrance examinations for the University, for which there is intense competition. They had learned their English at the fashionable British school in Rio. At length we all tried to sleep, with little success. Pete tried the floor and finally stretched out on the rear window ledge of the bus.

When the sun rose in a fiery red the next morning we were deep into the Highlands, the Planalto Central. The countryside was savannah, the *campo cerrado*, a rolling landscape covered with grassland, scrub and small stands of trees. The soil is a rich red, full of iron oxides, but thin and dusty. Of Man there was little sign – just the power line running beside the road, the single tent of a mineral prospector and, once, a gateway in the middle of nowhere marked Circle K Ranch, leading from emptiness into emptiness. Suddenly, in the depths of this wilderness, we came to a police post marking the boundary of the Federal District of Brasilia, and we pulled into a cafe alongside for breakfast. At 5,000 feet above sea level the early morning was raw and chilly.

We drove on into a landscape as utterly deserted as before. Then, like a mirage, there arose a skyline of tall modern blocks. The city of Brasilia lay before us. Soon we were passing along a wide boulevard lined with hoardings and shiny apartments. It was like a strange dream; people and cars were bustling everywhere, yet surrounding us were hundreds of miles of complete emptiness.

We left the two Carlos at the bus station, with plans to meet again in the evening. Pete was due back on duty next day, so he booked an evening plane back to Rio. Roger and I had more leeway, and booked a flight for the following day. This left us only the afternoon to explore the city together, so we took a guided tour in a VW minibus with a humorous old guide who spoke seven languages and claimed to be a nephew of Le Corbusier. The guide told us the history of the city as he took us round.

Since Brazil became independent the national dream has been to populate the empty interior by building the capital there. In the 19th century the idea was pushed by St John Bosco, the Italian educationalist priest who founded the Salesian Order. He had had a dream in which he saw a city named Brasilia at the confluence of three rivers. The idea was finally put into action by Juscelino Kubitschek, who was President from 1956 to 1961. A survey found that the best site, in the state of Goias, was indeed at the headwaters of three rivers: the Paraná, running into the River Plate Estuary; the São Francisco, running north-eastwards to the coast; and the Tocantins, a tributary of the Amazon. The watershed was dammed to create an artificial lake, and a 5,814 square mile area around it was designated the Federal District. The city was supposed to be self-financing; the government bought the land from cattle barons at one centavo per square metre and resold it to developers at 100,000 cruzeiros per square metre, the profit financing public buildings. The building workers were dumped in seven 'satellite towns' behind the hills, where they lived in shanties as they built the city. The first building materials had to be flown in, but then a road was built to the coast, the first of a network of highways cutting through unexplored regions of the Mato Grosso and Amazon and accelerating the destruction of the Amazon rain forest. By 1969 the population was 600,000, and was fed from newly-established local farms. The city has an aeroplane-shaped plan; the 'wings' are the residential areas and University, while the public buildings are in the 'fuselage' which leads down to the lake. It is the product of two architects, Lucio Costa and Oscar Niemeyer, both disciples of Le Corbusier. The competition was restricted to native-born architects; it was Le Corbusier's ambition to design a city and so he took on these two Brasilians as pupils.

They supposedly sent off the winning design on the back of a postcard.

We visited the opera house and theatre, built in the shape of a Mayan pyramid and covered with a frieze of concrete reliefs that is again reminiscent of the Maya, then the cathedral, a breathtaking fantasy built in the shape of a ferro-concrete Crown of Thorns, made of sixteen parabolic sections (symbolising the sixteen states of Brazil). When finished it was to be surmounted by a pentagonal structure incorporating the stars of the Southern Cross (to be lit up at night) and four bells, symbolising the four original ships of Columbus (one of them, the *Pilarica*, sank on the way across). A less deliberate piece of symbolism was the fact that the designer, Niemeyer, was a convinced Communist. For this reason the cathedral's completion had been delayed, although the Pope was now expected to consecrate it within a few months.

Next came the Government section, beginning with ugly office buildings, one of which had a burned-out second floor. The guide explained that the fire occurred the previous year, and since it was the Tax Department the fire brigade took over an hour to arrive while the citizens stood round and cheered. The Foreign Ministry was housed in a palace, the Palacio do Itamaraty, with a facade of glass and ferroconcrete and a watery moat set with a sculpture representing the shattered Earth. Inside all was light and air with a vast ballroom, luxurious conference rooms and a reception hall with an eight-ton cast-iron sculpture hanging from the ceiling representing birds taking flight.

The centre point of Brasilia is the National Congress Building. The office part is in the form of twin towers, connected to form an 'H'. In front of it are two concrete bowls: one contains the House of Representatives; the other, inverted, the Senate. The reason for this, said the guide, is that the House of Representatives is always holding out a begging bowl for money, while the Senate always clamps down on its demands. The bowls are mounted on a long, low building whose flat roof, accessible by a ramp, serves as a plaza. At this time both Houses were in permanent recess, having met once in 1968 to rubber-stamp a new dictator, General Medici. The previous dictator, General Artur da Costa e Silva, whose training in statesmanship was acquired as a tank commander, had fallen dangerously ill with polio.

Behind the Congress was a big parade ground, the Square of the Three Powers (Praça dos Tres Poderes). At one end is the Ministry of Justice, at the other the executive offices of the President in the Palacio do Planalto and in the middle a dovecote and a museum of historical speeches (inscribed on the walls). The President's actual home was the Palacio da Alvorada down by the lake. It is equipped with a swimming pool and a private chapel lined with 18-carat gold. Its grounds extend about a quarter of a mile out in all directions, so that the President is out of rifle shot, and are surrounded by a wire fence patrolled by armed guards.

We drove along one of the aircraft 'wings', past the University which was still under construction, and into a residential zone of the famous 'Super Squares' (superquadra). A Super Square is one of those integrated concepts in living so beloved by social planners. Each square is a total environment for 4,000 people, comprising eleven apartment blocks, shops, a cinema, a kindergarten and playgrounds. Underground parking is provided for two cars per household and the land within the square is given over to lawns and gardens. The idea is that the wives and children of the civil servant bread-winners can live their lives within the square and never venture outside, a frightening concept.

Our guide drove us to the airport so that Pete could catch his flight. We caught a taxi back to town and splurged out on a room at the Hotel Naçional, the most luxurious in Brasilia. We tried to keep our appointment with the two Carlos but could not find them, and eventually retired chastely to our luxury accommodation.

Next morning we visited a satellite town. They are called Free Cities (*cidadi livri*) because the inhabitants pay no rent, and the nearest one, also the oldest, was known as Nucleo Bandeirante (Pioneer Beginning). For only ten cents a crowded bus took us the twelve kilometres into the hills. There were two made-up roads and the rest was quagmire. The dwellings were made of packing cases and odd bits of wood; there was plenty of ventilation owing to gaping holes between the planks. Some of the houses extended precariously to two stories. Window glass was rare; usually the openings were covered, if at all, by wooden shutters. Almost all the shacks had TV aerials, many had battered cars standing outside and the population was neatly dressed. Most of them were well-paid construction workers who threw up these houses for themselves in the early stages of building Brasilia and preferred to stay rather than pay the high rents in the city. The place made up in colour for its lack of comfort. Huge signs proclaiming 'Hotel Paradiso' and 'Hotel Europa' presided over garish clapboard shacks. A favourite mode of transport was the donkey cart, using a pair of wheels and springs from an old motor car. The two streets were lined with shops and stalls selling everything under the sun, but especially hardware for the home construction enthusiast. We ventured into a meandering, festering market full of butchers' stalls, from which hung strips of gangrenous dried meat that crawled with flies. We found that we were enjoying ourselves. The people seemed full of life and were very friendly. There was a spirit here that was missing in the antiseptic paradise of Brasilia, the spirit of humanity.

With reluctance we came away and headed for the airport. Military police were everywhere, toting guns. One poster showed arsenals of weapons allegedly captured from Communist plotters, while another proclaimed the joys of military service – there is conscription at age 18. While waiting we amused ourselves by reading an account of the "Hudson-70" expedition in the *Brazil Herald*, the English language newspaper published in Rio and São Paulo. Ced Mann was featured in a photograph and described as the "Hudson mission chief". At last it was time to board, but the passengers had to pass through an intensive document scrutiny. A young Colombian couple in the queue with us said that this was because ex-President da Costa e Silva had died.

"But he died naturally, didn't he?"

"In Brazil you can never tell. It may be a *golpe*."

Our passports were locked away in the ship's safe, but I had my birth certificate which was sufficiently impressive to get me through. Roger had only his Canadian identity card and had to submit to a lengthy body search, after which we were escorted on board by lackeys who carried umbrellas to shield us from the rain. The little Japanese aircraft whisked us back to Rio in two hours via a short stop at Belo Horizonte where we were again searched.

We landed at Santos Dumont Airport and found Rio in a state of bustle. A flight of military trainers was landing at the airport and, as we passed the entrance to the naval base, a great number of buses roared in, packed with armed sailors. They were followed by two jeeps full of top brass in dress uniforms and some fast black saloons with screaming motorcycle escorts. We assumed that a coup was indeed in progress, but back at the ship we found that it was just detritus from the funeral of the ex-President, which had taken place with great pomp earlier in the afternoon. Ced Mann immediately inflicted some work on me, that of running down the gyroscopes for the gravimeter, which was not going to be used on the next leg. This took up most of the evening.

Pete Reynell had an interesting experience the night before. A wild-eyed intense man had come aboard, seeking a scientist who could speak

Portuguese or French. This being a Canadian ship none of those present could speak French except Pete, an Englishman. The man revealed that he was a flying saucer researcher and claimed to have discovered a cave in the Brazilian highlands near Varzelandia containing a series of prehistoric paintings showing spacecraft. He had published his experience in a fantastic book entitled *Flying Saucers and the Relativity Theory of Dr. Einstein*, of which he gave Pete some copies. The paintings certainly showed saucer- and cigar-shaped objects as well as astronomical symbols, although the text was somewhat overheated. The chances are that Senhor Hernani Ebecken de Araujo was way off beam, but I was sorry to miss him and hope that somebody has investigated his claims.

Friday, December 19, was our last full day in Rio. I spent the morning finishing the shut-down routine on the gravimeter and then went out to buy presents and souvenirs. In short order I assembled some Amazon butterflies and a large dried piranha fish whom I christened Percival Herbert Piranha and mounted in front of my porthole. His battered face, minus several teeth, is before me as I write.

In the afternoon there was to be a reception at the Canadian Embassy, but first I wanted to visit the Museum of the Indian. I found it housed in a musty old building in the shadow of the Maracanã football stadium. I was the only visitor. The displays were poorly researched and the atmosphere reflected an indifference to the culture of tribes who were now being exterminated. There were displays of headdresses similar to those of North American Indians, curare-tipped arrows with woollen balls as flights, ingeniously woven cane huts, a crude but efficient loom, and equipment for the complicated process of refining manioc. The root is shredded, pressed in long basket moulds to remove the deadly poisonous prussic acid, then made into cassava flour and bread. The remnants of the tribes who had slowly evolved these ways of coping with their environments were even now being destroyed by the diseases and rifles of the advancing white man. The forest is being cleared for ranches and agriculture, despite the fact that the soil is so thin that once the trees are removed its nutrients are leached away and it quickly becomes useless.

Emerging from the museum I hailed a taxi and thrust the address of the ambassador's residence at the driver. He had a droopy moustache and a very sad face and was mortified to discover that he did not know where the place was. He drove around at random, consulting his Rio road atlas, asking pedestrians and apologising profusely. For each apology he turned round and took his hands off the wheel, the better to express his woe. Eventually we reached the residence. It was out in Gavea, a district of rarefied elegance beyond Leblon beach. The ambassador's house stood behind high walls and a wrought iron gate on a winding mountain road. When I rang the bell a fierce dog came bounding out at me, suggesting that the ambassador did not like latecomers. However he was followed by a friendly butler who escorted me to the party.

My shipmates were standing around the swimming pool in states of undress sipping Cuba Libres, one of which was placed in my hand. They were being entertained by the attractive secretaries on the Embassy staff. I went over to the ambassador, a genial French-Canadian called Hardy, to apologise for my inexcusable lateness. He took this in good part and suggested that I have a swim. I changed into my trunks, plunged in and was soon joined in the pool by the ambassador, where we began an interesting aquatic discussion. The house, he said, waving his arm at the vast pink stucco palace in its superb grounds, was built in 1942 for a wealthy family and acquired by Canada in 1956. He had no desire to move to the wilds of Brasilia. The embassies were resisting, he said, and the move would not take place until the time of his 'successor', i.e. at least six years.

A large buffet supper was now laid out. I consumed my shrimps and turkey while talking to the wife of one of the Embassy staff. She was well advanced in pregnancy and looked rather tired. She spoke of the difficulties with security since the kidnapping of the American ambassador, Lincoln Gordon, earlier in the year. Children of senior officials were now escorted to school in locked cars, and the diplomatic residences in the area (the British ambassador lived down the road) had got together to hire a private patrolman. We took our coffee up to the terrace, which overlooked the pool and had a superb view of the steep wooded mountainside. The mountainside was, of course, covered with a favela, in which a few weak lights were beginning to show. The squatters would have the pleasure of gazing down upon functions such as ours. I suddenly felt ashamed of being rich, and wondered whether the urban terrorists who had kidnapped the ambassador were among those who dwelt upon that hill.

Later in the evening a bus arrived to take us back to the ship. As it was our last night ashore five of us launched forth and squandered our cruzeiros at a night club in Copacabana, preparing for the rigours of the voyage ahead. The next morning my head was in a strange state and my body seemed unable to rise from the bunk. Fortunately we were still in Rio, our early morning departure being delayed by the non-appearance of a new cook who was being flown down from Halifax. It was not until noon that we slipped away from the quay and bade farewell to the familiar landmarks. I had been overwhelmed by the impact of this new continent. Brazil seemed to be a violent cauldron in which grandiose technological planning rubbed along with primitive and poverty-stricken living conditions. Yet in this short visit I had gained no real understanding of the people, their customs or attitudes to life. I vowed to return one day.

The only man to do any scientific work in Rio was Peter Beamish. He had gone on a whaling expedition in Guanabara Bay in one of the ship's launches, and had harpooned a dolphin of the rare species *Sautalia brasiliensis*. This creature lives only in Guanabara Bay and had never been caught before; it had been described only from two skeletons found on the beach and from observations of its behaviour. Pete hung up his catch from the foredeck crane, producing a small lake of blood, and then cut it in two and stuffed it into the freezer in the after lab. It had already begun to putrefy, and so the *Hudson* sailed forth to the Southern Ocean dripping with blood and surrounded by the odours of corruption.

CHAPTER 5

ICEBERGS AND WHALES

At length did cross an Albatross,
Thorough the fog it came;
As it had been a Christian soul,
We hail'd it in God's name.

Samuel Taylor Coleridge.

T HE LAST ISLANDS DISAPPEARED and I gratefully dropped into my bunk. I remained there until raised by Roger at 4 a.m. to keep a geophysical watch. Fortunately neither the magnetometer nor the gravimeter was in action, and the watchkeeping was confined to the echo sounder and the satellite receiver. We were now recording the depth of the Deep Scattering Layer as well as the ocean bottom. At this latitude the DSL is very strong, and gives almost as powerful an echo as the seabed. It was fascinating to watch the DSL sink from near the surface to a depth of some 400 metres as the dawn rose; the deep-sea fish were returning to their homes after spending the night eating plankton at the surface.

A second long night was also spent watchkeeping, and then on December 23 we reached station 12, our first station of the new leg. This was at 27°30'S and was to be the first of 16 stations to continue the line down the 30°W meridian as far as 55°S. The bottle cast was now the first item on the schedule and we began soon after midnight. It was a perfect night, cool and moist after the heat of the day, and the full moon created a silvery highway across the calm sea. Two large squid, about six feet in length, appeared in the floodlit water beneath us. They glowed a violent red in surprise, then slowly changed colour to white before cruising lazily away in small spurts. A new face joined our winch-house club, the jovial and bespectacled countenance of Professor Pete Wangersky of Dalhousie University. Two of his graduate students, Bob Cook and Larry Atkinson, had accompanied Bruce and me in our bottle casting work on the first leg of the voyage. In between our Knudsen bottles they had fastened Niskin bottles to the wire. These are simply plastic water bottles designed to entrap a large sample, which is then passed through a fine mesh filter to catch the suspended detritus - known scientifically as particulate organic carbon (POC). A gentle but steady rain of this material, consisting of excreta and body fragments of living and dead creatures, falls from the well-populated upper layers of the ocean into the darker and more deserted depths. There it is scavenged by bottom-dwelling fish and re-enters the cycle of life. The concentration of POC is calculated by burning the sediment residue and measuring the volume of carbon dioxide produced. Bob and Larry had spent their voyage nursing the fearsome apparatus in which this measurement was done automatically, and now Pete Wangersky was aboard to take over the task.

While the deep cast was going down we were looking idly at the trace of the pinger on the echo sounder when suddenly a strong echo appeared at a depth of 3,000 feet. Bruce checked the sounder. There was nothing wrong; it was a real signal. Whatever was creating it was a large and very solid object.

"Too deep for submarines," said Bruce.

"Could it be a whale?" I asked.

"Surely not at that depth," said Pete.

"How about a giant squid?"

"Possible, I suppose, but a squid's body is almost all water. I don't think it would give such a strong reflection to sound waves."

Our giant visitor was a mystery. I wondered just how deep whales could dive, and later I dug amongst the books in the ship's library. I found to my astonishment that a sperm whale was once found entangled in a telephone cable brought up from a depth of 3,200 feet. The whale had drowned since; being a mammal, it needs to come to the surface to breathe. The pressure at this depth is a hundred atmospheres, and since a whale's lungs contain only the air inhaled at the surface they would have to contract to a small fraction of their original volume. Perhaps our mysterious friend was indeed a whale, but I prefer to hope that it was some great unknown creature that pursues its entire life in the secret depths of the abyss.

Whoever he was, our visitor had disturbed our cast, for when we drew it up we found that one of the bottles had slipped and that none of those below it had tripped. The cast had to be repeated, a long tedious task that lasted until noon, after which I retired to bed.

Emerging that evening into the lounge, I found it in a strangely quiet state. The normal background of quick-fire obscenity was missing, and even the Doctor, normally the most foul-mouthed of revellers, was unnaturally subdued. The reason was immediately apparent. Two real live women were aboard, and one of them was a sight for sore eyes. Dr. Carol Lalli of McGill University was a tall Grecian beauty with long brown hair flowing down her back. Together with Georgiana Deevey, she was aboard to study sea snails – or, as she preferred to call them, pseudothicosomatous heteropods. The ladies were sitting in a group of tongue-tied officers who were doing their unnatural best to make suitable small talk. They did not seem entirely relaxed.

The next day was warm and sunny, and Carol went sunbathing on the helicopter deck. This coincided with a painting effort on the part of the bo'sun. One of the seamen was at work up on the mizzen mast when he dropped his brush. After a preliminary "Lorjesus" he began to form his mouth into a suitable shape for that all-embracing Maritime curse whose victim has aspersions cast on his parenthood and on his preferences for incest and oral sex. Scarcely had the first syllable emerged when the seaman saw Carol. His face became a picture of frantically bottled energy, and the oath literally went off half-cocked. He stared in fascination for a full minute before returning to work.

In the days that followed there were many instances of crew and officers smothering their normal earthy prose in the presence of Carol, almost like guilty schoolboys in the presence of teacher. And a slight tension began to develop on the ship – nobody was at ease any more. Partly this was the result of silly rules; Carol and Georgiana were not allowed below on the crew's deck without an officer escort, for instance. And when Carol gave a lecture on sea snails in the lounge, a contingent of crew turned up for the first and only time, listened respectfully, asked no questions and left immediately afterwards. This was an extraordinary event because, although such lectures were theoretically open to the crew, in practice they never came because of the rigid class division whereby the lounge was a holy of holies for officers and scientists.

Carol's sunbathing day was also Christmas Eve. We did station 13 at 30°S in the afternoon, finding that the surface water temperature had dropped to 20°C from the 27°C found at the Equator. That evening in the lounge there was an abortive attempt to generate the spirit of Christmas. Everyone had a lot to drink and, with the aid of Pete Reynell's accordion,

Roger's battered ukulele and my guitar, we tried a singsong. Our efforts to arouse any participation were fruitless. Then Roger played his cherished "Je t'aime... moi non plus" record of a couple making love, we considered what we were missing, and the party broke up.

Christmas Day on the *Hudson* meant station number 14 at 32° 30'S, 30°W. Bruce and I did the shallow cast early in the morning and then knocked off for the official festive season which lasted from 10:30 a.m. to 2:30 p.m. This allowed time for free drinks in the lounge by courtesy of the Senior Scientist, followed by Christmas turkey and plum pudding. In the afternoon, instead of subsiding into bloated inaction, I had to go out and do the deep cast. The sea was silent beneath a cloudy sky, and suddenly the world seemed a very lonely place. That evening there was another feeble attempt at a party in the lounge. An evil-looking punch had been prepared in a five-gallon jar mixing every variety of cheap liquor with pineapple juice. I broke out a fruit cake which the kind Miss Otto had baked in Dartmouth and passed it around. Later the Doctor organised a game of liar's dice, a singularly inappropriate activity for the birthday of the Prince of Peace. So passed Christmas, which only the crew managed to enjoy in traditional seagoing fashion – they broke open a hoard of bottles and kept going until dawn.

To overcome the Christmas blues I rose early the next morning to watch the Isaacs-Kidd trawl. Dick Beamish had left us at Rio, and his place had been taken by Dick Zurbrigg, another biologist from the University of Toronto. We watched with familiar enthusiasm as the cod-end was emptied into the bath, and this time it yielded an interesting and aggressive specimen. It was a viper fish, *Chauliodus sloanii*, an angry deep-sea dweller, about seven inches long, which snapped at us as we laid it out for photography. Like other deep-sea fish it has photophores along its belly, but unlike most fish it has no scales, the skin pigment being patterned instead into a hexagonal scale-like mesh. Its most extraordinary feature is the 'fishing rod' on its back. The first dorsal fin-ray, just behind the head, is extended in the form of a barbel, with a luminous end which it waves about to attract small fish. Once lured the victim stands little chance, for the viper fish has a wicked pair of fang-filled jaws, operating on a hinged lever system like a snake's, so that they can open extremely wide and consume prey that is almost as large as the viper fish itself. This makes the viper fish well adapted to the deep-sea environment, where meals are available only at lengthy intervals and no opportunity can be missed to consume large or small morsels.

Dick's trawl was followed by a multiple net vertical plankton tow, carried out by Bob Conover, another new arrival for this leg. Conover used the hydrographic wire from the winch-house, on which he put three nets at 250, 500 and 750 metres. The wire was then slowly hauled in, and the differences between the catches in the three nets show which plankton species inhabit the three zones of 0-250, 250-500 and 500-750 metres. Bob Conover was an unkempt American from BIO, who had the endearing habit of humming tunelessly to himself. He was said to spend much of each morning at BIO in the toilet, humming away and perusing the morning's mail which gradually piled up around his feet. Bob replaced Chung I Choi and Walton Watt in the plankton work; we had also lost Ted Corbett at Rio and, prematurely, Jan Piechura because of an inflamed stomach ulcer.

Later that morning my spirits were uplifted by the first sight of the most beautiful birds in the world. Two sooty albatrosses appeared out of an overcast sky and joined our wake. From that day onward their displays of soaring and gliding were a constant source of pleasure and joy. They have a wingspan of about nine feet and their body and upper wing surfaces are speckled with brown spots. They were joined after a while by the larger black-browed albatrosses, which have white bodies with black heads and an outline of black around the wings, and finally by the greatest of all seabirds, the wandering albatross, *Diomedea exulans*. This magnificent creature is virgin white except for his black wingtips, and his wings may span twelve feet or more. I spent hours gazing at his manner of flight. He swoops down into the wind and glides along the sea surface, a few inches from the wave crests. His body is rigid, but his head is constantly moving from side to side as he searches for fish, or (in our case) for left-overs. Finally, as his glide loses speed, he takes advantage of the airflow over a steep wave crest to climb vertically into the air. With a flick of his wings he does a half-roll and soars off downwind to gather speed for another glide. He has the insolent grace of a ballet dancer, although he sometimes comes to grief when he misjudges his glide and has to paddle desperately to keep aloft when hit by an unexpected wave. He also looks awkward when taking off. He needs a long run-up, and in the final stages is actually scampering on the surface, frantically beating his wings to gain lift. When he lands he goes through a complicated process of folding his immense wings against his body. In the evening we would see the albatrosses floating asleep, heads buried in their breast feathers.

The legend that killing an albatross brings bad luck has been alleged by cynics to originate with Coleridge, and it is certainly true that some sailors used to kill albatrosses without compunction. Instead, they used pork fat enclosing a diamond-shaped metal hook which was towed behind the ship. A bird which took the fat got the hook caught in its beak and was hauled inboard. The flesh was cooked and the skin and feathers made into tobacco pouches. Once on deck, a captured albatross cannot take off because of the height of the bulwarks, so albatrosses could be easily kept in captivity. The sailors who did so noted that the birds had 'runny noses'. In fact this is an oil which is secreted from a tube above the beak, enabling the bird to rid itself of the excess salt which it accumulates from its diet and from drinking sea water. The wandering albatross roams the whole breadth of the Southern Ocean, and settles only on a few remote islands to breed. The nearest of these to us was Bird Island, off South Georgia, where the hillocks of tussock grass support a huge breeding colony. Our original plans called for a visit to South Georgia, but unfortunately this had been cancelled.

Our stations were now taking longer, because whenever the echo sounder showed a good depth of soft sediment we added a core to the station work. My Boxing Day enthusiasm enabled me to watch one of these operations. The coring tube is a 60-foot-long steel tube of three-inch internal diameter. It was stored along the starboard rail, and had to be slung outboard with the foredeck crane. A two-ton weight in the shape of a streamlined bomb is attached to the top end of the tube, together with a tripping mechanism which holds back a loose coil of extra line. The tube is lowered to within about sixty feet of the bottom, and then tripped so that it falls freely under its own weight. It plunges deeply into the sediment, which is thrust up into the tube. The tube is then hauled in. Today was the first core of the leg and things went wrong. The winch broke down while the core tube was still in the sea bottom, and as the ship drifted the force on the cable bent the tube. Roger Smith was in charge of cores for this leg, sending them back to his professor at Queen's University, and it took him hours to extract the core from the tube (the tube has a lining of plastic which normally slides out easily). This done, he spent the night on deck directly above my cabin wrestling the bends out of the tube with a noisy pipe-straightening wrench. A core provides a valuable record of the history of the ocean over the last several thousand years. In the South Atlantic the sediment is mostly an ooze consisting of the shells of minute protozoans called foraminifera, which sink to the bottom after the owner dies. If the salinity, water temperature or nutrients should change so that a certain species of foraminifera is no longer happy, it will move to new pastures and be replaced by a species with different tastes. Knowing the rate of deposition we can discover when these changes occurred by examining sections of core under the microscope.

By the time we reached 40°S the sea surface temperature was down to 14°C and dropping fast. We were passing through the Sub-Tropical Convergence, a zone where the warm surface water of the Tropics, called the Central Water Mass by oceanographers, meets cooler Sub-Antarctic surface water. This zone also marked our entry into the southern part of the great anticlockwise gyre in which the waters of the South Atlantic circulate. I have already mentioned the clockwise circulation in the North Atlantic, with the Sargasso Sea at its centre. In the southern hemisphere the effect of the earth's rotation is to turn currents to the left instead of the right, and this in conjunction with the winds produce an anticlockwise circulation. Just south of the Equator the waters run westward as the South Equatorial Current; they turn southward along the South American coast as the Brazil Current; then they turn eastward at higher latitudes; and finally flow northward up the African coast as the Benguela Current to complete the gyre. We were now entering the eastward flow, which itself forms a small part of the enormous eastward current around the globe at high latitudes called the Antarctic Circumpolar Current. As if to mark the occasion, a comet appeared that night, its long luminous tail pointing straight upwards from low down in the southern sky.

The new water mass also brought us new creatures. The next evening we stopped for a plankton tow. Looking over the stern I could see an amazing display of luminescent organisms being swept along by the slowly-turning propeller. Some were large diffuse blobs - probably colonies of luminous polyps - while the deep-sea fish showed up as bright darting lights. All of them were of a ghostly green colour. Dick Zurbrigg's tow with the Neuston net yielded a rich haul of lantern fish, and also an interesting siphonophore, *Physophora hydrostatica*. Like the Portuguese Man o'War this is an animal that is at the same time an individual and a colony. It is about three inches long, and looks like a cob of maize wearing a grass skirt. At the top is a pear-shaped transparent float, which holds the creature just below the surface. Then follows the cob which is made up of nectophores, little muscular tubes which pulsate in harmony to propel the creature along. The 'skirt' consists of a ring of bright pink palpons, or stinging cells, which serve as protection; the pink colour offers a friendly warning to enemies. Beneath the skirt is an inner ring of gastrozoids, the killing and digesting cells, which let down wavy tentacles into the water to kill the prey and haul it up to be broken down and digested externally. We had the little creature in the sink but, perhaps feeling annoyed and disturbed, it suddenly fell apart, and each of the individual cells tried to wriggle away.

The next day was New Year's Eve. We were on station 20 at 47° 30' S, deep into the Roaring Forties, and at last our good luck with the weather came to an end. The sea and wind had risen during the night, and when morning broke my cabin was a scene of desolation with every loose object on the deck. Percival Piranha, much the worse for wear, had flown gracefully from the porthole to lie with broken tooth and fin at the foot of my bunk. But the bottle cast had to go on. The ship was wallowing stern-on to the sea, and every few minutes it shuddered as a wave broke over the stern. This sent a flood of green water over the quarter deck and a fog of fine spray flew the length of the ship. Hanging over the Chains without benefit of safety line I was several times almost projected into the mountainous sea whose whitecaps boiled below me. The surface water temperature was down to 6°C, at which my survival time would be only a few minutes.

In the morning an iceberg appeared on radar, and it came into sight later that wild day. Seen through the curtain of mist and rain it looked like a mysterious wave-girt Gothic castle, rising to three jagged peaks. It had begun its life months or years earlier in the Antarctic as part of an ice shelf, a floating apron of ice which spreads out seawards from the ice sheet that covers the Antarctic continent. Stresses develop in the ice shelf from the action of wind and waves, and huge pieces break off and drift away. For this reason Antarctic icebergs are usually tabular in shape, whereas Arctic icebergs, which are formed by the calving of glaciers which come steeply down to sea level, are much more irregular and liable to capsizing. But here was an Arctic-shaped berg in the Antarctic. Clearly it was a fragment which had broken off a larger iceberg and which was now in an advanced state of decay as it drifted close to the northern limit for iceberg survival.

That evening we stopped for a short station in which Bruce Carson lowered the Bathysonde. I was on watch again, and at 10:02 p.m., which was 00:02 Greenwich Mean Time, I launched an XBT. The decade from 1970 to 1980 had been named the International Decade of Ocean Exploration by the United Nations, and so I had the honour of doing the first piece of oceanographic work towards this world-wide effort. However, the result was not a happy one. The XBT wire broke off early and was swept forward into the Bathysonde wire. I heard Bruce's anguished cry over the intercom:

"There are literally miles of XBT wire caught in the winch!"

It cost me several beers to restore his good humour.

The crew got started early on their own celebration of IDOE and by 10:30 all were unconscious except those on duty, who weaved from side to side. Once again we scientists were more civilised, or perhaps more inhibited by the presence of ladies, and New Year's Eve in the lounge was a tame occasion. At midnight Carol submitted to the embarrassment of being kissed on the cheek by various notables. I went to gaze at the vast grey sea and then lay down to sleep. The South Atlantic seemed as good a place as any to begin the 1970s.

As we crossed the 50th parallel Ced Mann ordered the stations to be more closely spaced. We were approaching the Antarctic Convergence, a second and more important convergence line at which sub-Antarctic surface water gives way to the true Antarctic water, immensely rich in nutrients, which supports a vast web of life. The first signs of this life soon appeared in the form of penguins. Four little heads popped up amongst our après-breakfast garbage and began bobbing and diving for titbits. They swam closer to the ship and looked up impertinently. They were small creatures, about thirty inches long, with black backs and reddish heads. I found a well-thumbed copy of *Birds of the Ocean* in the chartroom, and tentatively identified our new friends as Adélie penguins, which nest along the Antarctic coasts and sub-Antarctic islands. There was a vast increase, too, in the numbers of birds following the ship. The albatrosses were joined by Cape pigeons, small pure white birds with black heads; the larger sooty shearwaters and silver-grey fulmars; and the tiny Wilson's storm petrels. The little black storm petrel, known by sailors as Mother Carey's Chicken, dances frantically over the sea surface, dipping his feet in the water but scarcely ever settling. An old sailor's tradition is that this neurotic-looking bird contains the tormented spirit of a dead landlubber, while albatrosses are the reincarnations of the more noble souls of mariners.

More icebergs appeared, and during stations we would find ourselves surrounded by half a dozen at a time, standing round the horizon like the fallen megaliths of an ancient temple. Some had capsized, and looked like wedges of white cheese, while others were the normal tabular shape. The largest that we saw was a gigantic tabular berg, four miles long and 350 feet in height. It was impossible to believe that this incalculable mass was afloat; waves broke against it as if it were an island, and its cliff-like flanks glittered with a million diamonds in the fitful sunlight. But icebergs have a darker side. At 2:00 a.m. on January 3 I was suddenly awoken by a shuddering sensation. The whole ship was shaking to pieces, it seemed; the engines were screaming, and so was the Chief Engineer as he ran along the corridor outside. After a long and ominous silence the familiar throb began again and, having had a hard day, I went back to sleep. In the morning I found out that Pete Reynell had literally saved the ship from a 'growler'. This is a broken-off fragment of iceberg which has been so worn down by waves that it is virtually awash and does not show on radar in a heavy sea. However, it is still massive enough to sink a ship if hit at full speed. Pete was on watch on the bridge when he saw one of these fearsome objects bearing down on us, all unseen by the lookouts. He threw the engines into full astern and we stopped about fifty feet short of it. From that night on we always hove-to during the short hours of darkness.

Another unfriendly feature of the Southern Ocean is the size of waves that can be found here. The greater is the wind, the greater is the height and wavelength of the waves that it generates, and the Southern Ocean lies in the belt of powerful westerly winds. But to generate waves of the greatest possible height a wind must also have an infinite 'fetch', that is, it must blow over the sea surface for an unlimited distance. This makes the Southern Ocean unique, for only here can the westerly wind blow all the way round the world without encountering land as an obstacle. Therefore, even if there is no local gale, the ocean is always heaving with a long swell from some distant storm perhaps half a world away. The *Hudson* is a lively ship, so beyond 50°S the afterdeck was usually awash as a result of this motion. Ced decided to send a seaman down with me whenever I went aft to fire an XBT at night, as a safety precaution. On the first night of the new plan the victim was Mike Crimp, and by dividing our efforts we managed to squash my fingers in the breech block of the XBT launcher.

"Don't bother with the Doctor, the bo'sun will fix you up," said Mike, so down we went for ointment and bandages.

"Come on for'ard," said Mike casually. This was an important invitation, for the crew guarded the sanctity of the foc's'l with as much tenacity as the Doctor guarded the lounge. Hitherto I had unquestioningly accepted that my rightful home was the lounge, with all the social conventions that this represented. Yet my cabin was on the same deck as the crew's quarters, a deck below the panelled luxury of the scientists' cabins, and I shared with the crew the experience of being a long-term inmate. With a certain self-conscious trepidation I followed Mike into the noisy cramped foc's'l.

His cabin was wedge-shaped, and much of the space was lost to exposed pipes and stopcocks. It was also full of friends, whom he introduced.

"Have a drink," said Greg, the oiler. Rum was poured from a precious bottle. Silence returned. I felt like an intruder.

"Hey," said Greg suddenly, "is it you that I hear practising the guitar in your cabin? Why don't you bring it round and we'll have a party?"

The ice was broken. I played away as best I could with squashed fingers. Everyone sang lustily, songs that I knew and songs from the Maritimes that were strange to me. Liquid refreshment flowed. The noise attracted others, and there was a steady flux in and out of the cabin. Friendships began that were to last the whole voyage and enrich my life. These were men whom the Doctor described as 'scum', but I was at last waking up to the realisation that they were the finest kind of human being.

The party spilled over into the cabin next door. To my amazement two parrots were flying round the room, shedding feathers as they went.

"The green one's Pecos Pete and the pink one's Joe Carioca!" said Mike. "I got them in Rio."

"What are you going to do with them?" I asked.

"Take them right round America with me, of course," he said. "But you should have come in here a couple of days ago. We had a boa constrictor then, but he died yesterday!"

I was sure he was joking, but he wasn't. The pet snake had had an enjoyable time slithering over bunks and wrapping himself around pipes before succumbing to *Hudson* food, and had been buried honourably at sea. One of the parrots survived to Vancouver, whence Mike took him to Nova Scotia. At the time of writing Pecos Pete is still alive at the age of at least 40.

On January 3, as we reached 52°S, the sea changed colour completely to a deep organic green, and its temperature dropped to 3°C. Water bottles could be seen only down to a couple of metres below the surface. We had crossed the Antarctic Convergence at last, and were now in true polar waters. Plankton tows were now being done by Gus Vilks, a genial Latvian biologist from BIO. The day's rich sample of slime excited him greatly and, cradling the collecting bottle in his arms, he disappeared below to begin the patient work of preserving the sample and preparing microscope slides. Later I was able to peep down his microscope, and saw that the main cause of the sea's coloration was a tiny diatom called *Rhizoselenia*. The little needle-shaped plant is only ten microns long (one ten-thousandth of a centimetre) and untold billions of them are needed to give the water its colour and its broth-like consistency.

Where there are rich pastures of phytoplankton there must also be abundant zooplankton to feed off them, and in his evening trawl Dick Zurbrigg obtained an immense haul of euphausiids, small shrimp-like crustacea. The most famous and plentiful is the krill, *Euphausia superba*, which is the staple diet of the great baleen whales. As Dick preserved only representative specimens of his hauls, the epicures among us were able to carry off a bowl of krill to the pantry, where we fried them and ate them on toast. They tasted like a crunchy version of liver pate. A heated discussion began as to whether a whale can taste the food that he eats, and recourse to textbooks produced no enlightenment. A baleen whale feeds by cruising with his mouth open into a swarm of krill that he has previously located by sonar. He closes his jaws, entrapping a vast volume of water, since a row of parallel pleats beneath his chin enables his mouth to expand to more than its natural volume. Then he pushes his tongue forward and forces out the water through the sieve of baleen plates, leaving the krill behind. The whale then licks around his mouth and swallows his victims. Here, if anywhere, he needs tastebuds, in order to discriminate between krill and other types of plankton that may be poisonous to him.

Our southernmost station, at 55°S, was reached on January 5, and we deviated slightly from the 30th meridian to do a station over the South Sandwich Trench. This is a deep, narrow, crescent-shaped trough, of great importance to marine geologists, for according to the theory of seafloor spreading it is a 'subduction zone', where the moving Earth's crust (created at the mid-Atlantic Ridge) disappears downwards under a neighbouring plate. The trench is flanked by the Scotia Ridge, an undersea mountain range that pokes above the surface to form the South Sandwich Islands and South Georgia. In the Trench is the Meteor Deep, an 8,264-metre sounding made by the German *Meteor* expedition in 1925 and which is still the greatest known depth in the Atlantic Ocean. I think that Ced secretly hoped to better this. We stopped with 7900 metres beneath our keel, and began a bottle cast which had to be done in three stages: first the conventional shallow and deep casts, then a special cast to the bottom with extra wire spliced on the foredeck winch. Unfortunately the ship's drift during the cast took her into shallower water, and the deepest bottle went to a mere 7,400 metres.

I hoped that this was the end of bottle casting, but it was not to be. We were to sail west to the 40th meridian and do a closely spaced line of stations between 51°S and 48°S. Ced explained why. Along the ocean bottom runs a system of currents every bit as strong as those at the surface. The Antarctic Bottom Current is one of these, with a flow even greater than that of the Gulf Stream. It begins in the Weddell Sea, off the shores of Antarctica to the south of us, and is composed of very cold, saline water called Antarctic Bottom Water, which forms when growing sea ice expels salt downwards to mix with the waters beneath. The dense saline water that is created sinks to the bottom and heads north, the earth's rotation turning it westwards so that it hugs the east coast of South America until it finally loses its strength near the Equator. On its way north it must pass through two gaps in the Scotia Ridge, and here its speed is greatly increased. We were to study one of these gaps.

The next afternoon was bright and sunny, and as we plunged westwards great sheets of spray burst over the bow. I decided to take some photographs. First I tried the flying bridge, only to be drenched by spray. I retreated into the wheelhouse behind the Clear View Screen, where a rotating transparent disc keeps a window clear for the helmsman and lookouts. But the disc motor got in the way, so up I went to the Crow's Nest. This is a luxurious heated compartment, set amongst the radar scanners on top of the streamlined mainmast, and reached by a ladder running inside the mast. It is a far cry from the masthead barrel which sufficed for the early whalers and sealers. As I threw open the trapdoor into the Nest I was greeted by the surprised face of a seaman.

"What are you doing up here?"

"I was told to watch for whales a-blowing," he said.

"Do you know what they look like?"

"Lorjesus, no!"

I joined him in gazing across the boundless panorama of deep blue, flecked with white. In this second leg of the voyage we had been privileged in seeing the great chain of life in its simplest form. First come the phytoplankton, like *Rhizoselenia*, the microscopic pastures of the sea which drift in the sunlit surface water and convert its inorganic nutrients into the material of life. Then come the zooplankton, which browse on the phytoplankton and yet are active and vigorous enough to gather, like the krill, in great swarms. In this way they provide a concentrated source of food for fish, seals and the elusive baleen whales. In their turn the plankton-eating fish are consumed by larger fish and seals, ocean birds and toothed whales. But all life must end.

The bodies of the surface-dwellers sink down to the depths, where they feed the deep-sea scavenging fish and bottom dwellers. These creatures too must die, and the final essential link in the chain is the bacteria in the deep ocean, which break up this rain of dead organic matter and turn it back into mineral salts. The salts are carried by the deep currents to areas of upwelling, where they can once again reach the surface and nourish the phytoplankton. The cycle of life is complete, a cycle that is perfectly self-sustaining yet extremely fragile in ways that we do not yet understand. Today Man ignorantly tampers with all stages of the cycle; we pollute the surface waters with oil, sewage, detergents, DDT, heavy metals, radioactive waste, and insecticides which run off the long-suffering farmland of the earth into the ocean. And our carbon dioxide emissions from burning fossil fuels cause the ocean to heat up, become more acidic, and be less welcoming to life. Before we understand what we are doing we may break the cycle of life; then the sea will no longer yield its rich harvest and will become a barren, lifeless monument to the stupidity of the most destructive of all species.

That evening we began our new line of stations, and on the following day we were at last honoured by a visit from the whales. The seaman in the Crow's Nest shouted "Thar she blows!" (or equivalent) over the intercom, and we all rushed on deck clutching cameras. The first thing that I saw were four feathery blows, faint wisps of vapour, some way off on the starboard bow. We headed towards them, and then stopped our engines so that Pete Beamish could lower his hydrophone. Pete was understandably excited, and yelled over the intercom for the echo sounder to be switched off. The ship fell eerily silent, and we watched for half an hour as the whales circled around us. The occasional distant view of a dorsal fin inspired me to run off a hundred feet of the Institute's movie film. The blows were vertical, showing that they were not sperm whales. After Pete's tape had run out we set off in pursuit. The whales split into two pairs. We came near enough to one pair to see the long black backs and prominent dorsal fins as they arched out of the water very near the ship. Pete exclaimed, "I know what that is – it's the final dive of the fin whale!"

And so it was. One pair disappeared and the other drew away. I retired below to change reels. A few minutes later Roger rushed in, gesticulating at the porthole. The whole circle was filled with black flesh. I ran up on deck, to be met by an extraordinary sight. Two huge whales were swimming right alongside the ship, only a few feet from the port bow. They must have been making at least ten knots, and were oblivious of us. Their vast glistening bodies were at least seventy feet long, and left a foaming wake behind them. Pete was demented, screaming "Photograph! Photograph!" while his finger stabbed spastically at the trigger of an immense telephoto lens. One of the whales thrust its head out of the water, showing a huge eye, its mouth and a large white patch under the right jaw. The Doctor now appeared with a shotgun loaded with a whale-marking bolt. He took careful aim and fired. The bolt slid gently out of the barrel and plopped over the side, much to his chagrin. The whales now submerged right under the ship, leaving their bodies outlined in turbulent eddies. They were gone.

The episode had lasted only five minutes, but the excitement lasted the rest of the day. Why were the whales so unaffected by our presence? Pete thought that it was because they were feeding. At such times whalecatchers have been able to approach them at will. Pete had obtained his markers from the National Institute of Oceanography in England, which for many years had run a marking programme in the Southern Ocean. The bolts lodge in the blubber and are recovered by whalers, giving an idea of the migration routes of whales.

Nature was to give us one more spectacle in these fascinating waters. Two days later, while doing a bottle cast, I saw several shining bodies leaping towards the *Hudson* from starboard. Abandoning the cast to Bruce I ran down for the movie camera. When I emerged the sea was full of a school of pilot whales. These are small whales, a mere 25 feet long, and they are in the same family as dolphins. They were leaping out of the water with as much vigour as their smaller cousins, and were completely unafraid of us. There were at least 50 of them, and the sheer numbers filled me with a sense of the life-sustaining power of the ocean. Yet pilot whales have been seen in schools of up to a thousand - what a magnificent sight that would be! While one whale would thrust his bluff globular snout out of the water, his neighbour on the next wave crest would make a smooth arching leap, displaying his streamlined dorsal fin and black back with a big white patch behind the fin. Occasionally a whale would do a vertical dive in which his tail flukes were waving in the air. Another would fling himself bodily from the water, showing the clear white blaze that stretches back from his mouth, and then fall back with a splash. The whales kept us company for over an hour before going to play elsewhere. Pilot whales are too small to attract the attention of southern whalers, but they are still hunted in the Faroes by an ancient technique. Schools sometimes appear near the coasts, feeding on fish, and the local fishermen herd them into a confined bay or inlet, sealing off the entrance with a boom of boats. A bloodbath then begins, every available man setting-to with lance or gun until the bay runs with gore. In the Faroes this is a major source of fresh meat and oil for the winter. In Newfoundland the name for the whale – pothead – is an exact translation of the Latin name *Globicephala.*

Our new friends reappeared after supper for a new display. This time they played close to the bow, and I could see that there were many females with young calves. Pete Beamish took a shotgun up to the bow, hoping to take a baby whale as a specimen, but fortunately his aim was poor. The whales were so close that I could hear the hiss as each whale surfaced and blew, and I fancied also that I could smell the whales' breath, an odour like the interior of a butcher's shop on a warm day.

On January 11 the final bottle station was completed, and Bruce and I drained several bottles in celebration. The *Hudson* turned her bows from the Southern Ocean and headed for the warmer climes of Buenos Aires. The original plan had been to call at Mar del Plata, a seaside resort on the Atlantic coast of Argentina, but the harbour channel was found to be too shallow. We still stopped for the occasional station, but as these consisted only of plankton tows and reverberations I was able to watch them with benign tolerance. Orest Bluy and George Gill were much troubled by seabirds. When George flung his TNT charge over the stern it floated away beneath a bright red balloon, and many times a bird would swoop down to perch on this attractive object. George would shout and wave his arms, but usually the explosion and fountain of spray would subside to reveal a bedraggled but still airworthy bird staggering dazedly away. As the air grew warm the camp cots reappeared on the upper deck, and a group of us began a programme of jogging round the deck in an attempt to regain the use of our legs.

As we approached Argentina, Iver Duedall was busy working up the results of his oxygen measurements. On this leg he had been helped by Art Coote, a fine and gentle chemist from BIO, and by John Sharpe, a student of Pete Wangersky. Sharpe did a variety of projects on board; one of them was to stand in the bow each morning holding up a syringe with which he sucked in an air sample. He analysed this for carbon dioxide content, which varies over the ocean surface because of the varying amounts of phytoplankton; like plants on land, these produce CO_2 by transpiration during the day. Plankton, this time the animal plankton, are also the chief cause of the variation in oxygen which Iver found in his carefully drawn section of the South Atlantic. When water is at the surface it absorbs oxygen from the atmosphere, so water masses which were recently exposed in this way have high oxygen concentration. An example is North Atlantic Deep Water, found at mid-depths in the South Atlantic but coming from the surface regions of the North Atlantic. When water is isolated from the surface, its oxygen is depleted by the respiration of zooplankton and by the work of bacteria in decomposing organic material. Antarctic Bottom Water, for instance, is low in oxygen because of its long journey along the seabed from the far south.

On January 15 we finally made our landfall. Throughout the sultry morning various signs of land appeared – pieces of flotsam, a pair of harbour seals, some brown birds, and a water colour which changed from blue to green and then to brown. The Norwegian ore carrier *Skaustrand* passed us on her way to sea, the first ship that we had seen in four weeks. Just after noon Uruguay appeared over the horizon dead ahead. The first land in sight was the Isla Lobos, a low island at the mouth of the estuary of the River Plate (Rio de la Plata). It possessed only some scrubby vegetation and a lighthouse. Behind it the mainland soon came up, with a long white beach backed by low hills, and soon we saw the tall buildings of the city of Maldonado. We turned to port off Isla Lobos to enter the narrow dredged channel, marked by buoys. The estuary itself was still very wide; the Argentine side was over the horizon, while on the Uruguayan side a range of high hills slipped by, one of which was conical and crowned by a cross and was marked on the chart as Sugarloaf Mountain. Later in the afternoon we reached the pilot station off Montevideo. The pilot ship, painted in an arresting pattern of black and white bars, hove-to against the setting sun and despatched an ancient rust-streaked launch. Two pilots came aboard, one for the river and one for docking, and we began a cautious upstream passage. The channel was very narrow, and outgoing ships had to pass within a few yards of us.

Late in the evening I went down to the coffee room and found the dock pilot sitting alone. He spoke excellent English and we fell into conversation. The talk came round to politics, and he began to explain the philosophy of military dictatorships.

"In South America the military is big and powerful. This is why. Suppose there are six people who want to become Presidente, and I am the military. Each one will say 'If you help me I will increase your budget'. So I help first one, then another. After six I say 'Why should I let these weak corrupt civilians rule when I am powerful enough to take over myself?' So I do, and that is the end of democracy. It is like feeding meat to a baby lion – eventually he grows up and eats you. The people now are tired of disorder. They threw out Perón, but they do not know how to get along without him. Perhaps they will ask him back one day. But General Ongania, he may rule for many years. People have forgotten what freedom is. I do not like what is happening to my country."

We returned to the happier subject of piloting.

"There are eighty pilots for La Plata. Some are for the river, some for the port and some cover the local traffic to the Paraná River. The ship channel up the Plate is only thirty feet deep, and the tidal range is two feet. Many ships draw thirty feet, but this does not matter. The bottom is very soft mud, and the ship can push through it. I just came off the *Skaustrand* – she sailed out at five knots under full power. Sometimes the captains thank me for cleaning the barnacles off their keels, other times they ask me 'When am I going to be able to float out of here?'"

"But isn't the channel dredged?"

"Yes, but it is done by private companies who dump the mud only a little way out to sea so that it is brought back by the next tide. In that way they always have work for the future... This is an interesting ship. Where are you going from here?"

"Tierra del Fuego and the Antarctic."

"Ah, they are beautiful. For many years I was in the Navy and served in the Argentine sector of Antarctica."

His eyes twinkled.

"Of course, Great Britain claims that part too. The River Plate is an easy place to work. In Patagonia I once served in a place with a 38-foot tidal range and an eight knot tidal current. That was Puerto San Julián, where your Captain Drake hanged Mr. Doughty because he was planning mutiny."

His eyes twinkled again.

"I hope you like our city. The girls are very beautiful. And very friendly to Englishmen!"

CHAPTER 6

TRAVELS IN ARGENTINA

Our chief amusement [in Buenos Aires] was riding about and admiring the Spanish ladies. After watching one of these angels gliding down the streets, involuntarily we groaned out "How foolish English women are, they can neither walk nor dress".

Charles Darwin.

I WOKE TO AN unnatural silence. The engines were stopped, though the water was still slapping past the hull. I rushed up on deck and found us in the care of an ancient steam tug called *Mariden*, whose grim efforts to tow us caused her to emit fierce clouds of black smoke. I peered through the smoke screen and there, across the brown murky waters of the river Plate, was the city of Buenos Aires. The long, low waterfront was lined with oil storage tanks, power stations and factories. Further upriver, behind a wall of trees, rose the business centre of the city, a nondescript huddle of buildings above which loomed two or three new glass office blocks. For the largest city in South America this was not a very inspiring effort, but at least it was land, bringing the exciting promise of new experience and adventure.

Passing the commercial docks we were given the honour of berthing in Darsena Norte (North Basin), the nearest dock basin to the city centre. It seemed to be full of maritime relics, for on one side of us was the *Sarmiento*, an old three-masted steam auxiliary now used as a naval museum, while beside her was the British barque *Wavertree* with her masts removed but otherwise in good condition, waiting to be towed to New York to join the South Street Seaport Museum. Alongside a group of naval vessels Pete Beamish espied the graceful lines of the former research schooner *Atlantis* of Woods Hole Oceanographic Institution, now *El Austral* of the Argentine Navy. As soon as we were safely berthed the agents came aboard bringing the luxury of mail from home and a real English-language newspaper, the *Buenos Aires Herald.* I quickly digested the antics of the world's politicians then set off with Roger for a look at the city.

After leaving the dock area we came to a large and pleasant park, the Plaza San Martín, where we began to wander in a very disoriented way, struck dizzy by 'shore-sickness'. This disease, which took many hours to wear off, is caused by the simple and restricted nature of the environment at sea, making the mind quite unready for the thronging impressions which crowd upon it in a city: the sunshine, the flowers, the cars, the trees and the hordes of people. Most of all, the girls! Darwin was not exaggerating when he extolled their beauty and poise. And there was such a plentiful supply of them, lying around on the grass and munching their lunchtime sandwiches.

In the middle of the park is a tall clock tower, the Torre de los Ingleses, beneath which photographers plied for trade with primitive box cameras. A statue beside the tower was 'erected by the people of Argentina to George Canning', the British Prime Minister at the time of Argentine liberation. British influence in Argentina used to be immense; British capital controlled transport, banks, insurance and public utilities. The florid portico of Estación Retiro overlooking the park is an example of this, for Argentina's vast railway system, which did much to open up the country, was financed by Britain and built by Scottish engineers.

We crossed a wide boulevard with the lengthy name of Avenida Libertador San Martín (José de San Martín is the national hero) and came to the beginning of Calle Florida, the famous shopping street. In 1970 this narrow avenue was a pedestrian precinct lined with expensive leather-goods and jewellery shops as well as a department store called Harrods (no relation to the one in London). Its entrance was flanked by the drab concrete pile of the 26-storey Kavanagh Building, once famous as the only skyscraper in South America, and by the faded stateliness of the old Plaza Hotel. Nearby was a Bank of America branch where we changed our money into pesos. Lurking outside the door was the proprietress of a leather-goods store, and as soon as we emerged she used her charms and command of the English language to entice us into her emporium. Here she displayed a vast range of exotic articles produced by the slaughter of various forms of wildlife. We had just stepped ashore and our defences were down. I bought a pair of porcupine-skin gloves for my mother, and Roger was conned into buying a handbag for his girlfriend made from the skin of the *rhea*, or South American ostrich. This bird was once found in great flocks on the pampas but it is now very rare, thanks to the activities of souvenir-happy tourists like ourselves.

We took refuge from the heavy noon heat in a small Italian restaurant which was crowded with building workers. Over a meal of festering yellow chicken we decided to visit Montevideo the next day, as there was a new hydrofoil service across the Plate to Uruguay. Meanwhile we gamely set out again on foot. Buenos Aires looked a cultivated and civilised city, but it seemed to lack the colour and excitement of Rio. People on the streets appeared far too respectable and normal. We soon came to the main centre of the city, the Plaza de Mayo. On one side stands the Casa Rosada (Pink House), an ornate baroque building where the President conducts his business. It was guarded by grenadiers in fancy dress, but I imagine that there were more effective guards out of sight to protect General Ongania from his subjects. Behind Casa Rosada is the Home Affairs Ministry, still pock-marked from the strafing by fighter 'planes that it received during the 1955 coup which deposed the colourful dictator Juan Perón. By contrast, on the other side of the square squats the little whitewashed building of the Cabildo, or Town Council, where the declaration of Argentine independence was read out in 1810.

We went into the 19th century cathedral which stands nearby. Its impressive Roman colonnade gives way to an ugly interior where, amidst gilded scrolls, cherubs and gloomy paintings, rests the marble sarcophagus of San Martín, guarded by grenadiers. Around the walls are containers with the ashes of his lieutenants. San Martín was the great leader who liberated Argentina, Chile and Peru from Spanish rule. Later he was rejected by the countries that he had freed and he died in France in great poverty and bitterness.

After a while we came out on the Avenida 9 de Julio, which boasts of being the widest city thoroughfare in the world. It was built by the simple process of removing a city block, and it is short (14 blocks) because the planners came up against public buildings that could not be moved. It serves more as an open space than a road – the lanes are used mostly for car parking – and is adorned with fountains and large obelisks. On one side is the elaborate façade of the Teatro Colón, the most prestigious theatre in Buenos Aires, looking like a railway station with its cast iron verandah. Roger suggested that we take in a theatre show, but we found that the season at the Colón had not yet started. Buenos Aires is alleged to have 44 theatres, so we asked a group of three youths lounging nearby the way to the nearest one that was open. They turned out to be law students – a prolific breed in a country where a law degree is the passport to a comfortable career – and one of them, Hugh, spoke good English and elected to become our guide.

According to Hugh there were no theatre shows worth seeing, but he would show us some of the sights of the city, an offer which we gratefully accepted. The first sight turned out to be the synagogue, which Hugh wanted to visit because his girlfriend was Jewish. On the way Hugh suddenly stated that he was nervous and was taking tranquillisers. This soon became apparent when, after donning skullcaps in the antechamber, we were shown into the synagogue by a dinner-jacketed usher. Hugh immediately began to talk loudly, disturbing the small sprinkling of worshippers. Feeling that we were insulting somebody else's religion I rose to go, but Hugh began a heated discussion with the usher, continuing up the aisle and into the street where Hugh quit the place with various oaths and hand gestures. It seemed that he had asked for a book on the synagogue's history, and got angry when the usher explained that he did not have one.

Although Hugh kept up an interesting running commentary as we wandered round the city, we found his public behaviour rather alarming. Whenever a pretty girl passed by he would call out some ribald remark, such as "let me put my bread in your basket" to one carrying a loaf, and when an old woman in a hurry trod on his foot there was a major scene involving a choice exchange of language which attracted a small crowd. His friends shrugged as if they were used to it, but by this time we felt that we were in the hands of a lunatic. Following a standard Argentine dinner of gargantuan steak Roger and I pleaded urgent business aboard ship, and after elaborate expressions of thanks betook ourselves away with some relief.

Unfortunately we had told Hugh of our plans to visit Montevideo, and next morning at 7:00 I was awakened by the quartermaster who said that there was someone waiting at the gangway. It was Hugh, who announced his intention of escorting us to the hydrofoil jetty. Roger and I had a quick breakfast and then, finding Hugh still at the gangway in heated argument with the quartermaster, we dragged him to a taxi and set off for the hydrofoil jetty. The 8:00 hydrofoil had just sailed, and when we tried to buy tickets for the next boat we were informed that we could not leave the country unless we obtained a letter from the Captain to say who we were. We should then take this to the Immigration Office for the relevant hundreds of forms to be filled in.

On the way back to the *Hudson* we passed the training ship *Libertad* in dock, so we stopped to admire this lovely vessel. A splendid fully-rigged three-master, she was built in 1963 to train cadets for the Argentine Navy.

The smooth white lines of the hull sweep up to a classic naked wench at the prow, and I thought how colourful the dockside scene must have been in the heyday of the square-riggers. Her appearance was marred only by her super-structure, a stubby funnel and some popguns used for saluting purposes.

Back on the equally beautiful *Hudson* we persuaded one of the ship's agents to take us to the offices of Houlder Brothers, where we collapsed into ancient leather armchairs in a vast pillared hall. After much rummaging it was found that nothing could be done about the paperwork for Montevideo until Monday, so we acknowledged our defeat by red tape and decided to go inland to Córdoba instead. Politeness having failed to dislodge Hugh, we adopted the cowardly expedient of departing in a taxi while he was engaged in another street argument. We returned to the *Hudson* to find her crawling with shifty characters offering dubious goods and the procurement of girls. Mike and Greg were going on an afternoon coach tour of the Tigre marshes, so we decided to join them and leave for Córdoba by rail in the evening. An open house, when visitors were to be shown over the ship, had fortunately been postponed, so we had three days of freedom.

Our guide on the coach was a genial middle-aged Scotswoman called Janie, a second generation immigrant. We followed the coast northwards through the lush suburb of San Isidro, passing the private residence of the President, set in vast grounds and surrounded by tall railings and a thicket of trees. Then followed the more fly-blown suburb of San Bernadino and finally came a shanty town of wooden shacks. Here live the thousands of landless peasants who have flocked to the big city in search of a job. After travelling 30 miles we alighted at Tigre, a town on the Paraná Delta. The delta is a vast roadless tract where the Rio Paraná splits into a labyrinth of channels meandering among low, swampy islands, before coalescing with the Rio Uruguay to flow into the estuary of the Plate. The brown murk of the Plate is partly sewage and partly soil washed down from this region. We boarded a small motor launch called the *Mabel II* and chugged through the waterways, which were thronged with pleasure craft and swimmers. In this area the islands are used for summer cottages and yacht clubs, but the remoter parts of the marshes are sparsely populated and given over to fruit and vegetable growing; the produce has to be brought out by boat. One unassuming little cabin that we passed was the retreat of Domingo Sarmiento, an unusual man who was both a philosopher and one of the country's finest Presidents, serving from 1868 to 1874.

I started chatting with Janie, who chuckled when she heard of the rapacious saleswoman. She recommended a place called the 'Crazy Lamb', and on the way back the coach dropped us there. The owner, who clearly loved his work, showed us his workrooms and explained the techniques by which skins are cured. His low-key approach lowered our defences and, as I had left Halifax with little in the way of shore-going rig, I bought a suede jacket. The owner drove us back to the ship where we packed for our journey and caught up on the latest news. The Captain had just been down to bail the Chief Engineer out of gaol. There were conflicting accounts of how Sam got there: some said he was drunk and hailed a police car instead of a taxi, while others maintained that he had been waylaid by an engineer whom he had sacked. The engineers were jubilant at Sam's misfortunes, for he had refused to allow them shore leave in Buenos Aires apart from the normal breaks between shifts.

Mike Crimp decided to come to Córdoba with Roger and me, and we made a last-minute dash to the Estación Retiro in the immaculate old Pontiac of the ship's agent. Leaping aboard a few seconds before departure we then spent a tedious time being misdirected up and down the train by officials. At last we found our sleeping compartment, which must have dated from the Victorian era. The interior was of ancient, heavily varnished wood, with a musty odour reminiscent of old school desks. There were four berths, again of wood and without restraining straps. In between was an extraordinary piece of sanitary equipment, a wooden stand containing an enamel chamber pot, water jug, towels and soap, and a folding steel washbowl fed from a single tap marked 'Tire'. Small cupboards, smelling of dead rodents, opened at the head of each bunk for hanging clothes. Each had a little hole at the bottom to let the vermin out or to recover lost objects. The decor was completed by a veritable instrument panel of brass switches and buttons on the wall; we tried them all, with no detectable result. The level of lighting depended on the speed of the train; when stationary it was virtually nil. We now understood why we were charged only 13 dollars for a 450-mile journey by 'first-class sleeper'.

The fourth occupant of the compartment was a businessman called Manuel, who bore up well under the burden of three foreigners. We struck up a four-way conversation involving snatches of English, French, Spanish and Italian, and by some miraculous means we succeeded in exchanging ideas. We fed on the usual steak in the dining car and copiously toasted international friendship. Manuel pointed out the locomotive factory, some 40 miles from Buenos Aires, in which he worked. By now it was nearly midnight so, after balancing in turn over the hole in the floor at the end of the carriage which served as a toilet, we drew lots for berths. The upper berths, which had no ventilation, fell to Mike and me. Sleep was difficult because ticket inspectors kept coming round to collect parts of our tickets and stamp other parts. Eventually I dropped off, while the great level plains of the pampas fled past our wheels.

We were woken at 7:15 a.m. by the conductor, who said that we were half an hour from Córdoba. After washing with the sanitary machine we found ourselves entering the dusty suburbs of a large country town, set in a wide valley surrounded by the foothills of the Andes. Most of the suburban houses were one-storey dwellings of adobe, with peeling plaster and flat roofs on which were perched water cisterns looking like large dustbins. At the station we went into the cafeteria with Manuel for some tiny cups of their superb coffee. The walls were tiled, like an old grocer's emporium, and lined with cages containing songbirds from the countryside around. They treated us to a morning chorus as we bade farewell to our new friend and set off into the town.

It was Sunday morning and the streets were deserted. The mountain air tasted like wine as we wandered past baroque churches and pleasantly tatty houses. Presently there arose a faint chugging noise and an ancient Ford Model T truck came puttering down the street. Cars seem to thrive in this climate; there were so many old vehicles parked along the streets that it looked like a film set for *Bonnie and Clyde*. We soon came out on a pretty little square, overlooked by an old colonial church with twin towers framing the portico and an elaborate cupola decorated with mosaics. Several beggars were standing outside as the people filed in for the service. The town was waking up. In a little side street a crowd of children in identical uniforms was being taken by nuns to queue for a bloodthirsty Western film. The competing cinema next door was showing *The Loves of Isadora*, and the children were told to avert their eyes from the posters showing the heroine naked. In a small cafe where we stopped for a drink we asked the proprietor which were the best places to visit. He waved his arms.

"Córdoba is dead today, señor. Catch the bus to Carlos Paz."

He pointed up the road, which was the general direction of the bus station. We gathered that Carlos Paz was a resort up in the hills by a lake. The walls of the street were daubed with messages such as "Reforma", "Suelten a Ongaro de Tosco torres" (Freedom to Ongaro from cruel imprisonment) and various Communist slogans, indicating that all was not well in this seemingly idyllic town.

Córdoba is an old colonial city, founded in 1573 when Spanish expeditions from Peru crossed the Andes and came down the eastern flanks on the Inca highway. The Jesuits controlled the city for many years and founded the University, the oldest in Argentina, in 1613. Córdoba became the third city of Argentina, and in 1970 it had a population of 600,000 and a thriving car industry. However it was run on feudal lines by an alliance between the Church and an extreme reactionary group of the military known, paradoxically, as the Reds; the more moderate group who ran the national government at that time were called the Blues. A few months earlier, in May 1969, there were riots by workers and students after the government tried to impose a wage freeze on industrial workers and purge the University of dissidents. These riots were put down with massive brutality; little news was allowed to leak out, but I was later to learn more from an actual participant.

We came out on a main thoroughfare, Avenida General Paz, lined by science buildings of the University; the Engineering Department in particular looked small and squalid. At length we reached a large square, flanked by the administrative building of the University which bore the simple message 'Che!' in large red letters. On the square we spotted two attractive girls, so we nonchalantly sidled up and asked them the way to the bus station. Our luck was in, for they spoke some English. Sensing our inherent warmth and human loveliness they took us to the bus station where we all had a beer and exchanged life stories. One of the girls, Ana-Marie, was an alluring Syrian immigrant with long black hair and liquid eyes. She was a student of chemical engineering at the University of Santa Fé. The other girl, Alcida, was pert and attractive and worked in a photographic laboratory. Learning of our plans they expressed surprise.

"But have you not come for the Festival del Folklore at Cosquín?"

Cosquín, they explained, is a little town up in the hills some thirty miles away. Every year it is given over to a national festival of folk music, to which young and old come from all over Argentina. This sounded splendid stuff, and after judicious chatting-up we arranged to meet them at Cosquín in the evening. Meanwhile they put us on the right bus for Carlos Paz.

The road from Córdoba led westward past the Instituto Aerotécnico, a large Air Force establishment which designs its own aircraft. After a few miles we entered rolling mountains of green and purple, covered with scrub and bushes. This is the Sierra Córdoba, a chain of fold mountains that runs parallel to the Andes some 200 miles to the east of them. We skirted the foot of a mountain lake, Lago San Roque, and came to the dusty village of Carlos Paz. On the girls' advice we carried on a little way and got off by a bridge that spans the Rio San Antonio near its junction with the lake. Strung out along the road was a ribbon development of hotels and restaurants. The river is normally slow and meandering, and is ideal for swimming and sailing. Today, however, a dam was being sluiced out and the river was swollen to a raging muddy torrent, so we sought out a place to have lunch.

Along the road we found a restaurant which was crowded so, taking this as a good sign, we settled at a food-stained table on the verandah. We now encountered a phenomenon that we were to meet throughout these country regions, and that was the unaffected interest and friendliness of the natives. People at neighbouring tables would talk to us or come over and crowd round, proffering advice on where to go and what to see. Their friendliness was redoubled as soon as they learned that we were *canadienses* rather than *americanos*. Our conversations would be lengthy, for they had to be carried out in fractured Italian or in one-word chunks from my Spanish dictionary. Mike attracted particular interest as he was wearing his 'travelling hat', a felt thing with a large seagull feather in it. The waiter, however, was a shifty-eyed character who started questioning us about our cameras and then asked if anyone knew that we were here. Fearing that he was the secret head of a robber band we replied that we were itinerant karate experts. The food, when it came, made an interesting meal. The Argentinians eat almost every part of a cow, and one course consisted of blood sausage and assorted tubes which tasted gristly but quite pleasant. That is, until I translated the menu and found that they were fried large and small intestines. On closer inspection the sausage skin proved to be hairy on the inside.

Aghast, we decided to press on to Cosquín. At first we tried hitch-hiking, but without success. The road was alive with people, mostly young, in cars, mostly old, and they all had a cheery wave and a word for us which I was unable to find in the dictionary. We then tried to catch a bus, but none was going the right way. Buses in Argentina are extravagant creations covered with burnished chrome and with little chrome animals on the bonnet. We walked back across the bridge, where we saw an old woman with a llama, the first I had seen outside a zoo. It looked like a long-necked sheep, with matted brown wool. At last we found a bus for Cosquín, which took us along the lake side and then struck into the hills along the wide gorge of the Rio Cosquín, ending at the dusty bus station.

I shall always remember Cosquín as one of the nicest little towns that I have ever visited. It is set in an amphitheatre of purple hills, of which the most prominent peak, surmounted by a cross, is called Cerro Pan de Azúcar (Sugarloaf Ridge). The dusty streets were lined by trees, adobe houses and ancient cars. The people matched their surroundings by appearing unhurried and relaxed. Cosquín had been the site of the National Festival of Folklore for the previous ten years. The festival would be going on for a week, and already the streets were filling with young people; the heavy rucksacks that some carried showed how far they had travelled. Almost every exposed bare wall in the town carried a mural, vigorously executed, of country life in Argentina, mainly showing the ubiquitous gaucho with his blanket, spurs, guitar and ever-present horse.

We came upon a large park, with lawns and flowers and the usual monument to some general in the middle. Here stalls had been set up exhibiting folk craft from all over Argentina – ceramics, carving, metalwork and textiles – while in one corner an open air steak grill was under construction ready for the night's concert. Donkey carts rattled by in the street behind. Meanwhile Roger had discovered a souvenir shop, full of gaucho equipment and fine alpaca ponchos. We dragged him away and tried to find a hotel for the night, but without success, so, adapting to local custom, we sat down at a pavement cafe to watch the girls go by; these included the voluptuously shaped daughter of the proprietor. Again we became the centre of attention and were surrounded by a crowd of friendly locals.

Soon it was time to meet our two friends, so we went to the bus station and finally found them in the throng. People were now arriving in large numbers; every bus was packed, with cheerful children clinging to the roof racks. The girls led us to a large plaza at the edge of town called the Plaza del Folklore, where the all-night folk concert was to be held. It had been converted into an open-air auditorium with seats for 5,000 and a large stage; two loudspeaker towers were disguised as grotesque figures.

The concert was due to start at 10 p.m., and in the meantime we adjourned to a churchyard which had been converted into a bar and grill. The rustic tables were packed with happily drunken people; after several beers we were as happy and as drunken as the rest. The girls were lively company; Alcida spoke Italian which meant that I could communicate. They plied us with a local corn soup, and I explored the churchyard's toilet facilities, which consisted of holes in the ground in the close vicinity of some tombstones. By the time the concert started Roger and Mike were dead to the world. I retained partial command of my faculties, so I paid the bill and escorted the girls to the ticket office, where they charmed a policeman into letting us in at the front of the long queue. We returned through the dense crowd to where Roger and Mike were wandering in aimless circles, and herded them into the auditorium.

The concert was now in full swing. Each act was introduced by the splendidly swaggering figure of Julio Marbíz, the Master of Ceremonies. In a state bordering on ecstasy he would shout "Aquí Cosquín! Capital del Folklore!"

Then, in rolling waves of resonant phraseology, he would vent forth a torrent of praise for the forthcoming act, followed by an admiring reference to the Coca Cola Company's sponsorship support. Immense applause would follow, then the act would leap onto the stage and begin immediately. A typical group would consist of 3-5 guitarists, a side drummer and a bamboo flautist. Either everyone would sing in harmony, assisted by the audience, or else there would be a soloist with the other voices crooning a refrain. Dress ranged from a sweat shirt and *bombachas* (the baggy trousers worn by gauchos) to formal evening dress with the inevitable gaucho blanket draped round the shoulders. The most exciting and haunting rhythms came from Indian groups from the northern Andean provinces of Salta and Jujuy. The only distractions were the abysmal quality of the loudspeakers and the strident voices of the coffee and ice cream vendors hawking their wares round the benches.

Lulled by the music Roger and Mike sank into a deep alcoholic sleep. Complete unquestioning contentment is a state seldom attained on this planet, but there amid the fragrant smoke of frying steaks, sandwiched between two lovely girls who eagerly explained the good and bad points of each performer, I was very close to it. Heaven must be like this. The songs concerned the beauty of the pampas and heroes who committed murder, wasted away or died violently, all for the sake of *amor*.

I sat enthralled through four hours in which every performer poured out his heart and soul to the audience. Then Roger and Mike woke up and were anxious to leave, so after watching a folk opera which the girls translated, we set off. The music pursued us through the town, relayed by loudspeakers on every lamp-post. All the restaurants, bars and shops were open, and the main street was full of happy, tipsy people – grandfathers and grandmothers were dancing arm in arm. We slowly headed for the bus station where the girls planned to take a bus for Córdoba. While we had coffee in a bar Alcida went out and bought us each a little wooden doll in a tall hat (a local cartoon character) then gave us each a big lingering kiss. Then we said goodbye, feeling deep pangs of tender regret. I still have the doll.

Roger decided to sleep in the bus station and Mike to try the park. I went along with Mike, but it had turned cold and the loudspeakers were still in action, so, leaving Mike curled up on the grass in a multicoloured gaucho blanket, I returned to the bus station. It was filled with huddled bodies, amongst whom I found a few square feet of floor and stretched out on my coat. In front of me was a bench on which several peasants were sleeping sitting up, heads on each others' shoulders. Eventually the inevitable happened – the one on the end fell off with a thud. Nearby, two or three Indians in an advanced state of drunkenness were improvising wildly on their guitars, but despite this I drifted off to sleep. At 6 a.m. a policeman came round and delicately jabbed his toe into everyone in order to eject us.

It was getting light and we headed for the park, where a dew-covered heap on the grass resolved itself into a sleeping Mike. I stretched out on a narrow bench and slept for another hour, by which time people were crossing the park on their way to work and an ice lorry was delivering its slabs from door to door. We found a pavement cafe open and had coffee and rolls; despite the early hour the tables were crowded and again came the friendly but embarrassing attention. This little country town, bathed in the crisp wine-like air and sunlight of the eastern Andes, was clearly a place where foreign tourists were not common. Accompanied by one of the leading lights of the cafe, who offered to act as an interpreter, we returned to the ethnic souvenir shop where we overspent on ponchos, sets of bolas and drinking horns.

Loaded down with spoil we went into a quiet restaurant to eat. It was a shabby place with a high varnished ceiling, yet it too had a big mural on one wall. Whilst enjoying the best steak that I had ever tasted I thought how wonderful it was to be able to sit around in a quiet friendly little town on a sunny morning, an infinite distance in space and spirit from the cold climes of Nova Scotia or from my own home in England. Life's cares seemed to fall away. We all felt in the same mellow mood, and sat in splendid idleness into the afternoon until it was time to catch our bus back to Córdoba.

Córdoba, down at a lower altitude, was dusty and fiercely hot. We sought the shelter of the nearest bar, where the usual friendly crowd gathered around us. One of them spoke good English, a Jewish shopkeeper who ran a newsagent's business in part of the bar. His son Eduardo, a local student, offered to show us the sights of the town, of which he said there were only two: the zoo and the cathedral.

As we passed innumerable grandiose churches, Eduardo began talking of a students' revolt which had happened the previous May, unreported in British newspapers. He himself had taken part. Córdoba, he said, was a strong centre both of student radicalism and of the hated army which was running the country. The army sent the secret police into local factories and the traditionally autonomous University to report on malcontents. The students and the militant labour unions rose in common cause. There were riots and demonstrations in the streets, to which the military overreacted. According to Eduardo, someone started sniping at the soldiers from an upper window, the someone being a paid agent of the USA. The soldiers responded by firing indiscriminately at the unarmed demonstrators, killing 156 people. Eduardo himself was wounded in the side. News of the massacre was suppressed. The army finally brought in armoured cars to quell the revolt, as they feared that it would spread nationwide. Thousands were arrested and held in the military barracks. Most, including Eduardo, were released after a week, but many were given military trials and heavy sentences, and some had simply disappeared. Although the city was now quiet the causes of the trouble still remained. We listened with some incredulity, scarcely believing that such savagery could occur in such an apparently civilised and pleasant society. Yet of course we were hopelessly naive; this was only 1970 and still the age of innocence. Over the next decade, tens of thousands of innocent Argentinians would disappear in the 'dirty war' by which the military tried to perpetuate its power, and I have often wondered if Eduardo himself ended his life in a torture chamber or thrown out of an aeroplane.

By now our walk had brought us to the zoological gardens, which were laid out attractively (for humans) down the side of a hill in a labyrinth of plants and shrubbery. The first open-air cage that we reached contained a pair of short-haired grey monkeys who, on seeing us, began to copulate. The sign said 'Mono barrigudo común de Brasil', the Common Fat-Bellied Brazilian Monkey. A polar bear wilted in the fierce heat. A pair of sleek jaguars paced a cage with their young, the first to breed successfully in captivity. A huge aviary built into the side of the hill contained condors, the most magnificent of all birds. However, rather than display their 18-foot wingspans they preferred to sit hunched in their eyries, eyeing us unblinkingly. Mike began to tease a white llama to see if he would spit. He drew back his lips, revealing a convenient slit between his two front teeth, so we retired quickly.

Emerging from the zoo Mike decided that he wanted a sleep, so we left him lying in the park and walked up to a plaza which overlooks the city. From this elevated position Córdoba looked like a big dusty Italian town, dotted with spires and cupolas and bathed in the luminous glow of the late afternoon. We caught a taxi to the Cathedral, facing the busy Plaza San Martín. It had an air of heavy, faded majesty. It was begun in 1680 and finished in 1758 in the usual Baroque style. The portico, of shabby plaster, was surmounted by a statue of Christ and flanked by two ornate campanili decorated with Moorish arches. Behind its brave facade the rest of the Cathedral was built of ordinary brick, except for an elaborate cupola over the altar. Inside the main door we immediately encountered a large monument to the national army. The interior was opulent and very dark. We sat down near the altar, a monstrous lump of writhing metal overshadowing a tiny Crucifix. Eduardo said that the altar was carved in wood by Indian serfs of the Jesuit fathers who brought Christianity to the region, and was then covered in gold and silver from the local mines.

We emerged and dived into a side street where I spotted a music shop. Here I found a row of *charangos* on display and ended up buying one. The *charango* is a native instrument of northern Argentina and Bolivia. It has ten strings and is the size of a mandolin but the body is made from the shell of an armadillo, complete with hair. The master of the instrument was an Argentine composer and performer called Jaime Torres, and I had already bought one of his records in Buenos Aires. It is an unpromising instrument which is usually strummed as part of a group, but in his hands it seemed almost as expressive as Segovia's guitar. Further burdened down, we returned to the park, picked up Mike who was surrounded by admiring children, and invited Eduardo to be our guest for dinner. With some difficulty we found a restaurant that was open – it was only 8 o'clock and most Argentinians do not eat until 9 or 10 – and put away the customary steak washed down with copious toasts to international friendship. There was just time to grab a taxi and career off to the station, where the taxi driver with magnificent dignity flashed us a huge smile and refused to accept payment. We bade farewell to Eduardo, who was visibly overcome with emotion as we left him on the platform.

As the train pulled out I thought of the friendly people that we had found on this trip, simple country folk who by their natural warmth and hospitality put to shame the frantic self-centred society of the big city. And today I think of Eduardo and wonder whether he is still alive or whether his youthful idealism was destroyed along with that of the best young people of Argentina.

The train sped across the great flat grasslands of the pampas, a dark expanse broken only occasionally by the lights of an isolated farm. We stopped at tiny stations far from anywhere. At one the platform was thickly infested with huge flying beetles, who crowded into our compartment to share our bunks for the night. We had to conduct a ruthless massacre.

The train pulled into Buenos Aires at 8 a.m., just in time for Mike to get back on duty. I spent the morning answering letters, sending presents and changing money. At one o'clock the ship was thrown open to visitors and so, dressed in my best shore-going rig, I stationed myself in the console room and prepared to describe the equipment. The invited guests were Argentine scientists, naval officers, politicians, Western embassy staff and representatives of British and US companies. They were heavily outnumbered by casual wanderers and interested local citizens. To the first few I gave a detailed description of the computer, satellite navigator and geophysical consoles. The response would be "Aren't the flashing lights pretty?"

I therefore cut the length and content of my discourse until I was down to simple-minded drivel. To my embarrassment one of the visitors came back with a highly intelligent question about the satellite navigator. He was Commander Granelli, head of the Geophysics Branch of the Argentine Navy. His institute was planning to buy a receiver for its own ship, and he wanted to know the relative technical merits of the Magnavox and ITT machines. To my relief Al Grant appeared, having fortified himself with several beers, so I handed the Commander over to him and returned to face the crowd.

As the afternoon wore on I had a long chat with an old Scottish gentleman who had been chief construction engineer for one of the railway companies, and I was cheered up by the jolly fat wife of an Argentine officer who, on seeing the lights of the PDP-8, burst into uproarious laughter. The visitors were supposed to arrive in parties guided by crew members, but the sailors simply pounced on unaccompanied girls and left the rest to fend for themselves. This frustrated similar evil plans on my part. Fortunately Orest Bluy now appeared with some good news. While I was in Córdoba there had been a reception on board for the local Canadian Embassy staff. Mrs. Barbara Wilgres, wife of the Second Secretary, had been concerned that the lower orders among the scientists were not benefiting from official junkets to the same extent as the senior staff. She had therefore arranged a multiple date for Orest, George Gill and Iver Duedall with three embassy secretaries, a date from which Iver had fortunately dropped out. I hastened to fill the gap.

As soon as the open house ended I rushed below to smarten myself up, relishing the furious indignation of Roger who was busy writing a long letter to his Canadian girlfriend.

"I hope you get syphilis!" he said warmly.

A taxi took us to a large tower block where the Wilgres family occupied the third floor. We were welcomed by the Italian maid into an exquisitely furnished apartment, complete with spinet and copies of Renaissance frescoes. Mrs Wilgres appeared, a charming diplomatic lady in her late thirties, and we retired for drinks to the terrace, overlooking the luxurious residence of the British Ambassador. Like all true diplomats, Mrs Wilgres began some high-flown small talk which clearly left George ill at ease, for which he compensated by launching into a monologue about hunting, shooting and eel fishing in Musquodoboit Harbour.

At length the girls arrived and proved to be very attractive – at least, to a sex-starved mariner they seemed so. The nicest was called Dottie, a tall blonde from Alabama who worked at the US Embassy. The other two were Scottish: Flora was a dark, Italian-looking beauty with a snobbish manner but a loose silk dress which displayed her charms well; Pam was a chubby redhead with a good sense of humour. In the preliminary jockeying I seemed to emerge with Flora. Mrs Wilgres excused herself at a pre-arranged signal, and we decided to set out for a restaurant in Pam's ancient Morris Minor. The shattered windscreen, plastered up with Scotch tape, and her fervent demand that I fasten my seat belt, induced a certain amount of fear, confirmed by her brand of driving.

After several near-disasters we arrived safely at a restaurant recommended by Mrs Wilgres. It looked like a cross between a stock exchange and a pre-war dance hall, a great cavern festooned with pink marble pillars and gilded mirrors. To reach the tables we had to negotiate an obstacle course of potted palms. George was overwhelmed by all this sophistication, and recommenced his monologue with new fervour as we ate our way through the speciality of the house, '90 Day Chicken'. This is allegedly chicken killed at the age of three months, but my chicken seemed to have spent its brief life on a weightlifting course. Despite George's lack of couthness time seemed to fly, and only ostentatious yawning by the waiters revealed that it was past midnight and we were the only customers left.

We headed back to Dottie's apartment, passing on the way the new British Embassy building, cleverly designed with plate glass windows at the back in case of riots. Dottie lived at the top of a tall block in the south of the city. Her balcony had a magnificent view of Buenos Aires – a sea of lights, rooftops and warm orange smog. Down went the lights, on went the soft music and out came the booze. I made my first acquaintance with tequila, which tasted vile but had an immediate effect. All seemed to be going well and an orgy looked imminent. Unfortunately George, with amazing crassness, chose that moment to begin mending Dottie's bathroom window catch, which he turned into a major task. This effectively destroyed the atmosphere and hence my amorous hopes. The party soon broke up. Flora dropped me off at the ship, while George and Orest went off to their hotel – they had already left the ship and were waiting for a flight back to Canada. I burst into the cabin mouthing threats to murder George Gill, much to the amusement of Roger.

Next morning I settled morosely to write off my last batch of letters. The ship was sailing that evening for the Antarctic and I had missed my chance of a sailor's run ashore. Life looked grim. Suddenly the message was piped that sailing would be delayed until 9:00 a.m. the next day. Roger and I looked at each other with the same evil thought. Another chance! I rushed to the gangway telephone and, under the interested gaze of the quartermaster, got in touch with Dottie at the American Embassy. She found a co-worker called Dale to make up a foursome with Roger, and we arranged to meet at Dale's apartment in Avenida Córdoba. Orest came round in the afternoon and tentatively asked for the girls' addresses, but we professed ignorance. Roger, as usual, was late in finishing his letters so at 8 o'clock I set off by myself for Dale's apartment.

Dale also lived on top of a tall block with a superb view. Embassy secretaries are paid at US rates, which at a time of a collapsing peso gave them a higher income than almost every salaried executive in Argentina, so they lived in style. Dale's apartment was full of animals – parrots, fish and a turtle – while the floor was covered with a cow hide and a skunk skin, the latter retaining traces of odour. Dottie was wearing a ravishing transparent blouse, so I thoughtfully positioned myself close to her as we all exchanged life stories. Dale proved to be a quiet country girl from Arizona, newly arrived in Argentina. Dottie's story was more interesting: she had dropped out of college, joined the Diplomatic Service in Washington, and had served in Guatemala City and Santiago. Roger finally arrived an hour and a half later and we wandered onto the balcony with our drinks. Below us lay the slum-like pile of the Brooklyn Hotel, flanked by the courtyards of the University of Buenos Aires medical and law schools, while the tree-lined Avenida was a racetrack of wildly hooting cars.

Eating came next. We piled into Dale's Volkswagen and unpiled at a nearby *cantina*. A *cantina* is a restaurant, a pub and a social centre for the neighbourhood. The front was open to the street and the tables stretched back into a low, cavernous interior. It was packed tightly with local people, all shouting, eating, drinking, singing, kissing and generally enjoying themselves. The ceiling was thickly covered with paper chains, flowers, fishing nets, chandeliers and wine bottles, while amateur murals adorned the walls. We were presented with a menu as long as a book, which Dottie translated. I ate some rubber octopus and a giant steak, washed down by multiple carafes of red wine. An engagement party was going on at a long table by the entrance. All the participants were drunk. The happy couple was doused with ice cream and then wine was thrown over them, which they took in good part. Two women in the party then began serenading the couple in harmony. The first song was listened to by everyone in the *cantina* and rapturous applause followed it. Subsequent songs fell on deaf ears except at the table itself, where prolonged clapping and cheering took place each time. By now we had disposed of several carafes and clapped with gusto, as well as engaging in earnest and incomprehensible conversation with people at neighbouring tables. Dale had started out by being very quiet and shy, but suddenly, after draining her glass, she threw her arms around Roger and exclaimed "We're friends, aren't we Rog?"

Noting this behavioural change Roger kept ordering more carafes.

Some time after midnight we decided to leave. We paid the bill – with difficulty I dissuaded Roger from leaving a tip equal to the bill – and staggered out to the car. Here we found a little old man waiting, who explained that he had been watching our car and demanded money for this service. Roger was so taken with his audacity that he gave him a wad of pesos. Dale was nearly asleep so Roger took the wheel and with difficulty managed to insert the ignition key. There followed a frightening ride. Dottie and I cowered in the back as we weaved from side to side of the road, ignoring traffic lights and hooting at anything that moved. Reaching the apartment block we swept into the first-floor car park, narrowly missing a stanchion and a night watchman. Dale now began dropping delicate hints to Dottie and me.

1. Departure from Dartmouth, November 19 1969. Captain Butler on bridge wing. *Hudson* is flying Brazilian flag, for her first port of call.

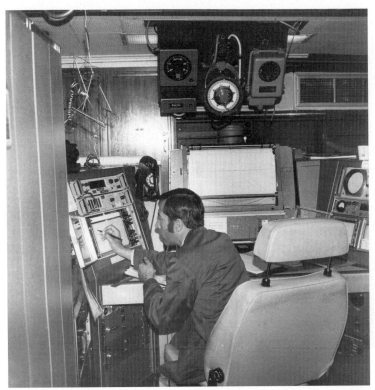

2. Bosco Loncarevic in the console room, marking gravimeter recorder. In centre is precision echo sounder, and on right the magnetometer recorder. Hanging from deckhead are gyro repeater and two logs.

3. Bruce Carson attaching a messenger weight to a Knudsen bottle.

4. Photographing whales in the tropical Atlantic. L. to r. Lew Rustige (ship's doctor); Peter Reynell; Peter Beamish; Peter Wadhams. On compass platform: Mark, the Doberman Pinscher.

5. Ced Mann marking the Bathysonde recorder in the console room.

6. Stan the winchman.

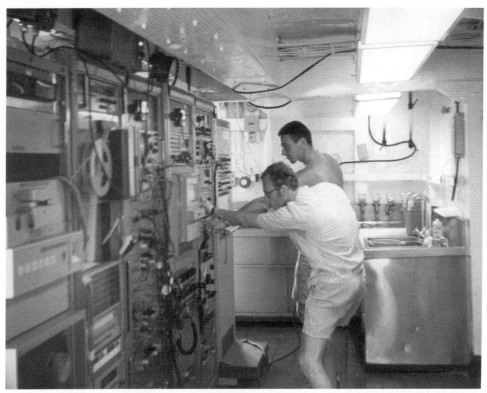

7. Orest Bluy (front) and George Gill recording acoustic data.

8. Night station: launching Orest Bluy's cone.

9. Gus Vilks (BIO) with a plankton net.

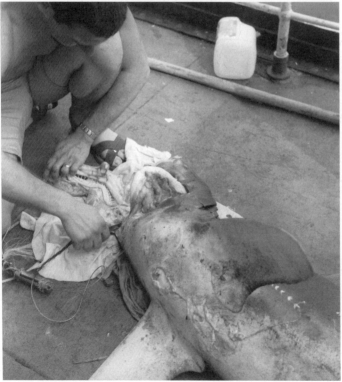

10. George Gill dismembers a shark.

11. An iceberg in the South Atlantic. Note flock of penguins hitching a ride.

12. Cape Horn Island (left). Deceit Rocks in foreground.

13. Deploying current meters in Drake Passage: the subsurface float and the topmost Braincon current meter enter the water.

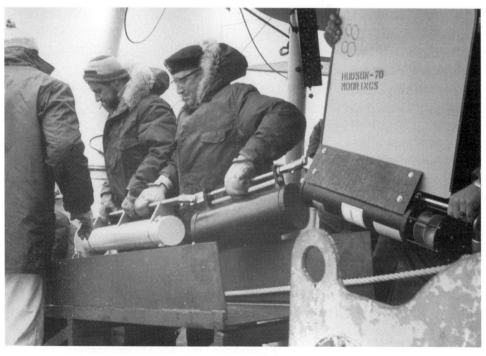

14. The Bo'sun easing a current meter down the slipway.

15. Bob Hessler (left) and Eric Mills (right) with an epibenthic sled.

16. The *Hudson* at anchor in Admiralty Bay, King George Island, South Shetlands.

17. Admiralty Bay: one of the graves of British scientists killed during occupation of Base G.

18. Admiralty Bay: whalebones on the beach.

19. Deception Island: twisted remains of Chilean base destroyed in 1969 eruption.

20. Deception Island: scientific staff, February 15 1970. Standing l. to r.: Roger Smith, Iver Duedall, Hugh Henderson, Ced Mann, Joe Avery (holding poster); Roy Edwards; Fred Cooke, Tom Foote, Bob Hessler. Seated l. to r. : Eric Mills, Lew Rustige.

21. Puerto Williams, Navarino Island, and a naval welcoming committee.

22. Navigating the Beagle Channel

23. Navigating the Beagle Channel.

24. Prof. George Pickard (Chief scientist, Chilean survey) in the Chains.

25. *Hudson* in Puerto Natales.

26. *Hudson* in newly-forming frazil ice in the Bering Sea.

27. Scientific planning in the Arctic. l. to r. Gus Vilks, Captain Butler, Bernie Pelletier, Roy Gould.

28. Bernie Pelletier and Chris Havard examine an Arctic Ocean core.

29. *Hudson* in the pack ice of the Beaufort Sea.

30. *Hudson* breaking ice in the Northwest Passage.

31. Arrival in Halifax, October 16 1970. Bedford Institute is on the far left.

32. Joe Greene (Minister of Energy, Mines and Resources) with Capt. David Butler and the medal awarded to *Hudson* and (as a smaller version) to participants.

"Are you sure that you want to come back to my place? Don't you think you ought to be getting back?"

When Dottie took the hint and announced that we were going home a broad smile spread across Dale's face as she said, "Do you have to go? We're staying here, aren't we, Rog?"

Dottie and I took a taxi back to her apartment. It naturally seemed to fall out that I should spend the night there. For a short while the cares, repressions and enforced coarseness of shipboard life dropped away and we were just two young people together. By the time the sun rose over the rooftops we had bared our souls to each other and were as close as two people can be. Then I realised with a wrench that my ship was waiting to take me away, and I felt the true frustration of a sailor's existence. A girl in every port is a poor substitute for the richness of a proper relationship. With promises to keep in touch, we parted. Curiously, Dottie did visit London a year later and tried to get in touch with me, but I missed her as my father had just died and I had taken my mother away for a holiday.

I got back to the ship about 8.30 to encounter the wrath of Ced Mann, who was about to send out search parties. Down below Roger too was seething with frustration. Instead of the intended night of passion he had to nurse Dale through several sessions of vomiting. Such are the joys of youth.

At 10 a.m. *Hudson* slipped her lines and we were towed slowly out of Darsena Norte, our place being taken by a rust-streaked Cypriot Liberty ship. The water was brown and dirty and the sun fiercely hot. The flat estuary of the Plate gradually widened out until the hump of Isla Lobos fell behind us and there was no more land to be seen. We dropped the pilot late in the afternoon. The porpoise playing round the pilot boat was a reminder of the cold mountainous seas that were ahead of us, while behind me lay memories of a countryside full of warm-hearted people and a city containing someone who had touched my heart. I stood at the stern in hopeless yearning: my soul was in the pilot boat, heading back towards Buenos Aires, life and love, but my body was aboard *Hudson*, heading for the polar seas. The gap could not be bridged. I tore myself away and went below.

CHAPTER 7

CAPE HORN AND THE LAND OF FIRE

The uttermost cape or hedland of all these Ilands stands neere in 56 deg, without which there is no maine nor Iland to the Southwards, but that the Ocean and the South Sea meete in a most large and free scope.

Sir Francis Drake

AND SO WE TURNED our bow southward, towards the icy gales and bleak shores of the most inhospitable region in the world. My imagination had gorged itself on the tales of Magellan, Drake and Anson, and now at last I was to see the fabled Cape Horn for myself.

Next morning, far off to starboard, the gleaming hotels of Mar del Plata appeared in the heat haze, and then the land rose to the gentle hump of Cape Corrientes and sank finally out of sight. We settled down to a steady 14 knots and began pounding our way towards the Magellan Strait. In 1970, even before the Law of the Sea had been negotiated, Argentina was claiming sovereignty over her undersea resources up to a distance of 200 miles from the coast, so to avoid offending her we did not stop for oceanographic stations. This was a godsend to me, as I was cowering in my cabin with a heavy bout of Argentine stomach trouble.

To enforce her claim, Argentina had put a man aboard at Buenos Aires, a Lieutenant Roberto Rebaudi of the Hydrographic Service. Anyone less like a policeman would be hard to imagine, for he was unfailingly jolly, friendly and courteous. He was also a proficient charangist, and I cajoled him into teaching me some chords. Armadilloes, he said, run wild on the pampas and the natives have a hard time catching them.

"Even if you catch their tail they can dig into the ground with their forepaws so quickly that they escape from you. The only way to stop this is to stick your finger up their backside, when they are so surprised that they stop digging."

"And did you ever catch one this way?"

"Yes, when I was a boy. But he looked up at me with his big, watery eyes and I had to let him go."

Although the seas were denied to us, the skies were not. We had an ornithologist aboard – Fred Cooke, of Queen's University – and also a marine biologist with an interest in birds, Eric Mills of Dalhousie University. During the next three days Fred and Eric spent the daylight hours standing on the upper deck in the steadily increasing cold, counting birds. They divided the day from 0900 to 2400 into five 3-hour periods, and tried to spend at least 45 minutes during each period on watch with their binoculars. It was an uncomfortable job but a rewarding one. They spotted 18 species of bird, and found two regions where birds occurred in unusual profusion, which they thought must be feeding areas rich in plankton.

The first feeding area lay just off Mar del Plata itself. This had been discovered by an ornithologist called Beck in 1914, who found 'an extraordinary intermingling of species from opposite ends of the Atlantic Ocean.' Fred and Eric found several warm-water species in this rich feeding ground, such as the Yellow-nosed Albatross and Cory's Shearwater, and were seeing over 200 birds per hour. The surface water temperature here was still 20°C, and the conclusion was that this is a region of upwelling, where cold nutrient-rich water from the deep part of the northward-flowing Falkland Current rises to the surface against the coast and is warmed by the sun.

The second feeding area was further south at 44°S, east of the Valdés Peninsula. Here there were even more birds – 800 per hour – but they were of a completely different, cold-water species. The Black-browed and Sooty Albatrosses (cold) replaced the Yellow-nosed Albatross (warm), and the Great Shearwater (cold) took the place of the Cory's Shearwater (warm). The sea surface was now at 14°C, and we were in the centre of the Falkland Current (or Malvinas Current, if you happen to be Argentine). The first Magellanic Penguins appeared here in small family groups, poking their heads inquisitively above the surface.

On the morning of January 26 land appeared on the starboard beam. It was a low, hummocky shore, of a uniform brown and seemingly devoid of vegetation. It ended in a low sand-spit. We had reached Cape Virgins, the entrance to the Magellan Strait. As a landmark it was disappointing, yet for its discoverer it had meant literally his salvation. Ferdinand Magellan, a Portuguese in the service of the Spanish King, had sailed from Seville in 1519 in five small ships in search of *el paso*, a fabled channel at the southern end of America that would lead to the great South Sea. He faced storms and a series of mutinies, for his crew and many of his officers had come to believe that the channel was a myth. Then on 21 October 1520, St. Ursula's Day, the pilot of the ship *Trinidad* wrote, 'We saw an opening like unto a bay'. At first people 'looked dubiously in the dark inlet', but then the rise and fall of the tide showed that the open ocean must lie beyond. Magellan named the entrance the Cape of the Eleven Thousand Virgins, after Ursula and her band of maidenly followers who on returning from a pilgrimage were set upon by Huns near Cologne and perished in spirited defence of their virginities.

We rounded the cape and saw that the low, brown coastline stretched far away to the west. This is where the pampas finally peters out into a windswept scrubland. In the centre of the vista was the lighthouse at Punta Dungeness, marking the boundary between Argentina and Chile. Further on, the shore was marked by oil derricks, many of them capped by the flames of burning natural gas. The Strait was now growing narrower, and the rugged coast of the original Land of Fire, Tierra del Fuego, appeared on our port beam. Magellan had seen columns of smoke rising from the campfires of the local Indians, and he named the island accordingly. Now that the Indians have been exterminated the only columns of flame are those that rise from the oil wells: oil was discovered here just after the Second World War, and has brought a minor boom to this inhospitable toe of South America.

After a few miles a higher rocky outcrop appeared to starboard, and in the lime-green water that washed its base lay the ribs of an old wreck, a sombre reminder of the Strait's evil reputation. The outcrop marks the entrance to a bight called Possession Bay, where the Magellan pilot boat was waiting for us. This turned out to be an extraordinary vessel, a former landing craft whose superstructure aft had been picturesquely extended into the likeness of a cottage, complete with flowery curtains at the windows and a little chimney for the cabin stove. The sailors all hailed us in fluent English and the gold-braided pilot climbed aboard with as much dignity as the rope ladder would permit. After the exchange of elaborate formal greetings he proceeded to the bridge while we threw a bundle of mail aboard the pilot boat together with some packs of cigarettes to expedite its delivery. Foam then appeared around the base of the cottage and the pilot boat chugged away, her Chilean ensign bravely fluttering.

We got under way and the land soon closed in on both sides as we passed through the First Narrows. For the early navigators the Narrows brought them to comparative safety, as the mouth of the Magellan Strait is characterised by extremely powerful tidal streams and strong westerly winds. Many an ill-found galleon has beaten its way laboriously almost up to the First Narrows, only to find the Strait giving an almighty hiccup and vomiting it far out to sea again. After the First Narrows a wide bay opened up, which soon closed in again to the Second Narrows. Now the Strait turned southward, and in the early evening we anchored off Punta Arenas, the southernmost city in the world, perched like an oasis of life on the bare deserted shoreline.

From the sea the city wore a dismal aspect. The 60,000 inhabitants lived in shabby houses of timber and corrugated iron which stretched in a grid-iron pattern for about four miles along the coast. A group of more substantial stone buildings, dominated by the large Cabo de Hornos Hotel, huddled together around the main square. The single mercantile jetty was crowded with small fishing boats, while far off to the left lay the hulks of several old barques. A sleek Spanish cruise liner, her lights blazing, was lying offshore. From the shore came the mingled odours of sewage outfalls and rotting seaweed which to us meant land, although landlubbers call it 'the smell of the sea'.

For all its shabbiness we gazed eagerly at the prospect, for in a few weeks' time we were due to spend several days here before starting on our survey of the Chilean fjords. Roberto plied us with lurid tales of the local girls and their friendliness to sailors, and the cold, windswept city looked more and more inviting. Our purpose in stopping now was to drop off one of our stewards, John Shanaghan, whose brother in Canada was dangerously ill. After John had been taken ashore in the care of the local customs officials we raised anchor and continued on our way southwards.

During the night we passed through the Magdalena and Cockburn Channels. I rose at first light, for today we were to make the tortuous and exciting passage through the Beagle Channel. At its southern tip the Andean backbone of South America comes down to the sea and breaks up into thousands of jagged islands, intertwined with labyrinthine channels and dangerous shoals, all forming a savage fringe to the west and south coasts of Tierra del Fuego. Chief among these waterways is the Beagle Channel, a narrow fracture only a mile or two wide, which splits Tierra del Fuego off from the final island remnants of America to its south. The region was first explored and charted in 1828 by Captain Robert FitzRoy in HMS *Beagle* and *Adventure*, following the suicide of his predecessor Captain King, and this remains the only complete survey. He named the islands and channels after officers of his ships and their friends and patrons. He returned with the *Beagle* to complete the survey in 1833 as part of a round-the-world voyage, this time carrying as his naturalist an eager young man called Charles Darwin.

After a hurried breakfast I donned my weather gear, loaded my cameras and took up position on the upper deck. The scene that confronted me was magnificent and violent. We had just left the Cockburn Channel and were close to the open ocean. A gale-force wind was piling up huge breakers on a protecting fringe of low skerries, and a long powerful swell survived as a reminder of the fury outside. Scattered all around were mountainous islands looming abruptly out of the sea and mist. Each one was of brown volcanic rock, deeply scarred and grooved by erosion. Off to port was the equally rugged Brecknock Peninsula of Tierra del Fuego. The turbulent flow of wind down the cliff-like mountainsides was generating williwaws, small waterspouts of spray which twisted their way across the sea surface. A scud of low-lying cloud blew like smoke off the island tops in untidy spumes. It seemed as if all the processes of Nature were at work at once.

The higher peaks on these islands were capped by snowfields, from which cataracts of melt water leapt down steep ravines to the sea. Some of these cataracts, especially on exposed western faces, were themselves frozen; and as we passed London Island we saw a waterfall that, in cascading over a sheer cliff face, was entirely blown away by the wind in a cloud of spray. On steep or exposed walls the vegetation was either non-existent or consisted of a thin fuzz of yellow-green moss and lichens clinging to the bare rock. On shallower slopes and in sheltered hollows there was wiry tussock grass and stands of the Antarctic beech, *Notophagus*, the only tree that can survive in these exacting conditions. The stunted and warped trunks, only a few feet high, lean wearily away from the wind, increasing the windswept appearance of the rocks. On the lee side of each island the sheltered coves were choked with the great kelp *Macrocystis*, which comes in brown strands up to 300 feet long anchored tenaciously to the rock.

Though the land was desolate the sea was full of life. A herd of sea lions would appear, leaping out of the water and plopping back in again. Wherever I looked the water surface would soon be broken by one or more cheery little

Magellanic Penguins, no more than two feet long, jumping from one wave to the next in their quest for fish. For much of the morning we were piloted by a dolphin, who expertly rode our bow wave or flashed from side to side of the ship.

The turbid green water is rich in fish and plankton, and they support a prolific bird life in addition to the sea animals. Fred Cooke pointed out the different species that were wheeling and swarming around us. The majestic bird with the huge wingspan was the Black-browed Albatross; the Great Skua, with his brown body and white wingtips, was almost as big; flying overhead was a Black-faced Ibis with his long, drooping bill and hawk-like wings; and behind came a King Shag, the local variety of cormorant. All of these are fish-eating birds. Later on Fred pointed to a distant mountain top and passed me his binoculars. There were seven black specks, circling and soaring effortlessly round the peak – condors, the most magnificent birds in the world. How proud they looked in their natural habitat as compared to the sorry specimens in Córdoba Zoo.

At 9 a.m. we passed Basket Island, set in the aptly named Desolate Bay. It looked like just another mound of bare rock, but this little island achieved fame as the home of Fuegia Basket, the only Fuegan Indian girl ever to see the shores of England. During FitzRoy's first survey in 1828 he 'acquired' four natives: one, whom he called Jemmy Button, he bought from a chief in return for a large mother-of-pearl button; while the other three, named York Minster, Boat Memory and Fuegia Basket (then an eight-year-old girl), were taken hostage after the theft of a whaler. The whaler had been used in a survey of these western islands, and the deprived crew were forced to return to the *Beagle* in a Fuegan canoe, which was made of skins stretched over a wicker frame and hence looked like a floating basket. Button was a Yahgan, while the rest were of the Alakaluf tribe. They were brought back to England and sent to a clergyman in Walthamstow for rapid civilising. They were presented at Court, where Queen Adelaide took a fancy to Fuegia and, according to FitzRoy, gave her a lace bonnet, a ring and 'a sum of money to buy an outfit of clothes when she should leave England to return to her country'. The four were returned to their homes during the second voyage of the *Beagle* in the hope that they would civilise the natives and convert them to Anglicanism. Fuegia and York Minster got married but immediately returned to their former primitive habits, while Jemmy, who seemed to Darwin the most civilised and engaging of the four, so forgot himself as to assist in the massacre of a later group of missionaries.

Later in the morning we passed Stewart and Londonderry Islands, whose bulk helped to shelter the channel from the sea. It was here that Francis Drake and the *Golden Hind* called in to take refuge from a terrible storm. The Fuegan coast on our left was still as rugged, and studded with long fjord-like inlets. Up one of these we perceived a small white shape, entirely dwarfed by the giant overhanging rocks above her. She looked like a small coaster, but in fact she was a large cruise liner, the *Anna C.* of Genoa. She sailed out of the inlet and overhauled us, her decks crowded with frantically-waving passengers. As I waved back I wondered grimly whether there is any corner of the world which is free of tourists. Here we were, doing the first scientific work down here since Darwin, and there was a luxury cruise ship following us, pricking our pretensions at being pioneers and explorers.

In the early afternoon we began to enter the Beagle Channel proper. First we passed Darwin Island, a shapeless pile close in to starboard. Then we entered a very narrow passage called the North-west Arm between Gordon Island and Tierra del Fuego; its breadth is less than half a mile, yet it is over 400 metres deep and the pilot had no difficulty in threading his way along. The splendour of the scenery now acquired a new magnitude as the great jagged rock masses closed in to either side of us and became yet higher. Simultaneously the weather cleared so that the snow-covered crags seemed to be floating through the sky above our heads.

And now we began to encounter mighty glaciers. The first were high up among the distant mountains, glinting white. Then they began to come down towards the Channel, hanging over us with the cracked and dirty ice of midsummer from which rivulets of meltwater streamed down. The greatest glacier of all, occupying a huge cirque between two mountains, was a deep blue in colour, and its run-off coalesced into a single gigantic waterfall which plunged hundreds of feet down the bare rock face. Behind it, shimmering in the distance and surrounded by snowfields, was the 8,000-ft peak of Mount Darwin, the highest mountain on Tierra del Fuego. Darwin forms part of a chain of mountains which separate the northern grasslands and forests of Tierra del Fuego from the myriad islands to the south.

On Gordon Island we saw the first sign of human life, a green wooden hut on a low spit of beach. It boasted a radio mast, and the Chilean flag fluttered from a pole. Four men were playing football on the beach. This was one of a chain of meteorological stations, whose occupants also tend the light buoys and beacons marking the most dangerous shoals in the Beagle

Channel. The staff must pass a psychological test to show that they can stand the loneliness, and they are all members of the Chilean Navy for, despite its remoteness, this is an area of tension. Argentina owns the eastern half of Tierra del Fuego and at this time laid claim to some of the islands to the south. Whenever domestic politics required a flag-waving exercise Argentina revived this claim and threatened to invade. The dispute was later settled by the Pope in Chile's favour. Later in the afternoon we passed a row of four unusual cone-shaped peaks which Roberto said are called The Pyramids. These mark the boundary between Argentina and Chile, and from now on there were small shacks on both sides of the Channel, keeping watch on one another.

I went below to eat and emerged to find us passing Ushuaia, a small settlement on the Argentine bank of the Channel with a population of some 3,000. It looked exceedingly remote, occupying a small lowland region at the head of a bay. There seemed to be just a few houses and a water tower in sight. To the west of the town was a long shed-like structure which, according to Roberto, was the notorious prison. Ushuaia has a chequered and unhappy history, forming part of the sorry tale of the extermination of the Fuegan Indian.

When European eyes first gazed on Tierra del Fuego there were three main tribes of Indians, numbering altogether several thousand souls. The Ona were hunters who sought guanaco (a wild species of llama) in the forests and grasslands of the main island. The Alakaluf and the Yahgan were nomadic canoe Indians who lived among the islands to the south, the Yahgan around the Beagle Channel and the Alakaluf in the western islets. Their lives were extremely primitive. They fished, caught seals and gathered mussels and berries. They lived in wigwams and went about naked except for a guanaco-hide cloak. To keep themselves warm they rubbed their bodies with seal oil and carried fires around with them in their canoes. Darwin hated their thieving tendencies and thought them the lowest form of humanity, but he approved of FitzRoy's efforts to save their souls. In the footsteps of FitzRoy came a trickle of Anglican missionaries; some were murdered while others starved. Last of all came Thomas Bridges, who founded Ushuaia as a mission station for the Yahgan.

Bridges was energetic and dedicated, and began agriculture and the work of conversion. He compiled the only Yahgan dictionary, finding to his surprise a language of 32,000 words. Much later, in 1898, he naively entrusted the manuscript to a Dr Frederick A Cook who was passing by on an Antarctic expedition aboard the *Belgica*; Cook published the dictionary in Belgium – under his own name (Cook also claimed to have reached the North Pole ahead of Robert Peary). Bridges was a liberal missionary by the narrow standards of the time, and did not try to distort the Indians' way of life too severely. But their nakedness was a sticking point. Devout supporters in England sent out cast-off clothing to cover the indecency of the natives, but the clothes carried the germs of measles, typhoid and pulmonary disease against which the Yahgan had no immunity. In 1884 an Argentine gunboat arrived at Ushuaia to claim sovereignty, and the sailors introduced a massive measles epidemic. In 1888, impressed by the remoteness of the region, Argentina set up a penal colony at Ushuaia for the worst criminals in the country including the famous white slavers. Epidemics brought by the prisoners killed the last of the Yahgan in Ushuaia. Undeterred, Bridges moved eastward along the Beagle Channel to found a new mission station called Harberton, which was carried on by his son Lucas. However, the decline of the Yahgan towards extinction continued. Meanwhile, in the grasslands to the north, the Ona were being actively slaughtered by settlers who were developing mines and sheep ranches. The Salesian order of Catholic missionaries collaborated with this process by shipping off survivors to virtual imprisonment on a mission station on Dawson Island in the Magellan Strait, where the victims died of disease or sadness.

The evil history of Ushuaia seemed to hang like a miasma over its shabby buildings. Passing this abode of misfortune, we continued along the narrow passage of the Beagle Channel, our path flanked by rows of stately mountains. The dark green vegetation, which clothed the sides of the ridges, ended in a distinct line at about 2,000 feet, above which the rock stood naked except for a crown of snow. Soon Navarino Island appeared to starboard. In front of its mountainous backbone this island has a sheltered lowland, where forests of beech can grow to a height of 25 feet or more. Here is to be found one of the most remote settlements in the world. Puerto Williams is a naval base and fishing village with a population of 800, and it claims the title of the southernmost town in the world as it lies only 50 miles north of Cape Horn. It nestles on the sunny south side of the Beagle Channel and we came upon it in the early evening, dropping anchor a few hundred yards offshore.

As soon as we anchored a naval pinnace came speeding out from the little jetty carrying three smartly dressed sailors and the commander of the base. While the officer presented his compliments to our Captain the sailors, anxious to give a good impression, stood stiffly at their posts as the boat wallowed alongside. We were given formal permission to lay offshore, and officers and scientists were to be allowed ashore the next day provided no cameras were carried.

As usual, I slept poorly in the unnatural silence, and at first light I went up on deck to look at this tiny enclave of humanity. In the unaccustomed sunlight the town looked bright and cheerful, like a Newfoundland fishing village. I could see a wooden church with a steeply pitched roof, a huddle of gaily painted cabins and a jetty with a cluster of small warships. Off to the right an airstrip had been hacked out of the forest. After breakfast our motorboat the *Gull* was brought round to the gangway, and we piled aboard and puttered away from the looming bulk of the *Hudson*.

As we approached the jetty we passed the Navarino Island Grand Fleet, whose principal unit was an old ex-Royal Canadian Navy wartime River-class frigate called the *Covadonga* (originally HMCS *Sea Cliff*). She appeared to be resting on the sea bed, her guns were removed and her upperworks had been extended with wooden planking. Her functions were to deter the Argentinians and to provide electric power for the village. Moored beside her were two torpedo boats, a patrol boat used to supply the light buoys, and a derelict supply steamer with her decks awash. Behind these vessels stood a workshop and barracks for the unmarried personnel. A tour of duty in the remote south lasts for two years, of which one year may be spent in the comparative luxury of Punta Arenas. The sailors are allowed to bring their wives with them, and most seem to have done so.

Behind the landing stage was an arc of huts comprising the post office, the 'travel agency', and a general store selling essential provisions which are usually paid for in scrip. From here a grassy track, rejoicing in the name 'Avenida Miramar', led off to the left along the waterside. We were met here by two people who were desirous of showing us round. One was an official guide provided by the Navy, a small chubby sailor who spoke excellent English. The other was an elderly chap wearing an impeccable accent and a tweed jacket. He introduced himself as Patrick Furness, a native-born Chilean of English origin and the supervisor of meat supplies for the base. He seemed very anxious to speak to English people, and he set off to escort the bulk of our party around the village.

Five of us, however, preferred to set out for the interior with our cheery Chilean guide. Our expedition was made up of myself, Roger, Fred Cooke, Eric Mills and another marine biologist, Bob Hessler from Scripps Institution of Oceanography in La Jolla, California. Fred, Bob and Eric, all keen naturalists, had come well equipped for hiking, complete with ruck-sacks, binoculars and stout boots. Bob also had a plastic bucket hanging from his back for botanical specimens. Rog and I, on the other hand, were woefully ill-equipped and we had completely forgotten to bring food with us. However I did have my sketch pad to make up for the lack of a camera.

Our path led off to the right of the base towards the interior of the island and an uneven ridge of peaks called the Teeth of Navarino. First we passed the commandant's house, a pleasant red bungalow with a fenced-off garden. A local fisherman was going in with armfuls of huge King crabs, for the delectation of Ced Mann and the Captain who were inside. Apart from the naval facilities the only activities in the village were a little sheep farming and a King crab fishery. The King crab or *centolla* (*Lithodes antarctica*), a relative of the Alaskan crab, is a delicious long-legged beast for which a fishery had been started at several small settlements in the Fuegan region.

Passing between the radio station and a group of small wooden houses the path led us over a rise and straight into the wild woods and another world. The first thing that struck me was the silence, absolute and complete, descending like a blanket. No bird sang and no breath of wind stirred the branches. A little black tarn lay limp and placid in a ring of trees, its surface disturbed only by bubbles of marsh gas. The atmosphere was not one of peace; rather it was one of death and decay. I recalled Darwin's words:-

> *In these still solitudes Death rather than Life seemed the guiding Spirit.*

It was midsummer and the vegetation was prolific. The soil is a black humus and the native woodland consists of several varieties of the Antarctic beech, some deciduous and some evergreen. There were also some very attractive trees with small fleshy leaves and delicate white flowers. The guide, who seemed to be something of a naturalist, called this the *canelo*, which I took to mean cinnamon. Many of the trees, especially the beeches, were dead or dying, and a tangle of fallen trunks made passage through the woods diffi-cult. The soil lacks nutrients, so that trees die off while still quite young; then the chill climate hinders their dissolution, and the result is more dead trees than live ones. Even the living trees were covered by fungi and lichen; one beautiful species hung down from the branches like tresses of green hair.

There was a dense undergrowth of bushes, thorns, ferns and rich grass. Some of the plants were very familiar - dandelion, daisy and buttercup.

Others were strange. The guide showed us a small ball-like fungus, the size of a pea, which grew on the trunks of the trees and which he said was good to eat. The balls were crunchy but completely tasteless. Next he pointed out a peculiar plant growing in clumps. It had large berries of a garish violet colour, and its leaves each had a vicious spine at the end. This is *frutilla del diablo*, Devil's Fruit, and it is extremely poisonous. It grows amongst clumps of a delicious blueberry called *calafate*, which has led shipwrecked mariners to eat it and die as a result.

Large areas of ground were covered with a pestilentially smelling marsh of soft black mud, called a *turbal*. As he diverted us around one of these our guide, who was evidently an Anglophile, began to reel off the names of First Division football teams and of countries in the British Commonwealth. By now our companions were rather restive. They had equipped themselves with an illustrated book called *The Birds of Chile*, and they were waiting for one to put in an appearance. The sailor indicated that bird life began higher up the hillside. Sure enough, after a while Eric froze, glasses trained on the middle distance.

"The Tufted Tit-Tyrant!" he breathed explosively.

Fred now began to utter his whistle, which he said resembles the cry of a generalised bird in agony. He proceeded up the track, whistling at intervals like the Pied Piper, and birds began to gather around us. Rog and I became carried away by the enthusiasm of our companions, and we learned to identify a few of the fleeting shapes in the trees. Some of the birds were similar to English species, like the swallow and the Austral Thrush, the southern equivalent of the robin. Then there is a group of tiny flycatchers, with exotic and lovely names – the Rayadito, which has a crested head and a bright yellow breast; the White-Crested Elaenia, with a little white crest on a jet black head; the Tit-Tyrants; and the Fire-Eyed Diucón, adorned with a crested plume. We saw a light brown hawk called a Chimango perched in the highest tree. With a raucous "Caw!" he swooped over us; such hawks will sometimes attack sheep and try to pick out their eyes.

The path ended in a clearing by a mountain stream, which was led off in a concrete channel to form the village water supply. A green cabin stood amongst the trees, and a family crowded to the door to greet us. Continuing up the mountainside, we came to an area that had been logged over and that was now covered with a dense secondary growth of thorn bushes which made progress slow and painful. Here I lost my new-found love of bird-watching, for in a solitary tree in the middle of a clearing Fred and Eric espied a mottled brown Ferruginous Pygmy-Owl. We crept silently up to it, scratching ourselves cruelly. Fred had his smuggled camera at the ready. When we were only a few feet away the owl nonchalantly withdrew into the dark inaccessible midst of the tree, whence he peered out at us with an amused pair of green eyes.

Fred, Eric and Bob decided to return to the village, while Rog and I gallantly pressed on up the mountain, afflicted by gnawing pangs of hunger. We reached a clearing just below the treeline, where time and exhaustion dictated a stop. I began to sketch a superb view. The Beagle Channel stretched out like a mirror far below, disturbed only by the tiny speck that was the *Hudson*. Across the waterway the great mountain ranges of Tierra del Fuego marched away to the horizon, capped by frowning black clouds. The desolation was complete. It was as if we were the first men on the face of the earth. Then clouds crept across the channel and started to empty themselves on us. We made what speed we could down the mountainside and caught the last boat back to the ship.

There was to be a reception on board at 7 p.m., and after dinner I stole a lift with the boat that was sent ashore to pick up the Chilean guests. I wandered at random into the little civilian settlement. The two or three rows of wooden houses had gardens hopefully marked out, though wiry grass was all that was growing. Each garden possessed a sheep, tied by a rope to a tree to keep the grass down. I got into conversation with the local dentist, who was busy untangling the rope from around his sheep's legs. He spoke fluent English, which he had learned at the Instituto Chileno-Norte Americano in Santiago. He said that his life in the far south was peaceful and beautiful, and that he was very happy with it. I could see the reason why when his wife appeared; like most Chilean women she was stunningly beautiful. On the outside wall of his home was a cage-like arrangement where he stored all his fruit and vegetables; the chilly wind performed the work of refrigeration. In another cage he kept his pet parrakeet, who seemed to appreciate the cold far less.

Further on I came to the 'square', a chained-off area of grass containing the usual monument, this time a bust of Admiral Williams who claimed this region for Chile in 1843. Flanking the square were the church, a small hospital and the *Escuela Pública*, built out of the worst brickwork that I have ever seen. Further on was a gymnasium with all its windows broken, perhaps by enthusiastic basketball players, and then, across a small creek, a cluster of tiny, decrepit and apparently deserted huts. Finding nobody about

I returned to the jetty, where a contingent of naval officers in dress uniform had appeared, together with their wives. We all crowded into the launch, and the officers and wives cowered below as sheets of spray flew across the cockpit. Back on the *Hudson* I changed into my shore rig and headed for the party in the lounge.

For once Bill Shaw had put on a proud show; Puerto Williams had never seen anything like it. The stewards were unrecognisable in spotless white uniforms, and Roy Gould was resplendent in acres of blue serge and brass buttons. Titbits of food worthy of the most nauseating cocktail parties were scattered about and, best of all, the booze was free. Everybody made the most of this and soon the party was well under way. Most of the Chileans spoke good English, which is one of their main subjects at school. One officer was a small, excitable chap, and as I was talking to him he dropped his glass. For a moment he gazed down in crestfallen stupefaction and then he exclaimed, "One minute it was in my hands - and then it was an invisible glass!"

He kept repeating this statement, so I looked around at the ladies. I found one of them looking at me – in fact, looking at everybody. She was small and curvaceous with long, flowing hair, a child's oval face and big round expressive eyes. Her husband, who introduced himself as the supply officer of the base, kept a firm hold of her and glowered at everyone around. Finally I spotted the commandant's attractive wife and began to talk with her.

We found that we had painting in common, for she had sketched the scene from the Teeth of Navarino many times. She had had a restricted traditional upbringing, and after she had graduated from University her parents refused to let her accept either of two jobs in the USA that she had been offered. She was now teaching at the local school which, she said, takes pupils as far as the eighth grade, although many of them are seventeen before they reach this level.

"The most intelligent pupils are the Indians. There are a few dozen pure-blooded Indians left – they live in accommodation provided by the Government on the outskirts of town."

I ascertained that these were the derelict huts that I had seen. She went on, "Of course, the Indians are very lazy; they never lift a finger to help themselves. Once they have left school they sit in their huts living on Government handouts."

I tried to point out that this is understandable when a people have had their land and their whole life's meaning taken away from them, but the point did not get across.

The party broke up about 10 p.m. and with some reluctance our new friends departed, many in an inebriated state. In fact, as they were transferred to the launch the Chilean pilot stepped straight into the sea clutching a bottle of Canadian Club to his breast. He was fished out by a member of the launch crew with the bottle intact. We who remained were also somewhat inebriated, and we propped up the bar until late at night while Bruce Carson told jokes from his inexhaustible reserve.

Next morning we raised anchor at 8 a.m. and drew out into the middle of the Beagle Channel for our first piece of scientific work – a bottom sample for Bob and Eric. This was carried out using an epibenthic sled, which is a metal contraption resembling a toboggan. The sled was lowered from the winch on the port side of the foredeck and allowed to drag slowly along the bottom for ten minutes. It scrapes off a sample of bottom life (benthos), together with surface sediment, all of which gathers in a nylon bag behind the sled's cutting edge. The bag was emptied into a tank on deck, where Eric, Bob and Allan Michael (a New Zealand-born graduate student at Dalhousie) began to delve amongst the gravel and sand in search of treasure. This first drag was made in 38 metres of water, and yielded mainly the wrinkled brown leaves of the kelp *Macrocystis*, each with a small bladder at the end. Copious quantities of animal life were also brought up: fleshy purple starfish; small brittle stars with long, thin, jointed legs; tiny spider crabs with mottled shells designed to blend in with the bottom; a flat beetle-shaped isopod; and a galatheid, a dwarf lobster only two inches in length. The sea bottom here was as full of life as the sea itself.

After finishing the drag we set off eastwards, leaving Puerto Williams behind. We also left behind a field party in the form of two scientists and the launch *Redhead*. The scientists were Ed Bousfield, a zoologist from the National Museum of Canada in Ottawa, and Jim Markham, a botanist from the National Research Council. While we were in the Antarctic they were going to spend an adventurous month cruising around Navarino and the far southern islands, collecting coastal animals and plants. The efficient Frank Durnford was their coxswain, and they carried on board a complete camping and cooking kit. Jim had been down here the previous year and had established very friendly relations with the Chileans, who contributed a knowledgeable guide in the form of Lieutenant Augusto Tapia from the Puerto Williams base.

It had snowed during the night, leaving a dusting on the peaks, and as we sailed a belt of low cloud loomed up and a fine rainbow arc appeared across the Channel as a mark of farewell. We sailed close by Picton and Nueva Islands, the two wooded specks that were the subject of the dispute with Argentina. We then came round to the south-west and headed for Wollaston Island, one of the wave-lashed group that marks the end of the continent. We hove-to some ten miles from its long, jagged shores and made two more sled hauls a few miles apart, in 58 and 73 metres of water, together with plankton tows. The prize specimen this time was a pale blue ray, some eighteen inches long with a ten-inch wingspan, still feebly flapping and pulsating.

At 6 p.m. we set off southwards again. The rugged rocky shores of Wollaston gave way to the equally forbidding Freycinet and Deceit Islands, fringed by a dangerous group of low skerries called the Deceit Rocks. From behind this screen there finally came into view Cape Horn Island itself. Its shape is known to every deep-water mariner; a long, dark, majestic mass that rears up at its southern end to a bluff headland some 1,300 feet high. The sky was wild with scudding cloud, though the sea was almost unnaturally calm. The sun appeared fitfully, making the water glint like dull grey steel. Bare of life, the Horn frowned morosely over the scene, as if unhappy that it could not summon up a storm to greet us.

After ten weeks and many adventures we had reached the very end of America.

CHAPTER 8

SOUTH TO THE ANTARCTIC

And ice mast-high
Came floating by....

Samuel Taylor Coleridge

WE WERE OUT IN the free immensity of the Southern Ocean at last, and we spent the next day searching for a place to lay our first set of current meters. This was one of the most important parts of "Hudson-70" and one of the original justifications for mounting the expedition. The Southern Ocean is the only body of water to completely encircle our planet, and it is driven by powerful westerly winds – the Roaring Forties - which move the surface waters eastward to form the world's most powerful current, the Antarctic Circumpolar Current or West Wind Drift. In the days of sailing ships this band of wild ocean was a major thoroughfare. Vessels outward bound from England to Australia would sail far to the south of the Cape of Good Hope before turning to 'run their easting down' in the Roaring Forties. The homeward journey was made by way of Cape Horn so that once again the westerly winds could be used to blow them half way home. This great wind-driven highway has only one bottleneck, the comparatively narrow stretch of water between Cape Horn and the Antarctic Peninsula known as the Drake Passage. Here the water flow is restricted to a smaller width and so the current should become faster. This makes it the best place to measure the flow of the Southern Ocean, but nobody had succeeded in doing so before "Hudson-70". Our current meter moorings would each carry three meters – hanging near the surface, at middle depth, and near the bottom – to give a complete picture of current speeds and directions.

Ced Mann spent the day glued to the echo sounder. Each mooring was designed to rest on the bottom using a weighted anchor which required a bottom slope of less than 1 in 17. At last, near midnight, a suitable site was found about 120 miles SSW of Cape Horn at 57° 49'S, 68° 20'W. To pass the time before dawn Ced ordered a bottle cast, so once again Bruce Carson and I found ourselves together in the winch-house with the familiar figure of old Stan at the controls.

This time we were joined by two chemists from Woods Hole: Pete Brewer, an English exile from Liverpool; and Pete Sachs, a New Englander. They proposed to add some enormous 30-litre Niskin bottles to our cast, from which they hoped to filter enough particulate organic carbon to be able to do direct chemical analysis on the residues. The drag of these vast bottles meant that we had to lower away very slowly, and the cast was done in three parts instead of two. Pete Sachs also had a turbidity measuring device called a nephelometer which he put on the end of the deep cast. A laser beam shines from one end of the instrument onto a photomultiplier which is slightly offset from the direct beam so that it receives only light scattered from particles in the water. The intensity of the scattered light is encoded and sent to the surface in the form of a time delay between two pings of a pinger. The most turbid parts of the ocean are the surface water (due to plankton) and the layers close to the bottom, where the sediment is stirred up by bottom currents.

The whole business took us nearly eight hours, occupying the brief Antarctic night and a morning of calm sea and mild easterly breezes – nothing like Cape Horn weather. I went straight to breakfast afterwards and then to bed, missing the lowering of the first current meter mooring. I also missed the second mooring, which took place the next day at 60°S, another 120 miles to the southward. Again I was in bed in preparation for another night-long session in the winch-house.

This next session began at 9.30 p.m. It was still daylight, and there was a mystical beauty in the air. The sea was absolutely calm except for a long, very low swell coming from a distant part of the ocean. There was not a breath of wind to disturb the few flakes of snow that were gently falling. All around the horizon a break in the cloud left a band of gold at the rim of the sea. As the sun descended into this gap the ship was illuminated by an unearthly orange-red light, as if her plates were glowing from intense heat. To complete the unworldly feeling, we were visited soon after midnight by an inhabitant of these regions. Pete Reynell, who was on watch, had been shining a searchlight from the bridge wing onto a shoal of small fish that were feeding at the surface. Suddenly a large shape appeared in the beam. It was a big leopard seal, placidly paddling around and gazing inquisitively at the ship. His long whiskers twitched as he sneezed, then he dived lazily and swam near the surface for a while before disappearing. He was a beautiful mottled brown in colour and about ten feet long, and his peaceful appearance belied his reputation as a voracious predator who lives on a diet of penguins.

We finished the cast at 4 a.m. just as Pete Reynell was coming off watch, so we went off together into the lounge to celebrate, followed by a bacon and egg orgy in the pantry. Pete was now regularly on the 12-4 watch, and as my nocturnal labouring was becoming a habit we would often end our work by a pleasant hour of yarning in the deserted lounge or Pete's cabin amongst the rye and records. Pete Reynell was a loner, one of that fine breed of independent, adventurous and completely straightforward people that England still produces and whom you meet in the most distant corners of the world. He was born in a boat on the Solent, this being his parents' home at the time. His father, temporarily penniless, was an old Etonian who had led a footloose life and who would later run a successful coastal shipping company in Borneo. Pete went to Pangborne Merchant Navy Academy and thence to sea, to deep-sea tramping and to container ships in the Caribbean. He retained a deep love for England, combined with a strong aversion to settling down there. He had a beautiful girlfriend, as independent as himself, who had followed him from England to Canada and then had gone to Argentina to work. Their happy reunion in Buenos Aires had helped soften Pete's loneliness in an environment of taciturn Nova Scotian officers. The finest things about Pete were his intense love of life and his quiet shy manner that concealed a deep goodness. As I write this, I recall again how we talked away the hours of dawn, with the infinite ocean invisible behind the shuttered windows and silent except for the slap of waves against the drifting hull. All the promise of Pete's life ended tragically two years later when he was drowned.

The diet of night stations caused me to miss the third current meter mooring through being in my bunk at the time. As ship's photographer I was supposed to record such important operations, so I made a point of staying awake to film every stage of the fourth and final mooring, which took place on 3 February at 63° 26'S, 67° 06'W. I shall describe the operation in detail, as it is typical of the complexity of modern oceanographic techniques.

The whole business was carried out over the stern by a burly gang of Bedford Institute technicians led by Tom Foote. First over the side was a subsurface buoy that served to support the chain of meters. It was orange and the size of a large bomb, with a metal surface to provide a good sonar reflection, a radar corner reflector on top, and a pressure-activated radio beacon. All these are aids to assist in its detection and recovery after the experiment is over; when the anchor is released by a remote signal the buoy floats to the surface and may need to be found in a very rough sea.

The buoy was lowered by crane from the helicopter pad into the water. Attached to its underside were a depth recorder, a continuously-recording thermograph and the first current meter. From the current meter ran the stout wire on which the whole instrument chain was to be supported; this was wound on a winch at the stern just under the helicopter pad. When the buoy was floating safely in the water the *Hudson* sailed slowly ahead at 3 knots while 1,350 metres of wire were paid out from the winch. A second set of instruments was then attached, consisting of a current meter, a thermograph and a transponder. The transponder responds to sonar interrogation by providing one minute of pinging for location purposes. This set of instruments was launched down a chute over the stern, and then more wire was paid out.

Meanwhile the depth of the bottom had been very accurately calculated using the echo sounder and *Matthews' Tables*, which correct for the variation of sound velocity with depth. The aim was to set up the mooring with the buoy 150 metres down and the third set of instruments 100 metres from the bottom; the second set is then 1,500 metres down. When the calculated length of wire had been paid out the third and final set of instruments was attached and launched, consisting of the third current meter, a thermograph and a strain gauge (to record any unusual stresses on the mooring). Finally the acoustic release was attached to the wire. This vital link responds to a 10 kilocycle coded sonar signal by releasing the whole chain above it; the release must function if the meters are ever to be recovered.

Now the final 100 metres of wire were paid out and the anchoring system was fixed to it. This consisted of two old railway wheels, attached to parachutes to slow their descent. When the wheels splashed into the water and the parachutes were cleared the job was done. The wheels sank to the bottom, pulling down the buoy and establishing the instruments in a vertical chain. This is known as a 'taut wire mooring', which presents no hazard to navigation. A simpler system is a 'slack wire mooring', where the buoy floats on the surface and the instruments dangle loosely beneath it; this is liable to drift and is also a danger to shipping. The *Hudson* had to remain at the scene until a good satellite fix was received, in order to give the exact position of the meters. She then tested the 1,500-metre transponder and confidently sailed away, leaving an unmarked Southern Ocean and a very expensive set of instruments. An experiment two years earlier in terrible conditions off Greenland had resulted in the loss of nearly all the moorings that had been laid, so we were gambling both with the weather and with the skill of the instrument designers.

The Braincon current meters themselves were beautiful instruments, reflecting the advances in instrumentation during the 1960s which turned oceanography from an adventure into a technology. They have a fin which aligns with the current and a cupped Savonius rotor which measures its velocity. Obviously a true direction must also be recorded independent of the meter, and this is achieved by a magnetised freely spinning disc which carries a phosphorescent marker. The rotor is connected by reduction gearing to another transparent disc which also carries a phosphorescent marker, and a third reference marker is attached to the wall of the meter. Finally there is a luminous electric watch beside the disc. The whole scene is recorded on photographic film by means of a clockwork shutter which exposes a frame for 20 minutes and then winds on. The film sees all the markers. Since the fin is attached rigidly to the meter body the magnetised disc and the reference marker together give the current direction, while the speed of the current is given by the arc of blurred phosphorescence traced out in 20 minutes by the disc attached to the rotor. Thus an independent measurement of speed and direction is made every 20 minutes for as many weeks as the clockwork will function. The thermograph works in a similar way by photographing the silhouette of a mercury thermometer against a phosphorescent plate.

Having filmed the current meter operation I looked around me in daylight and realised just how far south we were. The wind was biting, and a crowd of tiny Chinstrap Penguins was sporting in the choppy grey sea. The little creatures were only two feet long, with white heads and shirt fronts and a black band round the neck which gives them their name. We were surrounded by birds who swooped and dived at our garbage; I recognised the familiar Cape Pigeons and tiny Wilson's Storm Petrels from South Atlantic days. Around the horizon lay a few small icebergs, like floating cheeses. Feeling inspired, I stayed awake the next day as well, despite another night-long bottle cast, and spent the day filming sampling operations on deck. Roger was doing plankton tows with Roy Edwards, an English biologist now at Trent University, Peterborough, Ontario, and a former student of my hero Sir Alister Hardy. Rog and Roy had just lost their coarse mesh net which disappeared into the sea when a swivel gave way, and were reduced to a fine mesh net which took much longer to filter the plankton. In the afternoon Eric Mills did a dredge sample. The deep-water dredge is a less sophisticated instrument than the epibenthic sled and consists of a heavy steel scraping edge which is dragged along the bottom, gathering the sediment into a canvas bag. The returning dredge was hauled high over the foredeck, the bottom of the bag was opened, and a great torrent of mud gushed down into a waiting tank, splashing over the waiting photographer and his Bedford Institute cameras. Luckily I cleaned the cameras quickly, for we soon came up close to a very large tabular iceberg, perhaps half a mile long. Erosion had left a shelf or beach running round its edge near the waterline, and this provided a resting place for dozens of penguins, who periodically retreated when a large wave broke against their refuge. The flanks of the berg shone blue in the weak southern sun, displaying horizontal striations which record each year's accumulation of ice. The berg had never capsized, and so must have broken off its parent ice shelf quite recently. The sea around the berg was dotted with small growlers which had broken off their parent, leaving mysterious dark blue caverns as scars.

This magnificent iceberg was the harbinger of the true Antarctic, and I looked forward eagerly to my first glimpse of a new continent. We had crossed the Drake Passage in a week, laying four current meter moorings in conditions of unbelievable calm. I had worked all night and slept most days, and was scarcely aware of how far south we had come. Now, as dawn broke on February 5, we were approaching the South Shetland Islands off the Antarctic Peninsula, to sample and dredge while we waited for the current meters to do their work.

We entered the island chain from the south-west, and when I came on deck we had already passed Smith Island, so that the snow-covered crags of Deception Island provided my first sight of Antarctica. The island is seven miles long, with a forbidding aspect of black slag slopes and jagged low peaks, but as its name implies it is a deceptive place. From Bransfield Strait it appears inaccessible, but it is really the peak of a volcano, and the sea has breached a narrow entrance into a flooded crater which provides a perfect landlocked harbour. This is the best harbour in the South Shetlands, and was used as a major whaling base until about 1930 and then as a scientific station.

However, our first port of call was to be Livingston Island, where we anchored in South Bay. This is a huge arena surrounded by looming grey crags and snowfields, and with glaciers which end at the sea in great ice cliffs.

The water was glassy calm and filled with small pieces of brash ice from the glaciers. Occasionally penguins popped up their heads, creating circles of ripples, and in the clear grey water we could see snake-like strands of jelly drift by, speckled with red blobs. These were salp colonies. We did sled and plankton tows, and a Smith-McIntyre grab sample in which a spring-loaded pair of jaws is lowered to the bottom and snapped shut on a sample of sediment. Bob Hessler gloated over the resulting lump of mud since it contained several long, thin bottom worms as well as the normal sponges and starfish.

After two hours we sailed again. I set to work processing station data on the computer, while the mountains of Livingston Island slipped by, the highest peak buried in cloud. The sea teemed with Chinstrap Penguin who made the water boil as they erupted in a body from the surface ahead of our bows. The sky was filled with Kelp Gull, an unfamiliar species which nests in these islands. As I worked I was joined by Fred Muise, who began trying to fix the broken-down satellite navigator. He looked very ill and I asked him how he was.

"Haven't been able to eat for days," he said, hollow-eyed. "Keep throwing everything up."

He looked terrible, but worked doggedly away, helped by Hugh Henderson, until the machine was working. Then he tramped quietly off to his cabin. I remembered not seeing him for meals recently.

In the afternoon we entered English Strait between Greenwich and Robert Islands, and hove-to in Discovery Bay on Greenwich Island. This is a large sheltered bay surrounded by low mountains, and with a spit of land near the entrance supporting a Chilean scientific base. We could see bright orange tents and huts, radio masts, a cemetery and a ship lying alongside. She was the naval supply ship *Yelcho*, and we honoured her with a blast on our klaxon to which she gave no reply. This was possibly because of the ludicrous political situation in the Antarctic whereby the South Shetland Islands and the Antarctic Peninsula are claimed by three nations: Britain, Argentina and Chile. Each nation maintains a high density of scientific bases in order to lend credence to its claims, and Argentina has even invented new names for some of the South Shetland Islands. Each nation sends its supply ships down in summer to fly the flag around the bases, and quite possibly the Chileans were puzzled by this unfamiliar vessel. Could it be a fourth country making land claims? According to the Antarctic Treaty of 1961 all these claims were set aside for 30 years (later extended) and the continent was to be regarded as a free area for scientists of all nations. This philosophy has not penetrated to the Foreign Offices of the three claimant states, who continue to maintain more bases than they need, while Britain continues to issue stamps for the 'British Antarctic Territory'. Canada, of course, was innocent of all such nationalist entanglements, so we sailed blithely into the bay and did our sled, grab and plankton tows, then sailed back out into Bransfield Strait leaving *Yelcho* emitting clouds of black smoke as she tried to get steam up. *Yelcho*, for all her dirty appearance, bore an honourable name, for she is named after the Chilean tug which succeeded in rescuing Shackleton's marooned men from Elephant Island in 1916.

Our final call for the day was Marion Cove on King George Island (Isla 25 de Mayo on Argentine charts), which we reached about 7:30 p.m. A very narrow strait separated us from Nelson Island. The cove is filled with a great glacier of deep blue ice, sweeping down to a cracked and gnarled ice cliff containing a sea-filled grotto of exquisite beauty. The water was perfectly calm, and our bow wave as we entered the cove broke in a great fountain of spray inside the grotto. We carried out our sampling under a vertical lichen-covered rock face, watched by a small group of penguins loitering on the shore.

We spent the night out in Bransfield Strait where Bruce and I had to do the inevitable bottle station, and next morning we entered Admiralty Bay, a deep fjord on the south coast of King George Island. This great convoluted inlet is surrounded by tall mountains and glaciers. It is about twelve miles deep, and its innermost part is divided into two coves, Martel and Mackellar Inlets, separated by a mountainous promontory known as the Keller Range. We entered Martel Inlet and anchored opposite two glaciers that plunge into the sea on either side of a rocky pile called Stenhouse Bluff. To our left stretched the Keller Range, a line of conical peaks in front of which lay a small ledge of foreshore ending in a shingly beach. Here lay the three huts of an abandoned British scientific base, Base 'G' of the Falkland Islands Dependencies Survey (now the British Antarctic Survey). The Captain decided on a run ashore to explore this base.

I jumped into the first launch. The beach slopes very gently so the launch had to lie offshore and land us by dory. We landed on shingle amongst large smooth rocks and lumps of stranded sea ice. We saw to our amazement that the shoreline was a charnel house of great whales. Vast quantities of whale bones were piled up along the foreshore; huge vertebrae, ribs, jaws and shoulder bones, all bleached and grooved by exposure and lying in complete confusion. They are mute testimony to the heady and wasteful early days of Antarctic whaling. When the Norwegian captain Svend Foyn perfected the harpoon gun and fast steam whaler in 1864 he made it possible to hunt the fast-swimming rorquals (blue and fin whales) who dwelt in the Antarctic and who could not be touched by sailing whalers. The first Antarctic steam whalers had shore bases in the South Shetlands to which they towed their whales for processing; sometimes the bases were old liners, permanently moored in sheltered harbours. The 'processing' consisted simply of boiling out the blubber in time-honoured fashion, and the meat and bones were discarded and left to float around in the bay. These shore stations came under the jurisdiction of the Falkland Islands Dependencies, and the British Government taxed them and later tried to control their activities when the whalers' rapaciousness led to a catastrophic decline in whale stocks. This stimulated the whaling companies to invent the whale factory ship, which sails independently of any shore and knows no control save the ultimate one imposed by the extinction of all great whales. Admiralty Bay had been a shore station until the 1920s; now only the bones remain as a memorial to mass murder.

I climbed ashore and explored along the beach. In pools between the rocks there were brown leaves of kelp and small ferny seaweeds, and just above the high tide mark large areas were covered by a spongy yellow-green moss. Otherwise there was no vegetation. Animal life consisted of two Gentoo penguins standing by the water, who did not object to being approached. They were handsome creatures with pink feet, white breasts with a crisscross ribbed pattern, brown backs and red bills. At length they waddled off with their flippers held out behind them in true Chaplin fashion, and plunged into the sea.

Next I climbed up to Base G. The main hut was a wooden building about 80 feet long, set on a gravel platform some 200 yards from the sea. The windows were boarded up but the door was open. Iver Duedall was already inside and had found some candles, with which we looked around. There was a sad smell of mildew and decay, but the building and contents were quite sound. In one end room were two generators in a well-oiled state, with plentiful supplies of fuel oil, tools and spares. At the other end of the hut was a full bunker of coal. There was a kitchen with a large coal-fired stove and various pieces of crockery; a bathroom; and an empty radio cabin with peeling photographs of Cambridge on the wall and QSL cards of station VP8DT, South Orkneys, run by A. Sharman. A. Sharman must have been a Cambridge man, and I could understand his nostalgia for the Bridge of Sighs. Next door was the base leader's office, with a desk and cupboards full of meteorological charts. The most evocative room was the library-cum-lounge. One wall was covered with bookshelves still filled with mildewed volumes; each was stamped 'Falkland Islands Public Library' or 'Falkland Islands Company'. Scattered about the room were easy chairs and a coffee table, and an amateur decorator had painted one wall red and covered it with crochets and quavers. Lying on the table were some old 78 rpm records of Bach and Eddie Cantor. A table lamp had been made out of a whisky bottle and a flowery shade. In short, it was a bachelor's idea of how a home should look.

Leading off the lounge were a darkroom, still equipped with trays and rotten chemicals, and a record office. Here I found files full of messages and copies of telegrams. I reproduce one of the regular radio messages sent back to London by the base leader; it gives the flavour of what life was like for a small party of scientists cooped up together for two years at a time:-

> *G/201/59. Fortport. Generally pretty rotten weather rain snow gales record low pressure with barograph dropping off chart. Geological party returned to base on 22nd having completed map of rock outcrops on Hennequin and found fossils and morraines. While field party away Watson and myself did Met OBS and Stokes now included as regular member of Met team. In spare time some skiing enjoyed and darkroom popular while amateur radio station having more success ... Ice fast to gates no change during past two months Bransfield pack ice six to ten tenths to horizon ice formed inlets 2nd May all fast by June 6th thickness 1.3 to 1.5 metres sea temperature constant at minus 1.7 C - Stansbury.*

The ice report shows that these deceptively temperate islands are actually embedded in the Antarctic pack ice zone for at least six months of the year, so that much of the scientists' time is spent 'wintering', i.e. huddling in their huts through days of twilight and darkness until the brief summer comes again.

Base G was set up in 1948, expanded for the International Geophysical Year in 1957-58 and then abandoned in 1961. It was left as a refuge for castaways, and is described as such in the *Admiralty Pilot*. It was resupplied in 1964 for this purpose and was equipped to support life for several months. We found the food store full of thousands of cans, most of which were still good. We also found a special equipment store containing skis, snowshoes, pitons, ice axes, waterproof clothing and two aluminium canisters of medical equipment. This made the subsequent actions of the *Hudson* visitors especially shameful. What now began was indiscriminate looting, not just of harmless souvenirs and keepsakes, but of the life-saving equipment from the store. Snowshoes, skis and axes disappeared, and soon a regular ferry service of spoils was under way back to the ship. Officers and scientists were smitten by the same mad fever as the crew, and the base was systematically stripped of items of no particular value to us but of possibly life-saving value to a castaway. The most solemn code of seafaring men was broken, and by a ship of science no less.

Disgusted, Roger and I turned away from the huts and came upon a low promontory bearing four stark rocky cairns topped with wooden crosses. The inscriptions on the crosses told everything that needed to be told:-

> *Dennis Ronald Bell. b. 15:7:34, d. accidentally Base G, 26:7:59*
> *Eric Platt. Geologist. Base Leader. d. on duty 10:11:48 aged 22*
> *Ronald Gordon Napier. Base Leader. b. 29:1:25. Lost at sea 24:3:56*
> *Alan Sharman. b. 29:12:36. d. accidentally Base G 23:4:59 (radio operator)*

So Alan Sharman had never again seen the Bridge of Sighs or punted along the Backs. Four adventurous young lives were surely too high a price to pay for the base.

We were joined by Mike Crimp in his travelling hat, and soon a breathless Tom Foote appeared, who had just climbed the peak behind the base and glissaded down again on his back. We felt the need to escape from Base G so we set off to emulate his feat. It was a stiff climb of nearly two hours up snowfields and scree slopes. Mike was attacked mercilessly by Antarctic terns, who aggressively swooped and pecked at his feathered hat. Finally we scrambled onto the summit and could gaze down on the *Hudson* floating like a toy in Admiralty Bay. Sea ice was now drifting into the bay, and soon a bank of low cloud swept in, enveloping us in flurries of snow and blotting out the scene below. We knew that it was time to descend. There in front of us was the steep snow slope, a rapid path to the foot of the mountain. If Tom could do it, so could we. Mike went first, lying on his back and holding on to the bottom of his parka. I followed in his tracks. Initially the acceleration was frightening, but the wild ride became exhilarating and I ended up near Mike at the bottom with my gloves full of snow but with no injuries. Roger followed, but his special sou'wester fell off en route so he had to climb back up the mountain to retrieve it. Together with Bruce, we caught the dory from shore, which had to thread its way between drifting ice floes to regain the ship.

The biologists were already busy doing a grab and a sled haul at the anchorage, finding a mass of grey mud full of benthic life. The *Hudson* sailed immediately and, as if to punish us for our tardiness, Ced ordered Bruce and me to do a bottle station straight away. We were only four miles from King George Island and in only 370 metres of water, but we dutifully did our cast and found the surface water near freezing point. Then, our good fellowship undiminished, we repaired to Bruce's cabin to partake of his particular piece of loot, a stone jug of immensely powerful 1958 overproof Navy rum.

"Where did you find this?" I asked.

"Well, I'll tell you," replied Bruce in his most innocent voice. "Iver and Tom Foote and I were looking around, you know, when we saw this trapdoor in the roof. Nobody else had seen it. We got up there and found this wonderful attic space, full of good stuff. There were all these boxes of dynamite, see, and right by them these two wonderful gallon jugs with Her Majesty's seal on them. There was even a set of shot glasses to go with them!"

I looked with admiration at the stylish glasses from which we drank.

"What I figured," he said with continued innocence "was that with an abandoned base like this, being visited by looters all the time, there was a real danger of an accident. You know, if a rum jug got smashed and a guy like Iver dropped his candle on it with all that dynamite around, the whole place could go up. So I thought that the rum and the dynamite should be well separated."

He proceeded to crank up a portable gramophone. "Like to hear *Greensleeves*?" he asked. "Iver found this up in the attic, too!"

As a postscript to the Admiralty Bay affair it is ironic to note that a year later there was a real need for the refuge facilities of Base G, when the Norwegian cruise ship *Lindblad Explorer*, laden with rich American matrons, went aground in the bay. The passengers had to spend a night at the base, and found conditions in the despoiled hut so unpleasant that the Lindblad Company faced several lawsuits for 'mental cruelty'. The base even maintained its reputation as a killer, for in 1971 Jacques Cousteau visited in the *Calypso* and lost his Chief Mate down a crevasse. And to complete its bizarre history it was the location of a UFO sighting by scientists aboard the USS *Glacier* visiting in 1961. Today the hut is almost a museum; a glossy new Brazilian base has been built just a hundred yards away, and the personnel keep a benign eye on this relic of early Antarctic exploration.

We sailed east out of Bransfield Strait with intentions of further Antarctic cruising, since the current meters required several more days of undisturbed data gathering, but we were stopped in our tracks by a terrific storm. By midnight we were facing 70-80 knot winds and 25 foot waves, and the next morning found us hove-to with waves breaking over the foredeck and flying spray hitting the bridge windows. More dangerously, the lines and cranes on the foredeck were becoming heavily iced. The sea was viciously short and steep, since the wind was coming from the south-east and had only a short fetch. Towards noon we resumed way, and crept cautiously round to the northwest of King George Island to shelter from the gale. This side of the island is very rugged and intercepts icebergs on their eastward drift in the Circumpolar Current. Eric Mills wrote in his diary:-

> *Few sights have impressed me more than this view of the white north side of King George Island, where the jagged islets rise offshore and the icebergs crowd along the smooth, snowy glacial shore. It is the ultimate in inanimate hostility.*

In the early evening rumours began to fly around the ship about a change of plans. A procession of scientists and officers called on Ced Mann. At last it was announced that we were to head straight back to Puerto Williams to drop off Fred Muise, who had suddenly become very ill indeed. Now the whole tragic story came out. Fred and his wife had been looking forward to Fred's voyage as a means of saving enough money to buy a house for themselves and their small son. Then, just before sailing, it was confirmed that their son had a brain tumour. They faced an agonising decision, but came to the conclusion that Fred should sail. At Rio Fred received news that his son was worse and at Buenos Aires that he was dead. Ced offered to fly Fred home but he refused. His mental agony brought on the eruption of an old stomach ulcer, and the resulting inability to keep down food made him weaker and weaker. In the recent storm he had become delirious. Unfortunately Fred had to cope not only with his illness but also with the attentions of the Doctor, who locked him in Iver's cabin (a woman's cabin with toilet and shower) with a heavy sedative. The Doctor then lost interest in him, having diagnosed psychosomatic illness. Naturally, when Fred awoke at last and found himself imprisoned he went somewhat berserk and tried to kick the door down. From then on the Doctor was taken off the case and relays of scientists kept Fred company. We sailed north at full speed through the night of the 7th and all day on the 8th, entering the Beagle Channel on the morning of February 9.

The eastern end of the Channel was calm and shimmered like a fish's scales. Gulls and skuas crowded the air and penguins sported in the sea. Autumn was on its way, however, and the mountain peaks of Tierra del Fuego bore the dusting of fresh snow. As soon as we anchored at Puerto Williams the commandant came out and the matter of Fred's disembarkation was settled. He went ashore in the care of Bob Reiniger, a physical oceanographer from Bedford Institute. They awaited a military flight to Punta Arenas and then a commercial flight home.

The long-lost launch *Redhead* also appeared, and Jim Markham and Ed Bousfield came aboard to report on the success of their coastal collecting expedition. They had experienced storm, snow, rain, engine breakdowns and a sinking dory, and were very happy with their results. In fact one of Ed's specimens, which he found in the intertidal zone, was later found to be new to science and of a genus that was believed extinct. It was a tiny amphipod, or flea, less than half an inch long, but it was one of the major discoveries of "Hudson-70". It was in the initial stages of evolving from a marine creature, with powerful swimming legs, into a land-based beach flea. All other amphipods have either moved completely onto land or have remained in the sea. Ed had found a case of 'arrested evolution', where a process which was finished millions of years ago in the rest of the world is still in progress in Tierra del Fuego.

The *Hudson's* engineers overhauled the launch's engine, and then Ed and Jim set out for more collecting. We ourselves sailed late in the afternoon, leaving as a parting present a large slick of diesel oil, pumped out by an engineer's mistake. We passed Cape Horn in the night, and hove-to off the Diego Ramirez Islands south of Cape Horn next morning for some biological sampling.

Now we began to work slowly southwards, picking up the current meters and running a chain of closely spaced oceanographic stations down the Drake Passage. At the first station Pete Sachs and Pete Brewer lowered their giant bag. This was a 2,000 litre neoprene bag which was lowered from a davit in a rolled-up state and was then unrolled at depth by a release triggered by a messenger weight. The aim was to collect a gigantic sample of water which could be analysed for trace elements and for particulate organic carbon. A second messenger was used to close the mouth of the bag after it had filled. The full bag was hauled slowly up, and the ship listed to starboard as the unwieldy two-ton weight was swung over the rail and secured on deck.

Next Bruce and I set to work on the first of an apparent non-stop series of bottle stations which soon reduced us to physical and mental wrecks. Ced gave us no warning of what was in store, nor any explanation of the purpose of the stations, otherwise we would have worked with better grace. Instead, one station followed another with only short gaps, at all times of day and night. Sleep came in brief snatches at irregular intervals, meals were lost and tempers became frayed. We started to make mistakes, like forgetting to close the air vents in the Knudsen bottles so that the bottles drained as they came out of the water. Bruce's lot was even harder than mine, since he had to do Bathysondes as well. We considered forming a Bottle Casters' Union and going on strike, but somehow suffered through it. Probably the dismal weather and the long period at sea had started to give us 'cabin fever'. Our most frustrating experience would be to come into the lounge after several hours in the bitter cold to find Ced placidly playing chess or watching the evening movie.

The general spread of cabin fever led to the Talking To Loved Ones Project. Fred Muise had a little electronics workshop adjoining the drafting laboratory, where he ran a ham radio station, VEOMX, operating on the 14 megacycle band. He and Phil the radio operator, whose shack was just opposite, had a great feud. Fred would spend long hours at his radio, raising Halifax or other hams in Antarctica, and people used to crowd round his rig to listen in. Phil, with his big official Marconi Marine rig CGDG, felt his position pre-empted, and so when Fred had raised an interesting contact Phil would often come over and insist that Fred get off the air as he had to send a Morse message. With Fred gone the radio remained, and now Eric Mills went on the air with it and succeeded in raising San Diego so that Bob Hessler could talk with his wife via a 'phone patch' in which the ham in San Diego connects through to the wife by telephone. Eric was now inundated with requests for contacts, but found that conditions were never again good enough to raise North America.

The retrieval of current meters provided one of the few opportunities for me to sleep, so I missed all of these operations except the second, on February 12. I filmed this for BIO. When we reached the estimated position a hydrophone was lowered and the coded acoustic identification signal sent out. The transponder 1,500 metres down, responded perfectly with a minute of pings. Next the coded command signal was sent out to activate the acoustic release. After a few anxious minutes the bleeping of the buoy's radio beacon came through loudly on our radio direction finder to tell us that it had reached the surface safely. The Bedford Institute technicians grunted with relief, and after a few minutes' steaming the orange bomb came into sight. It was hooked on to the foredeck crane and the whole mooring was winched on board. This was typical of the smooth recovery of all four moorings, in sea and wind conditions that had now deteriorated a great deal.

After "Hudson-70" it took two years for Ced to process the current meter data, and the results were startling. The surface meters recorded the expected massive flow of water from west to east, the Antarctic Circumpolar Current. The mid-water meters, however, recorded very little net flow, while the bottom meters recorded a flow from east to west. Adding up these two counter-currents it was found that during the eleven days of the recordings there was almost no net flow of water through the Drake Passage! We now realise that the recording period was too short, that the ocean has a 'weather' of eddies and varying currents which can overwhelm its 'climate' of long-term average flows unless lengthy records are taken. The results of the "Hudson-70" measurements were enough to jolt oceanographers out of a complacent feeling that they understood the broad features of global oceanic circulation, and during the 1970s longer-term current measurements were done in a programme called International Southern Ocean Studies. It is now agreed that the net eastward flow is in fact huge, some 150-180 Sverdrups – where a Sverdrup is a million tons per second.

Despite the onset of Antarctic autumn we were still not deserted by the prolific marine life of the Drake Passage. During one station a school of about fifty pilot whales swam past the ship, arching out of the water and displaying their strange pot-shaped foreheads and big white dorsal patches. On passage further south we were joined by a school of ten porpoises, who swam with us at 14 knots. Later when we slowed down they closed in and started playing beneath the bow, darting to and fro and twisting and turning in the water as if they were playing tag. They would shoot across the bow from one side to the other so that I could admire their fine lines and beautiful black bodies with white patches. Killer whales also appeared one day. A small pod cruised past, oblivious of us, showing only their tall triangular dorsal fins and a little of their backs. In the Antarctic these kings of the sea hunt seals both in the ocean and on ice floes, by tipping them off in concerted group attacks.

With all the moorings collected we found ourselves at the southern end of Drake Passage with time for another brief visit to the South Shetlands. The morning of February 15 found us approaching Deception Island. It loomed up behind a bank of mist as a mysterious rugged line of black crags and steep lava flows. The island is roughly circular and about seven miles in diameter, but the entrance to the lagoon is less than two hundred yards across and is easily missed. We felt our way slowly towards it and crept through, overwhelmed and awed by the vertical rock faces on either side. The entrance passage is called Neptune's Bellows, and it must be terrifying to negotiate in heavy weather. On our port side lay a reminder of this, the rusty wreck of a whalecatcher under the cliff face. She was the *Southern Hunter* of Leith, wrecked in 1956 on the Raven Rock, which lies treacherously awash within the entrance passage. The sheer brown rock face to starboard, riven by cracks and fissures, is called Fildes Point after Robert Fildes, a sealer who discovered and charted Deception Island in 1820. His discovery brought a rush of sealers to use the perfectly sheltered harbour as a haven and base for their operations. In the years 1821-2 alone, more than 320,000 seals were killed in the South Shetlands by ships based at Deception, and by 1829 the local population of fur seals and elephant seals was extinct.

Neptune's Bellows opens into the calm lagoon of Port Foster, the great crater of the Deception volcano. It is a magnificent anchorage five miles by three, ringed by conical peaks reminiscent of South Wales slag heaps. Just inside the entrance lay a little semicircular cove called Whalers' Bay, containing the derelict huts and airstrip of a deserted British base and the larger buildings and oil storage tanks of the old Hektor Whaling Station. Whale factory ships started to use Deception Island in 1905, and by 1912 there were twelve old liners moored in Whalers' Bay, wastefully processing the victims of 32 whalecatchers which roamed Bransfield Strait. The ships, mostly Norwegian, lay stern to shore in a line, taking advantage of the reliable fresh water supply found in wells around the bay. The resident British magistrate reported 3,000 rotting carcases floating around in the bay, and this stimulated the British authorities to grant a licence for a land station which would be more efficient. Whaling ceased here in 1931 after the floating factory ship with a stern slipway made whalers independent of the shore. The more recent desertion of the scientific bases, however, was due to quite another cause – a sudden increase in the volcanic activity of the island, which we were soon to encounter for ourselves.

We continued into the lagoon, passing the Argentine scientific base on our port side, and came to anchor in Telefon Bay. The launch was lowered and this time only scientists were allowed ashore; perhaps the Captain had learned from the destruction at Admiralty Bay.

We headed east for a mile in the launch, and reached shore at Pendulum Cove, the site of the wrecked Chilean base. As we drew near, we could see the water in the surf zone actually steaming, like the River Styx, while more vapours rose from a volcanic peak behind the foreshore. To the right of our landing place was a rounded hillock, covered in ash and bearing three radio masts, but the foreshore ahead of us was just a bleak expanse of black mud and ash engulfing the twisted ruins of the scientific base. As we entered the surf zone we were enveloped in warm, saline, sulphurous vapours. The beach was steep and we had to land in the dory; I stepped out into hot acidic water which bleached my red rubber boots. The black beach was scattered with old oil drums, and behind it we found a 10-foot high escarpment of dust and ash. This was the product of the recent 1969 eruption. The Chilean base had flourished until 1967, when an eruption from a crater above the base rained ashes and cinders on the buildings and forced the inhabitants to flee in the middle of the night to the British base. The whole island was then evacuated. In 1969 came a second eruption which brought down a 'lahar', an avalanche of burning mud and ash, which engulfed the Chilean base and also damaged the abandoned British huts. Now only the Argentinians seemed interested in the island, for we had seen a few tiny figures as we passed their base on the relatively inactive side of Port Foster.

We climbed the escarpment via a ravine carved by a meltwater stream (part of the ash flow covered a glacier, which had been melting ever since) and reached the wreck of the base. There must have been a complex of corrugated iron buildings, with a large wooden hut set somewhat apart. The iron sheeting had been torn and mangled into fantastic shapes with rivets, bolts and screws forced out. All the wooden beams had been turned into charcoal sticks. The former floor level was now eight feet underground, and the ruined shell stood like the wreck of the airship *Hindenburg*. All that stood undamaged was a breezeblock archway that was the former main entrance of the base. Of the wooden hut all that remained was the front facing the sea, where a couple of window frames were still joined together by a few boards bearing peeling green paint. In front of the base was a cairn, built of stone and cement and once surmounted by a large wooden cross, which now lay at a crazy angle on top of it. Behind the base was a radio mast, and nailed to its foot was the nameplate of the base, a metal plaque partly eaten away by extreme heat and bearing the words:-

FUERZA AEREA DE CHILE
(-----) ANTARCTICA
'PRESIDENTE AGUIRRE CERDA'

Now we split up to explore further. I wandered along the beach, finding a complete absence of intertidal life except for some boiled seaweed which had probably been cast ashore in a storm. A few whalebones poked out above the ash, and I recovered a vertebra which I carried back to the dory as a souvenir. Offshore, through the veil of steam and sulphur fumes, the stern of a wrecked Chilean landing craft could be seen. I turned my attention to the volcanic peak behind the base and began to climb it in the company of Allan Michael, who was familiar with the volcanoes of his native New Zealand. As we climbed higher the slope became steeper and loose cinders and lava boulders replaced the fine ash. The soft surface was riddled with cracks and fissures from which steam or sulphur dioxide oozed forth. Fumaroles, said Allan. Eventually we reached the lip of a crater which had opened in the most recent eruption. The mountain higher up was wreathed in smoke and steam and looked most uninviting. The crater was 200 metres across, and the walls were streaked with red and silver veins from solidified lava flows. At one point there was a deep channel lined with pure native sulphur. The acid stench of sulphur dioxide was everywhere, and the footing was treacherous. The whole scene was diabolical, and unlike anything that I had expected to find in the Antarctic. In the distance the *Hudson* floated in the tranquil green lagoon. To the right of her lay the long flat north side of the island, where Sir Hubert Wilkins built an ash runway for the first Antarctic flight in 1928. Far off to the left an Argentine supply ship was creeping into Port Foster to replenish the base.

At a signal from Ced we reassembled on shore and were ferried back to the *Hudson*. I cradled a whale vertebra, and also spirited away the nameplate of the Chilean base. Back on board we did plankton tows, a benthic haul and the inevitable bottle cast in the lagoon. There was a depth of 164 metres and a water temperature of 1.2°C, surprisingly unaffected by the surrounding geothermal heat. At 6:30 p.m. we sailed and passed back through the

Bellows. An hour later, with Deception Island fading into the distance, we came to a perfect tabular iceberg, with a flat top and gleaming white vertical sides. It was a symbol of the austere beauty of these Polar regions, which has enslaved explorers and in which Deception Island seems so out of place. Astern of us the towering peaks of Livingston Island sparkled in the setting sun before a luminous mist descended over them and the island sank away. We turned from the Antarctic and began our long journey towards the opposite end of the world.

CHAPTER 9

THE SOUTHERNMOST CITY IN THE WORLD

Them girls of Chile are hard to beat;
Always pulling on the old main sheet.

Sea shanty.

THE NOISE IN THE corridor at midnight told me that a gang of drunks was on its way. Sure enough, Bruce, Roger and Iver burst into my cabin and dragged me off to the lounge together with a bottle of Cinzano that I had hoarded since Buenos Aires. We settled down to a ghastly concoction of vodka, Cinzano and raw egg mixed with gusto by Bruce. Iver brought in his looted wind-up gramophone from Deception Island and we played mildewed records of 1950s' love songs that filled us with inexpressible longing.

We all yearned to get ashore and relax. Many of the scientists would be going home from Punta Arenas, including Ced, Bruce, the chemists and the current meter party, and the scientific staff for the next leg through the Chilean fjords would be supplied by the University of British Columbia. Many of the crew were due to change as well, but not, unfortunately, the Doctor. Long-term inmates such as Iver and I planned to make the most of our call at Punta Arenas, and Roberto Rebaudi had promised to produce an enormous number of Chilean girls to assist our recovery. So the voyage north from Deception Island degenerated into a series of parties in which the consumption of alcohol cemented old friendships and eased the dying days of the cruise. The helicopter hangar was one gathering place for such sessions. Here Ron Shaw, the seaman son of the Chief Steward, had rigged up an amplifier and loudspeaker system for his electric guitar. We found that there were four guitars on board as well as accordions, ukuleles and spoons, and an evening concert with accompanying booze became a regular and pleasant way of passing the time. Here in the hangar officers and crew were on neutral ground, so the rigid divisions of shipboard life could for once be relaxed.

On the morning after the egg orgy I awoke with a hangover to find us sailing through heavy fog near Elephant Island. The island had been named after the elephant seals found there, but acquired lasting fame in 1916 as the refuge for the crew of Shackleton's *Endurance* after she was crushed in the ice. From here Shackleton set off on a 600-mile voyage in the tiny 22 ft boat *James Caird* to fetch help from South Georgia. To my disappointment we saw nothing of the island in the fog. Instead, we stopped for a benthic haul. This was the first and last time that the Captain, to his credit, chivvied the scientists into doing more work than they had planned. There was ship time in hand and the Captain, inspired by the creatures that he had seen emerging from sled hauls, went into the lounge and suggested to Eric Mills that he do another station. Eric was reluctant, since his gang was relaxing after processing the material from the Deception station, but he finally agreed. *Hudson* hove-to in shallow water, but drifted over the edge of the continental shelf and the sled haul was done in 2,560 metres. This was the only deep-ocean benthic haul of the cruise, and it yielded a magnificent array of creatures.

Bruce and I were also not allowed to relax. After the haul *Hudson* sailed northwest for 80 miles to clear the South Shetland chain, and then Ced ordered a bottle cast. The water depth was 5,200 metres and the cast took us ten hours of exhausting work. After only three hours of steaming this was followed by yet another bottle cast, the 47th of the voyage and the very last on this leg. With infinite relief I took the final bottle off the wire and calculated that I had screwed and unscrewed more than a thousand since the beginning of the voyage.

Two more days flew by and then, on the afternoon of February 19, the familiar landfall of the Beagle Channel entrance came into view. We passed close by the disputed Isla Nueva, and then stayed off the east coast of Navarino Island for the rest of the day doing sled, grab and plankton sampling. A magnificent procession of cumulo-nimbus clouds drifted over the sunlit peaks of Tierra del Fuego, while across the Beagle Channel a perfect rainbow appeared in the centre of a great wall of dense slanting rain, with a complete secondary bow above the primary. As the sluicing rain belt moved across the Channel the rainbow arc became cut off in mid-air. There was a smell of life around us again, which gave a great lift to my spirits.

In the evening a pilot boat came out from Puerto Williams and gave us a pilot who guided us in to anchor next morning. We recovered the *Redhead* along with Jim Markham and Ed Bousfield, who came aboard laden with King crabs and Chilean wine; a welcome pile of mail also appeared. However, the hitherto friendly Chilean authorities had now turned hostile. They objected to the presence on board of Roberto, whom they said was a spy. They also said that they could not spare us any fuel oil, although the Chief had been hoping to replenish his tanks. With hindsight I suspect that our oil slick had been discovered in our absence. So we sailed out again without landing and came round to the south side of Navarino Island where Jim wanted to sample in a bay that he had not been able to reach by launch. As soon as we left the shelter of the Beagle Channel, however, we were struck by a 60-knot wind, so we simply did a sled and grab station north of Wollaston Island and then headed for Punta Arenas.

The Chileans had forbidden us to pass through the Beagle Channel again with Roberto on board, so we had to take the long route around the outside of Tierra del Fuego. This involved sailing through Le Maire Strait between the south-eastern corner of Tierra del Fuego and Staten Island (Isla de los Estados). Staten Island presented an ironbound and jagged profile; it has no safe harbour and hundreds of sailing ships have been wrecked against its evil cliffs. Windjammers often chanced Le Maire Strait to save a few hundred miles on the eastward passage round the Horn, but its storms and treacherous tidal streams led many of them to disaster. Fred Cooke and Eric Mills returned to their bird watches, and north of Le Maire Strait they found a third 'feeding area' even more extensive than the two that they had discovered on the voyage south. The sky was crowded with great shearwaters, South American terns, Parasitic jaegers and King cormorants, while Magellanic and Rockhopper penguins were numerous in the sea. Again they suspected upwelling as the cause of the bird concentration.

The whole of the next day was spent steaming up the east coast of Tierra del Fuego, and I did my best to catch up on my computer processing work so as to have time free in Punta Arenas. We entered Magellan Strait in the early evening, and on the morning of the 22nd we came to anchor off Puerto Percy, a small fuelling station on the Fuegan side of the Strait some 25 miles above Punta Arenas. Here we were to pump the oil that was refused us at Puerto Williams. We moved to one of several buoys lying a mile off a low shoreline that displayed only a few houses and some oil storage tanks. A launch came out and began attaching us by a long floating hose to an underwater pipeline which emerged at one of the buoys. The task of pumping 500 tons would take all day so a shore party of scientists was arranged for the afternoon, officially to study intertidal fauna, in fact to get us away from the ship.

Thus at 1.30 p.m. a small force landed from the *Gull*, comprising Fred, Eric, Ed, Bob Hessler and me. At first glance there seemed little to explore. To the right of the jetty stretched a series of oil storage tanks and pumps, while to the left was a maintenance area with a few warehouses. We followed an unmade road off to the left, where we suddenly found ourselves in what appeared to be a London suburb. The road abruptly became metalled, with pavements, grass verges and neat stucco bungalows with flowery front gardens. Children played on bicycles in the street and there was even a speed limit sign. A modern primary school and a little ambulance station stood side by side, while the familiar British weeds of dandelion, thistle and nettle grew between the paving stones. We were completely taken aback, and concluded that the State oil company ENAP (Empresa Nacional del Petróleo) must have found that a simulation of suburbia was the only way to attract workers to this inhospitable region. Feeling faintly ridiculous in our polar gear we tramped on until the 'town' finished as quickly as it had begun. After passing a windswept children's playground proclaimed as the 'Mickey Mouse Club' by the sign and grinning face over the gate, the road disappeared into Magellan Strait.

We descended to the beach, accompanied by a crowd of friendly and inquisitive children. Here we found smooth stones covered with a mass of limpets, scallops and giant blue mussel shells. Seaweed littered the beach, big brown leaves of the familiar kelp *Macrocystis* and a strange pink fleshy weed looking like a heap of intestines. Ed was wearing thigh waders and began searching in the shallows for intertidal animals with his landing net, to the great amusement of the kids. Bob got the kids together for a group photograph, then we wandered onwards collecting shells.

Bob and I were some way ahead of the others. Suddenly, on a promontory outlined against the sky, we saw a guanaco. This rare and shy creature, *Lama guanicoe*, is the wild species of llama that used to roam freely over the grasslands and mountains, but which is now almost extinct after ruthless hunting by settlers. He frisked his tail at us, but as soon as we made a move towards him he jumped like a startled colt and disappeared. We climbed up from the shore to follow him, but saw only the wide grassland of northern Tierra del Fuego stretching into the distance, the continuation of the Argentine pampas. There were butterflies, bees and other insects flying through the tall grass and scrub, while a breeze from inland wafted a summer smell reminiscent of an English country lane. The sun shone, the steel-grey sea was calm, and we might have been on the coast of Norfolk.

After a while a *camioneta* (American pick-up truck) came bumping along the coastal track and the driver offered us a lift. We scrambled over the tailboard and were driven for two kilometres as far as Punta Zegers, a low headland marked by a concrete tower. Here Eric, Ed and Fred Cooke stayed to birdwatch, while Bob and I started slowly back across country. We ended up by the shore again, since we had seen big flocks of oystercatchers feeding in the offshore shallows. With their black backs, white breasts and large flat bills they were distinctive birds but rather shy ones, for when Bob crept up on them in approved fashion with his Leica they flew away. We followed the beach, picking up beautiful specimens of the cup shell, or *Cymbiola*, then turned inland again. The bird that we could see everywhere was the Military Starling, *Pezites militaria*, which is similar to a thrush but with a bright red breast. He darted through the heathland and rooted through the small squares of cultivated land, enclosed by high windbreaks, where the local people grew their vegetables.

It was a real delight to see such peaceful countryside again. In a few weeks the first bitter winds of winter would sweep across these exposed plains but now, briefly, it was as gentle as home. We caught the launch back to the *Hudson* and as I went below I saw two white-backed porpoises flash out of the water beside the ship. It was a good day.

In the evening we had a party in Pete's cabin with booze, my guitar and Pete's accordion. I gave the first performance of a mildly obscene song that I had written in honour of Professor Christiaan Barnard, entitled *Organ Transplant Blues*. The chorus went:-

> *With the blood of a bull and the liver of an ox;*
> *The pancreas of a giant eel, the kidneys of a fox;*
> *The legs of a carthorse with a pair of metal shoes -*
> *The Doctor's left me here to sing the 'Organ Transplant Blues'.*

When the booze ran out we moved to the lounge where we had the unprecedented experience of being bought drinks by the Chief Steward. His wife had just remarried, he said, saving him 180 dollars a month in alimony. At 11 p.m., pumping complete, we set sail.

We arrived at Punta Arenas two hours later and anchored offshore for the night. The morning broke clear and beautiful. The sun shimmered on the calm waters of Magellan Strait and the sky and sea were filled with great flocks of gulls and skuas. I went up to the fo'c's'l to gaze at the view. Ahead stretched the city, along a shoreline which sloped gently up towards a range of low bare hills. The red corrugated-iron roofs of the small houses glittered in the sun in a cheerful way. Off to the left at the southern end of town was the naval dockyard, where three old Cape Horners from the 1870s were lying. Two, the *Falstaff* and the *Hipparchus*, were mere hulks, careened on the beach, but the third, the Glasgow-owned *City of Peebles* that used to carry jute from India to Dundee, was anchored offshore and still had her masts and lower yards. She was being used as a storehouse. The mercantile jetty lay directly opposite me, while behind it was the business centre dominated by the Cabo de Hornos Hotel. At the north end of town was the tall spire of the Salesian church of Santa Maria Auxiliadora, while off to the right lay the airport.

I was joined on the bow by Peter Sachs, who was bemoaning the quantity of drink that he had consumed the night before. As we reminisced about the voyage the ship completed her customs formalities, weighed anchor and edged slowly into the single space remaining at the end of the mercantile jetty. Our companions were an interesting collection of vessels. Opposite us was the Spanish luxury liner *Cabo San Vicente*, the same ship that we had seen here a month earlier, although in the meantime she had done a cruise to the Beagle Channel. Next along was the *Hero*, a neat green wooden vessel built like a small trawler and run as a research ship by the National Science Foundation of the USA. During the summers she was based at Palmer Station on the Antarctic Peninsula, and during the winters she carried out oceanographic cruises from South America. She was stoutly built to resist ice, and carried a ketch rig of sails for 'quiet work' such as acoustics or whale sound recording. Today she is in retirement as a museum in Oregon. On our side of the jetty were the disreputable looking government coaster *Isabella* of Valparaiso, and the government passenger steamer *Navarino* which ran a fortnightly round trip up the coast to Valparaiso.

After lunch a party of us set out for the town. We carefully avoided the Doctor, who went ashore ostentatiously with his dog on a leash and a long knife in a leather belt round his waist to protect himself against the natives. A thin drizzle trickled down as we walked towards the main square. Here we found solid baroque buildings, mainly banks, dating from the heyday of Punta Arenas in the late 19th century. The city was founded in 1843 and soon became a flourishing centre for sheep farming, as well as a coaling and victualling port for the increasing number of steamships that passed through Magellan Strait. It acquired a very mixed population of immigrants from Britain, Germany, France, Spain and Bosnia, the last being refugees from the Balkan wars of the early 20th century. As a result the city took on the character of a North American pioneer town, with little Latin feel about it. Then came a mortal blow. In 1914 the Panama Canal was completed and ships no longer needed to use Magellan Strait. Punta Arenas was instantly relegated to the fringes of the civilised world. The mutton and wool industries declined, and soon the town was a shadow of its former self. But then after the Second World War oil and natural gas were discovered in the area and the town staged a recovery. A canning industry for the *centolla* was established, a naval base was built and tourism began. By 1970 the city was flourishing again.

After stopping to change our dollars into ever-depreciating escudos we reached the pleasant tree-lined main square, dominated by a monument to Ferdinand Magellan. The doughty navigator is cast in bronze as a Spanish grandee with a forked beard, gazing aggressively southwards as he straddles a cannon. The plinth is supported by a pair of lovely mermaids and a pair of sullen Fuegan Indians. On the west side of the square is the cathedral, a brown stone building with an attractive bell-tower and a corrugated iron roof. We found it locked, so we asked the way to the British consulate like true traditional tourists, hoping to obtain some information about the city.

We were directed to an impressive stone building with an exquisitely polished brass nameplate bearing the simple inscription 'The British Club'. We climbed a flight of stairs and found a door marked 'British Consulate'. This proved to be a single office with a bench running down the middle. The decor consisted of a large pre-war photograph of the Queen Mother; a poster bearing a yellowed portrait of Churchill with cigar in teeth, uttering his famous words about 'In Victory, Magnanimity'; some ancient notices about the registering of British nationals; and pictures of the Queen and Prince Philip in their youth and Prince Charles as a baby. It was a time capsule. The staff maintained by Her Britannic Majesty consisted of a small, evil-looking one-eyed Chilean with two teeth in the front of his mouth. He spoke good English, however, and told us that the Club itself would open at 3:45 p.m. precisely.

Our party now split up. Pete Reynell and I went off to the Cabo de Hornos Hotel to await the opening of the British Club. The hotel was a ten-storey yellow brick building, constructed recently out of a government grant and maintained by a large subsidy. The government had reasoned that Punta Arenas could not flourish as a tourist centre without at least one decent hotel. In the foyer was a travel agency where we asked for information. The agent, though born in Chile, was English down to his tweed sports jacket. He gave us a street map on which he marked the one discothèque and two of the brothels ("Try this one first - everybody goes there, including the governor of the province"). We moved on to the bar, where some Hudsonians were already well established, and ordered pisco sours. Pisco, an aptly named beverage, is the national drink of Chile and Peru, and is a coarse aquavit made from muscat grapes. In pisco sour it is mixed with lemon juice and a little white of egg to give it froth and improve the flavour. After two or three of these we felt quite happy and accepted an invitation from Roberto to visit the town's nightspots later in the evening with him and his friend Patricio, a Chilean naval lieutenant who was hydrographer for the Punta Arenas area.

Meanwhile we returned to the British Club. By now quite merry, we marched up the wide staircase chanting "Rule, Britannia." First we were met by some hunting prints, then the full splendour of the club struck upon our eyes. It was like a scene from Somerset Maugham or the stage set for an Edwardian melodrama. The first room was the lounge-cum-library, full of ancient stuffed leather armchairs and musty books. The library was last replenished about 1930, and consisted of forgotten novels and biographies of Victorian earls and First World War colonels. On the wall were portraits of distinguished Former Members, with a bronze plaque commemorating those who fought in the two world wars. There was a baize noticeboard with cards of visitors dating back to the 1930s. A list of present members put the strength of the Club at 182, and the visitors' book showed that they had recently entertained the officers of HMS *Endurance*, the Royal Navy's ice patrol ship. Leading off the lounge was a bar, with a local barman quietly polishing glasses, and then came the dining room with a magnificent high ceiling from which the plaster was peeling. A sepia portrait of Queen Victoria hung on the wall and there were writing desks, a dining table, bookcases, magazines and newspapers including the inevitable airmail edition of the *Daily Telegraph*. A billiard room with three tables was next door. The whole club conveyed the image of a cosy upper-middle class England marooned in gentle seedy decay at the fringe of the inhabited world.

Early in the evening a party of us assembled in the Cabo de Hornos bar to await our guide Patricio, who turned up many piscos later. He proved to be an engaging character with a limp and a roguish smile. He took us first to a restaurant called the 'Centro Austral', which he said had the best food in Punta Arenas. It was an unmarked green wooden building on a corner, with a clean spartan interior heated by an old wood stove. A party of scientists including Ced, Eric, Ed and Fred was already there. We had steak and King crab, washed down by superb Chilean wine. As we sat on in mellow conversation the door opened, and to our mutual surprise a new party arrived consisting of the Captain, Doctor and First Mate. The Captain and Doctor each had a woman in tow who, by their decayed appearance, we judged to be ladies of ill repute. The Doctor glowered, but the Captain behaved with aplomb and introduced his girl as his sister.

About 11 p.m. our party set off in Patricio's car for the Naval Officers' Club, where he planned a few drinks before conveying us to the only late-night entertainment in Punta Arenas, viz. a house of pleasure. As we pulled up at the club, to our astonishment we ran into the wife of the supply officer at Puerto Williams, the girl with the glowing eyes who had made such an impact. She was emerging with her three children, but Patricio, who obviously knew her, persuaded her to stay. We found ourselves alone in the club, and after ordering pisco sours we fell to talking to Nena, for that was her name. She spoke not a word of English, but this didn't seem to matter. We played with her children, giving them piggyback rides and letting them beg the loose change from our pockets. After a while Patricio announced that it was time to take Nena and the children home. They disappeared. Half an hour later Patricio and Nena returned minus the children and the party continued.

In the early hours of the morning we divided our forces and Patricio set off with Iver, Roberto and me, leaving Roger and Nena in the club to be picked up later. I left Roger my Spanish phrase book. As we got in the car, Patricio said enigmatically: "I am giving him the greatest opportunity of his life!"

Afterwards Roger told me what happened. As soon as we left a great change came over Nena. She moved up close to Roger, took the phrase book and pointed to significant phrases such as 'I like you' and 'Where shall we meet?'. The message was unmistakeable, but the language barrier made arranging the details very difficult, especially as the suspicious steward came in at five-minute intervals. Nena would then slide over to the other side of the sofa and look prim. Trying to write down a time and place was equally difficult, as Nena's handwriting was indecipherable, and arrangements were not in place when Patricio returned an hour later.

Our own expedition led us to what is undoubtedly the most extraordinary and famous bordello in the southern hemisphere. Known simply as 'Maria Teresa's', it is but a stone's throw from the jetty, and has a neat corrugated iron façade like any ordinary residence. It was destined to become a home from home for the *Hudson*. We knocked on the door and a girl ushered us through a drab corridor into a large smoke-filled room. Shouts of welcome went up as we entered, and to our surprise we saw virtually all of the officers, crew and scientists – in fact, the entire off-duty contingent. The room had a bar at one end, staffed by an incredibly ugly crone, and a 'band' (organ, drums and guitar) at the other. Easy chairs round the walls left the centre free for dancing. The Hudsonians were being entertained by a large number of girls of varying degrees of attractiveness. The whole room was in wild and glorious confusion and an uproarious party was in progress. Patricio insisted on dragging us out to visit the other houses in town, just to show that this was the best, and gave us a lightning tour of three decrepit edifices on the outskirts of town, involving hiking through mud and across open sewers. They all consisted of sad, smoky bars inhabited by shifty-eyed locals. We returned to Maria Teresa's.

The party was still in full swing. One of the Newfies was doing a Newfoundland step dance in the middle of the room, to the incredulity of the natives. A scientist disappeared into one of the bedrooms with an attractive redhead, accompanied by cheers all round. Roberto disappeared with the other attractive girl. Patricio left and reappeared with Roger, who told his frustrating story. Patricio smiled.

"She has just become separated and is on the loose," he said.

After 4 a.m. the party started to quieten down. Brawny Nova Scotian quartermasters tearfully told their life stories to understanding girls who stroked their wrinkled foreheads. We prepared to set forth. The Chief Steward by now was quite helpless. He fell off his chair and tried to crawl back into it as if it were a bed. Obeying the unwritten mariners' code of not abandoning a shipmate, we carried him back to the ship and poured him into his cabin.

I slept until lunchtime and then set forth to visit the Salesian Museum. I found the large brown stone church of Santa Maria Auxiliadora facing a shabby square at the north end of town, and the museum lay alongside. It has since been modernised, but was then a gloomy cavern cluttered with a mixture of rubbish and priceless artefacts. The most important material consisted of relics, paintings and photographs of Patagonian Indian tribes, taken while their natural way of life still existed. The Yahgan are shown first in their original guanaco cloaks, kneeling in their leaky bark canoes; and then, after 'civilising', they stand shivering in wet cotton shirts and dungarees, gazing in a puzzled way at the camera as they strive to make sense of their imprisonment on the mission station. The museum also contained many relics of the Ona, those ill-fated guanaco-hunters of the grasslands. They used tepees, bark canoes, headdresses and amulets which were very similar to those of the North American Indians. These tribes had been the real pioneers of America. Their history, if they had been allowed to tell it, would be a fantastic odyssey from Siberia through the length of North and South America, pushing on or being pushed by the tribes that followed, until, with nowhere further to go, they finally made their home in these chilly rain-swept wastes. Like the Eskimo they flourished in adversity, adapting to their rigorous environment, until Western man decided that their souls must be saved. One must admire the fervour and strength of purpose of the Salesian missionaries, whether seated on their horses in full priestly habit or celebrating Mass in the wilds, as shown in devotional paintings around the walls. Yet the result of their activities was the establishment of two concentration camps (one for men, one for women) on Dawson Island, in which these same Indians sank into hopeless despair or died of imported diseases. Now the history, religion and myths of the first Americans will never be known, for none remain alive to tell the tale.

On my way back to the ship I noticed an enormous hoarding of a grinning face on the wall of a large villa, with the name 'Tomic' written underneath. I had also seen 'Viva Tomic' daubed on various walls in the city. I learned from Roberto that Chile was in the throes of an election campaign and that the villa was the local headquarters of the Christian Democrat Party. President Frei, an efficient and popular Christian Democrat, had ruled for six years but under Chilean law was not allowed to stand for a second term. Therefore his party had to find another candidate, and chose the colourless Raoul Tomic. His chief opponent was thought to be the right-wing Alessandri, but there was also a left-wing candidate, a conventional bureaucratic Marxist called Salvador Allende who had been a minister in the 1940s and to whom nobody gave much chance. The election was held just after our visit. Allende was as surprised as anyone when the unpopularity of the other candidates let him in as President. His poorly judged attempt to impose socialism on the individualistic Chileans provided an excuse for the CIA-sponsored coup of 1973 that destroyed Chilean democracy and installed the vicious Pinochet dictatorship which disfigured the later history of the country.

That evening there was a crowded cocktail party in the *Hudson's* lounge, attended by many of the British colony. I met the headmaster of the British school in Punta Arenas, a young Englishman with a beautiful wife. Most of the students were Chilean, since a British education was very fashionable, and the students were forced to speak English at break and lunchtime as well as in class. Then I had the pleasure of meeting Rod Maclean, a young Scot who managed a large sheep estancia 70 miles away. He was a friend of Fred and Eric, who had stayed at his estancia while touring South America before joining *Hudson*. Rod invited me out for a visit; I eagerly accepted. Then I met Bill Waldron and his wife Jane, specimens of the old-fashioned British settlers. Bill was a quiet man with a toothbrush moustache who looked like an ageing schoolmaster. He had been a landowner in Patagonia for nearly 50 years. His wife had a strident voice which was painful to the eardrums. She boomed out: "I hear you're a Cambridge man. What were your sports? Did you reauw?"

Not meaning to be rude, I replied truthfully, "Neauw, I just did tenpin bowling." In fact I had indeed bowled for my college.

She smiled bravely at my lack of breeding and invited me to dinner. Bill introduced me to Sven Robson, the honorary British consul and another emigré of long standing who arrived in 1930 to work in a packing factory. I didn't see him at first, but then looked down to discover a small, mild, white-haired man with thick spectacles who simply poked a glass in my ribs and said, "I say, do you think you could get me another little whisky?"

Lastly I met two guests of the Captain, a young girl and an aged dame, both local ladies of the night. They behaved impeccably, and gave out a different story to everyone they met. To me they said that they were tourists on a motor camping holiday.

Before he left, Rod Maclean said that he would return next morning to take Rog and me out to his estancia, so we rose early and packed. I saw Al Grant and formally took over the ship's computer from him. Also, unfortunately, I met Ced who ordered me to return in two days' time as he wanted to see me again before he himself left the ship.

Rod now appeared, looking very bleary-eyed, and Roger and I eagerly threw our bags into the back of his Fargo *camioneta*. We wound away from the jetty and out through the northern suburbs of the city, where crab canneries and mutton freezer plants mingled with new houses and flats for the increasing population. Rod had spent the night at Maria Teresa's, where he had heard a long sad story from his girl about how she was forced into this work in order to support her child. At length, the transaction complete, she had offered Rod a drink.

"I have everything," she said, pulling from under the bed a bottle of champagne and various other liquors. Rod replied that he just wanted a beer, whereupon she produced a crate of Oland's Schooner Beer, the source of which was obvious. By then Rod's *camioneta*, marked with the name of the estancia, was parked outside in broad daylight, so he had crawled over to the *Hudson* and collapsed in an empty cabin for a couple of hours' sleep.

Outside the city the road followed Magellan Strait through rolling grassland until we were stopped by a police roadblock about ten miles from town. An outbreak of foot-and-mouth disease had occurred, and we had to have our tyres and shoes washed with disinfectant before we could proceed. Thirty miles further north the road left the Strait and turned westward to cross a hilly isthmus which led us to the shores of Seno Otway. 'Seno' is a word used interchangeably for inlet, bay or fjord; Otway is almost a lake, with a narrow entrance channel from the Pacific. It was first surveyed by HMS *Beagle*, and was named after one of FitzRoy's lieutenants. The road was now a gravelly track, and as we bumped along we disturbed great flocks of Black-necked Swans, *Cygnus melanocoryphus*, looking most unusual with their jet-black necks and pure white bodies. Later we came upon a group of pink flamingoes, stalking awkwardly through the chilly blue water by the shore.

Eventually the hilly shore opened into a wide grassy plain, and there beside the peaceful waters of Seno Skyring, which opens out of Seno Otway, we came upon the buildings of Estancia Rio Verde. There was a neat English-style bungalow and a small village of farm buildings, all built of white weatherboard and enclosed by white picket fences. The estancia was huge – 45,000 acres – and contained 22,000 sheep. Rod's parents lived there and he had a sister Gillian at school in Santiago. Inside the bungalow we found a home away from home, a perfect British nest which brought on waves of nostalgia. A plump Chilean girl brought us mutton stew for lunch, then we toured the estancia with Rod.

Passing the neat cottages of the farmworkers we came to the shearing sheds, with their electric shearing machines and hoppers full of raw greasy wool. Then we toured the home fields and paddocks in the company of Rod's sheepdog. The estancia was owned by a British company, and the Macleans were managers. President Frei's Land Reform Act of 1967 threatened all such large farms, and the estancia was due to be subdivided among the local landless labourers. Rod loved the land so much that he hoped to be allowed to buy a small portion of the estancia for himself.

We wandered across the windy plains where the estancia horses galloped ecstatically, then back in the haven of the bungalow Rod told us his life story. It was a simple one – he had spent most of it here on the wide plains of Patagonia. His parents had sent him to agricultural college in New Zealand, a place, he said, of boorish louts and frequent fights. One particular bully who had tormented Rod received his desserts one night when Rod crept into his room and padlocked his testicles while he slept. Rod was thenceforth known as 'the Padlock Man'.

The pleasant evening was followed by a night in a real bed, a luxury after weeks in a heaving bunk smelling of diesel fuel. Next day we went out with Rod and Pedro, the head man, to shear the faces of some sheep. The wool must be removed so that the sheep can see where he is going, and the job must be done by hand. At this time most of the shearers were on strike, inspired, so Rod hinted darkly, by Communist rabble-rousers imported from the north. Rod showed us how to do the job. You must first throw the sheep on its back and hold its head firmly between your legs – it immediately becomes completely docile, either through fear or stupidity. Then you clip vigorously around each eye. Rod assured us that the eye is recessed so there is no danger of damaging it, but it was still a curious experience to cut away at matted wool and then suddenly see an eye peering up at me from under the blades of my shears.

At lunchtime Rod's parents arrived by car after a visit to a neighbouring estancia. They were accompanied by Gillian, a beautiful and intelligent English girl. Mr. and Mrs. Maclean were continuing to Punta Arenas, so to keep my appointment with Ced I had to accept a lift with them and forgo the pleasure of Gillian's company. I heaped curses on Ced's head during the drive back. Roger was free of such shackles, and stayed behind at Rio Verde. He was due to leave the ship at Punta Arenas and fly to Germany for a holiday with his girlfriend, rejoining *Hudson* at Valparaiso.

On my return I announced myself breathlessly to Ced, only to find that he had forgotten why he wanted to see me. He introduced me to the new Senior Scientist, Professor George Pickard of the University of British Columbia, a mild-mannered Englishman and former nuclear physicist at

Oxford, who had built up a leading oceanographic institution from small beginnings in Vancouver after the war. The rest of the UBC contingent had also arrived, bringing their own water bottles, so I set to work adapting the computer programs for the calibrations of the new bottles.

Several days of frustrating inactivity followed; frustrating for Pickard, who wanted to begin his cruise, and also for me, who was tied to the vicinity of the ship. The ostensible reason for our endlessly delayed departure was the need to wait for a second pilot for the Chilean fjords. The real reason, we all thought, was the Captain's *grand amour* with a lady of the waterfront. To pass the time I visited the ships berthed near us, the *Hero* and the Norwegian cruise ship *Lindblad Explorer*, where I met the jovial Lars-Eric Lindblad himself. The ship was one year old, and with it he was pioneering the concept of comfortable risk-free 'expeditions' for rich Americans to remote places at fantastic cost. This has since grown into a wildly successful business, although last year, under new owners, the ship herself sank after hitting a very small iceberg.

I also took up Bill and Jane Waldron's invitation to dinner. As I had expected, their apartment was immaculately furnished in a thoroughly English way. Bill seemed quiet-spoken and insignificant until he started to talk of his years in Patagonia. In his heyday in the 1920s his holdings covered nearly a third of Tierra del Fuego. Most of his shearers then were Fuegan Indians, and they organised a strike against the miserable wages that they were receiving. Some of Bill's overseers took the ringleaders out to sea with chains round their ankles and threw them overboard.

"They were so strong that they managed to swim to land, though," Bill added with a sigh of regret. He hurriedly added that this was done without his knowledge, but he admitted that at one time a bounty of £2 was offered by the estancia-holders for a pair of Indian ears.

"It sounds cruel," he said blandly, "but really it was them or the sheep. The Indians just used to steal sheep; they thought that the place belonged to them."

He blinked inoffensively behind his glasses, still indifferent to the fact that he was describing an act of genocide.

Jane met Bill in England in 1924, and knew him for only five weeks before he left again for Chile. She followed in a cargo steamer. Their first house was a wooden shack on Tierra del Fuego. They had to cover the windows with newspaper because the Indians used to creep up and stare in wonder at the strange habits of the white man. They built up their stock with Merino sheep imported from Australia and New Zealand. These were quarantined in the hulks which we had seen lying off the naval base. Now they had sold up almost everything. They were bitter that they had received no royalties from the oil discovered on their land, and they looked forward to retiring to the peace of Berkshire. The Waldrons were the real stuff of which the British Empire had been made, and it was fascinating to meet them.

Thus far I had fastidiously avoided a transaction at 'Maria Teresa's', yet here we were trapped in a town full of beautiful Chilean girls, certainly the most beautiful girls that I had ever seen, and with the prospect of more months at sea ahead. What to do? I started girl hunting. One afternoon I ran across an attractive girl who proved to be a reporter on the local newspaper *El Austral*. She spoke good English and we wandered around town in pleasant and lively conversation. She readily agreed to my suggestion of a dinner date, and we arranged to meet at seven at the entrance to the 'Cabo de Hornos'. All seemed set fair. Pete Reynell accompanied me into town and proceeded into the hotel bar, leaving me to wait – and wait. Eventually I retreated to the bar as well, where over a pisco we decided to sample the commercial yet more reliable delights of Maria Teresa's.

We banged on the purple door of the establishment, and were admitted into one of the most bizarre scenes that I have ever experienced. Can you imagine a formal banquet in a whorehouse? The visit of the *Hudson* had made such a fortune for Maria Teresa and her girls that they had decided to offer their thanks gracefully by laying on a decorous and entirely civilised meal. The supplies, of course, had mostly come from the *Hudson* via the Chief Steward, but no-one was prepared to quibble. Pete and I were conducted to two spare places laid with the best silver, three wine glasses and snowy napkins. The Captain presided at the head of the long table, and the Hudsonians were interspersed with Maria Teresa girls, whilst other girls acted as waitresses. The food and wine were superb even if my waitress had a habit of thrusting a large spangled bosom directly into my face as she served me. I was fortunate to be sitting beside Maria Teresa herself, famous throughout the seven seas, a mountain of middle-aged flesh with a formidable voice and an earthy English vocabulary acquired from visiting seamen.

"You like this fucking steak?"

"Erm, yes, very good indeed."

"Well, eat up and have some more. You look fucking thin."

Our dinner table conversation was not quite at the level of College dining nights at Cambridge, but the company was certainly more interesting, and probably more honest and hard-working as well.

This remarkable evening lacked one vital ingredient, since it was an off-duty night for the girls. Then the next day a fearsome bug struck my stomach. Clearly Maria Teresa's kitchens were not of the cleanest. The repeated vomiting reduced me to such a pitiful state that I made the mistake of consulting the Doctor. He cursed me roundly, then finally gave me some vile fluid that he had picked up in Buenos Aires. He forbade me to leave my cabin. That evening I felt much better and was gratified to hear that Rod Maclean and Gillian were on board. I went up to the lounge to join them and spent a pleasant evening in their company. After I had retired to my cabin the Doctor burst in without knocking, screaming that he had forbidden me to leave my cabin, that his word was law and that he would get me thrown off the ship. The spectacle was terrifying and ridiculous at the same time, and reminded me how dangerously deranged the Doctor actually was. Naturally nothing came of it.

The pilot had finally arrived and the next day was to be our last in port. I decided to do some quiet sketching in town. I settled on a bench in the plaza and began a drawing of the Magellan monument. Suddenly a familiar figure approached from across the square, accompanied by two small children. It was Nena, the bewitching companion of our first night in port. She smiled, sat down beside me and we began an intense conversation by means of my dictionary. She wanted me to show her children over the ship, after which she would take them home and accompany me to dinner. This seemed a fair exchange, so I endured the curious stares of my shipmates as I escorted a small boy and a smaller girl around the *Hudson*. Later Nena and I went off to a restaurant with a dance floor and discothèque. It was my last night in port, and despite my illness I did my best to keep up with Nena's vivacity and inexhaustible energy.

We danced the short night away, and it was already light when in the small hours of the morning she took me home to her apartment near the Officers' Club. There followed a night of passion such as I had never known before in my excessively sheltered life. Afterwards I wandered empty-eyed through the busy morning streets to the *Hudson*, and as we sailed I went below to avoid the pain of seeing the city disappear.

CHAPTER 10

IN THE WAKE OF DARWIN

One sight of such a coast is enough to make a landsman
dream for a week about shipwrecks, peril, and death.
Charles Darwin, of the Pacific entrance
to Magellan Strait.

T HAT DAY WE DID one station in Magellan Strait and then hove-to
for the night. On the following day, March 4, we did six stations,
taking us down the Whiteside Channel and into Seno Almirantazgo
(Admiralty Inlet). Whiteside Channel separates from Magellan Strait at
Dawson Island, bleak home of the Salesian mission camps, then Seno
Almirantazgo continues south-eastward like a slender finger for fifty miles
into the mountainous interior of Tierra del Fuego. The day was grey and
overcast as we sailed past a grim line of rounded bare hills along the north
side of the inlet. The summits were dusted with snow and the treeline lay
very close to the sea, leaving two thousand feet of barren grey rock in
between. We coasted back along the south side of the inlet, where the steep
Marinelli Glacier swept down to the sea from a small inland ice sheet in a
chaos of dirty brown crevasses.

It was a pleasant experience to watch other people doing bottle casts.
My job was merely to compute the results on the PDP8, but when I came to
do so I found that Al Grant had left the library of computer programs in a
sorry state. One vital program, which corrects each thermometer reading
according to the instrument's calibration curve, did not work at all. I spent
the whole day fruitlessly working on it, helped by Hugh Henderson and by
Danny Winter, a new technician sent out by Bedford Institute to replace
Fred Muise.

In the evening I found to my horror that we were returning to Punta Arenas for the night. We all knew why, and only Dr. Pickard was puzzled by the magnetic attraction that this tatty city held for the Captain. We arrived at 8 p.m. and anchored off in the Strait. Local regulations forbid visitors to land in ships' boats – to ensure work for the local boatmen – but in our case the rule was waived because of the economic benefit that we had brought to the service industries of the town. An hourly ferry service of launches now began and I faced an agonising moral decision. The experience with Nena had shaken me completely and I finally decided to let our one night remain in our memories unaffected by further complications. More to the point, I was frightened of being disembowelled, or worse, by her husband.

The morning found us still at anchor, but the final launch from shore was scheduled for 10 a.m. I went ashore to send off some letters and found the Doctor and Chief Steward waiting at the jetty, both looking damply malevolent in the heavy drizzle. Their final visit to 'Maria Teresa's' had revealed a deserter, Ron Shaw, who had gone missing two nights earlier by falling asleep in the establishment and who had been cared for by the ladies against our return. Back on board I expected us to sail immediately, but found that we could not because two people were still missing, one of them being the Captain. I set to work once again on the computer programs, but eventually I was forced to go to Dr. Pickard and confess defeat. He immediately decided to use the old Bedford Institute thermometers, whose calibrations were safely in the computer, rather than the thermometers that he had brought with him. He went straight off to the winch house to change the thermometers around. Later, at 8 p.m. we finally freed ourselves from the insistent clutches of Punta Arenas and set off southwards down Magellan Strait, bound for the fjords.

A new and exciting stage in our expedition was beginning. For the next month we would be cruising through an intricate maze of inlets stretching for over a thousand miles northward from Tierra del Fuego to Puerto Montt. This labyrinth of narrow channels and fast tidal currents is almost uninhabited, poorly charted, and seldom visited by large vessels. Most of the fjords had never seen a scientific ship, while others had not been investigated since FitzRoy and Darwin on H.M.S. *Beagle*. Their oceanography was completely unknown. Pickard's institute in Vancouver specialises in the study of fjords, and in twenty years of surveying they had covered most of those in British Columbia and Alaska. Now the virgin waters of Chile lay ahead, and so there was tremendous enthusiasm in the UBC contingent. The infectious excitement filled the Chileans too. We had seven Chilean scientists on board as a gesture of courtesy and thanks for being given permission to work in Chile, and this was the first time that many of them had seen these southern waters of their own country.

In the lounge that first evening I did my best to get to know the large batch of new faces that had brightened the ship. Dr. Pickard's second-in-command and chief biologist was Brian Bary, a New Zealander of Irish extraction with an expression of worldly ruggedness and a hook in place of one hand, lost in a nautical accident. Then there was Murray Storm, the technician in charge of the field equipment and thus UBC's equivalent of Bruce Carson. His assistant was Dave English, a tall young ginger-haired Vancouverite. Two professors from Oregon State University, Steve Pond and Wayne Burt, had come along to assist with the stations, and Dick Brown, a former Oxford ornithologist with the Canadian Wildlife Service, was on board to study the bird life of the fjords. The Chileans were exceptionally friendly and lively, but it was hard at first to fit names to all the faces. The most senior of them was Professor Hector Inostroza of the University of Concepción, and another leading figure was Bernardo Uccelletti of the Hydrographic Institute in Valparaiso, who had worked at Oregon State University. The others were all young: Nelson Silva, a chemist from the Catholic University of Valparaiso; Chano Chuecas and Ramón Ahumada from the University of Concepción; Riccardo Montaner from the Hydrographic Institute in Valparaiso; and finally Francisco Rey from the University of Chile at Valparaiso, friendliest of all and known to everyone as Pancho. The pilot that we had originally picked up at Punta Arenas was a Lieutenant Fernando Espinoza of the Chilean Navy, a frosty and distant officer who was under the impression that he was on board for a two-day run to Valparaiso. After being enlightened he had demanded to be put ashore. Unfortunately for him, he had to stay, because only one of the two civilian pilots requested for the voyage had agreed to join the ship. His name was Hernan Hernandez, a jolly middle-aged man who confessed that he knew very little about the fjords. His colleague, Espinoza's replacement, had taken one look at the size of *Hudson* and gone straight home again.

During the first night at sea we rounded Cape Froward at the southern end of Magellan Strait, and ran some way up the western arm of the Strait where we did one station. Next morning we entered the narrow Canal Jeronimo (Canal = channel) which leads off the north side of the Strait and opens into Seno Otway. Here we were once again in the fjord that I had seen from the bouncing cab of Rod Maclean's truck. The weather was ferocious. A 70-knot wind kicked up a vicious chop in the fjord, and each time that we stopped for a station the ship took up a list to leeward, with waves breaking over the quarterdeck. Through the grey scud I could see the familiar scenery of the south – steep bare mountains, with tortured beeches crowding their lower slopes, snow dusting the peaks, and the occasional gleam of a glacier coming down to the sea. Otway is fifty miles long by twenty miles wide, and we did six stations along it, ending near the entrance to the narrow FitzRoy Channel which leads into Seno Skyring. Here a consultation was held. Rod Maclean had shown me a telephone line strung low across the channel, and when this was mentioned to the pilot he suddenly remembered it too and pronounced the channel impassable to a large ship. Pickard wanted to send a launch through the channel to sample in Skyring, but the rough sea made this impossible so we reluctantly sailed out the way we had come in, and were unable to pay our respects to our friends at Rio Verde.

That evening Dr. Pickard gave us a talk on the oceanography of fjords and on the results from Almirantazgo and Otway which had now been computed. A fjord is a deeply drowned river or glacial valley with a maximum depth of perhaps 600 metres. Usually the valley was gouged out by a glacier during one of the ice ages, and when the glacier later retreated the sea advanced to fill up the deep U-shaped trough. A glacier in motion piles up the material that it has excavated in a great heap beyond its snout called a terminal moraine, and when the glacier retreats the moraine is left behind. In a fjord the moraine forms a shallow sill near the mouth which partially separates the deep water within the fjord from the deeper water out in the open sea. This sill is the key to the oceanography of the fjord.

The water mass in a fjord consists of two layers, a thin surface layer originating from the run-off of rivers or glaciers and consisting of fresh water with some admixed saline, and a lower layer of saline water similar to that of the open sea. The surface layer is constantly fed from the run-off and therefore flows out towards the sea. Mixing occurs at the boundary between the layers (most rapidly when the wind disturbs the fjord surface), and saline water tends to be entrained upwards in preference to fresh water mixing downwards. The result is a net loss from the lower layers which has to be replenished; thus a deep current flows in over the sill from the open sea into the lower part of the fjord. This balance between an outward surface current and an inward deep current is called an 'estuarine circulation', and a vigorous circulation is essential to bring oxygen and nutrients into the fjord to replace those used by the marine life within it. If the sill is shallow enough to protrude into the surface layer, then the deep layer is cut off from the open sea and cannot receive fresh nutrients. Aerobic (oxygen-consuming) bacteria, which feed on organic detritus, use up all the oxygen and the fjord is then incapable of supporting life. The largest and best example of such a stagnant fjord is the Black Sea, which is literally black in its lower layers because anaerobic bacteria (non-consumers of oxygen) are all that can live there, and these produce hydrogen sulphide gas as a by-product of their disgusting metabolism.

One fascinating effect which can be seen in fjords is the telltale slick of an internal wave. A normal ocean wave occurs at the boundary between two fluids, water and air, which are very different in density. An internal wave is just the same but occurs at the boundary between two layers of water, so that the difference in density is very small. This gives the wave some strange properties. It can have a very great height while carrying only a tiny amount of energy – of course this height cannot be seen because everything is happening underwater. It moves very slowly, and it may take half an hour for two successive wave crests to pass a point. The only surface evidence of an internal wave's presence is a series of long narrow slicks, like oil slicks, which move very slowly at the speed of the wave. These are caused by the wave at the boundary between the two water layers setting up a series of vertically circulating cells within the upper layer, and where two cells meet the surface water converges along a line and forces any grease or floating detritus to come together into a slick. These slicks occur in ordinary river estuaries too, and I have seen them in the Thames off Southend Pier. Internal waves were first studied by Fridtjof Nansen in the Arctic Ocean. He deliberately froze his ship *Fram* into the ice in 1893 in an attempt to drift to the North Pole. Sometimes during summer when the engine was started the ship scarcely moved; this phenomenon had been known to generations of Norwegian fishermen as 'dead water' but was not understood. Nansen and his colleague Ekman showed that in fact the propeller of *Fram* was at just the right depth to excite an internal wave between two water layers, the fresh upper layer being caused by melting sea ice; the energy wasted in this way could not then be used to drive the ship.

Both of the fjords that we had studied so far had a vigorous circulation, and were rich in dissolved oxygen at all depths. Their shapes were similar; each had a maximum depth of about 500 metres and a sill depth of 100 metres. The surface water layer was about 50 metres deep, with a temperature of about 9°C, dropping to 7°C in the lower layer. Thus the sills were far too deep to cut off the fjord from the sea. Our echo sounder profiles, which gave us the shape of the fjords, would be passed on to our Chilean friends, who would later use them to improve the sparse soundings on Chilean Navy charts of the area.

Early in the morning of March 7 we entered Golfo Xaultegua near the exit to Magellan Strait, and the launch *Redhead* was lowered to carry a party led by Pickard up the tortuous and shallow Canal Gajardo. This channel opens into Seno Skyring, and Pickard with characteristic thoroughness was trying one final means of getting into Skyring. Once again he was foiled, for at one point the launch's echo sounder showed just six feet of shoaling water, and so he had to return reluctantly to the ship. Meanwhile we had been doing stations in Xaultegua through another grim, grey day. At one point a remarkable little island suddenly emerged from the murk, looking like Edinburgh Castle, in other words an almost perfect volcanic stack. The solidified lava of the main vent showed as a squat pillar in the centre of the island, while the rest of the volcano had been eroded away.

The *Redhead* returned in the afternoon. She came along to the starboard side and her occupants scrambled aboard *Hudson*. She was then secured fore and aft to the davit and hauled out of the water. When the davit winch had brought her almost to her resting position the for'ard fall suddenly broke away from the block and the bow of the *Redhead* plunged down. It hit the starboard rail with a great crash, mangling the steelwork and staving in several planks in the launch's bottom as well as dislodging her keel strake. Nobody was hurt, but we suddenly realised the danger that we had all been in: to give a big open working area on the port and starboard quarterdecks of *Hudson* the designer had simply suspended the two launches above everybody's heads, held only by the cable falls and with no chocks to rest on. This accident could have happened at any time, with people working underneath. At once two strong hawsers were put around the other launch *Gull* to hold her safe. The *Redhead* was tied down where she lay on the quarterdeck; as far as the present cruise was concerned the damage was irreparable. This was a grave blow to "Chile-70" (Pickard's name for this phase of "Hudson-70"), for Pickard's intention was to use the sounding launches to precede *Hudson* in unsurveyed waters, so that oceanographic work could be done safely where no ship had been before. Without the launches the ship could not safely run into unsurveyed fjords, and so these had to be deleted from the cruise programme.

Next morning we entered the final system of fjords that leads off Magellan Strait. It consists of a bay, Bahía Beaufort, followed by a 'roundabout' of inlets with a group of three islands in the middle. First we nosed into the southernmost inlets, Seno Glacier and Seno Icy, narrow channels only a few hundred yards wide. Their names derive from an enormous glacier which shone in perfect whiteness among the mountain peaks above us. The mountains here are no higher than in the earlier fjords, but gave an impression of overwhelming majesty by rising sheer from the water on all sides. The rock walls loomed above us, riven by cracks and fissures. Beeches somehow clung to the lower slopes, mosses and lichens hung on tenaciously half way up, while crannies and hollows of snow crowned the peaks. We tried to get round the 'roundabout' by way of a very narrow channel called Canal Cascada, but the pilot entreated us to turn back so we re-entered Seno Glacier and proceeded into Canal Swett, lying deep within the mountain chain.

Here we saw an extraordinary phenomenon. Coming from the head of Canal Swett was a pale green milky water, which gave way abruptly to the dark clear water of the fjord. We crossed the boundary between the two liquids, a line as sharp as a knife edge. Dr. Pickard explained that the warm weather must have caused an unusual melting in the glacier that feeds Canal Swett, hidden behind a bend in the fjord. The large run-off carries 'rock flour' into the fjord, a ground-up rock powder produced by the glacier scraping over its bed. The flour stays in suspension in the surface water layer, giving the milky texture, and the sharp boundary shows the limit of the run-off. Pickard described how he makes use of this effect to find the depth of the surface water layer. A weighted bucket is lowered to a measured depth and then pulled up quickly; if it has reached beneath the surface layer it will bring an upwelling of dark clear water with it.

As the day wore on the long-lost sun emerged from its grey shroud and we did our last station in Canal Swett to the accompaniment of a magnificent sunset. The mountain wall close beside us was lit up eerily in warm orange light, throwing into deep shadow its pattern of cracks. The ice sheet among the mountains shone with a beautiful shade of lilac and glistened like icing sugar; the sun reflected off it tinged the sea with red. As the sun went down among the peaks the sky turned to yellow then glowed orange and red, while the islands silhouetted in the channel passed through blue and purple to black. High cirrus cloud stood out in bold scarlet streaks. Finally a matt half-light was left in which the mountains and sky looked like the background to a Leonardo painting. It was the finest sunset that I have ever seen, and an almost religious experience in the complete silence of this wild fjord.

During the night we left Bahía Beaufort and turned north, emerging at last from Magellan Strait and the gloom of the far south. The last island on the west side of the Strait was surveyed by Captain John Narborough in the 17th Century and aptly christened Desolation Island. It ends in Cape Pilar, the famous Pacific landfall to Magellan Strait, which we passed in the early hours of the morning. Our goal was an intricate maze of fjords that penetrates inland almost as far as the Argentine border. The innermost fjord, Estero Ultima Esperanza (Last Hope Inlet) is graced by the village of Puerto Natales, one of only two 'towns' in the entire thousand miles of fjord coast.

We approached the maze through Canal Smyth, a narrow but deep inland passage which runs north between the mainland and Isla Manuel Rodriguez. Then we turned the corner into Seno Union, the beginning of the maze, and did several stations in this inlet and in the long narrow Estero de las Montañas which leads off it. I was busy all day with the computer and its many problems, and saw little of the scenery. We anchored for the night at the southern end of Canal Santa Maria to await a dangerous passage through the narrow entrance of Canal Kirke, the only way into the innermost fjords.

The morning broke fine and sunny to find us lying very close to shore, near a narrow beach and a gently sloping island covered with beech trees. Canal Kirke is navigable only at slack water, and 11 a.m. was the time predicted by the pilot for this to occur. As we approached the Narrows we had to breast a current of several knots, and it was clear that the pilot's estimate of time was far out. The channel is blocked by three islets, leaving a passage barely 200 metres wide which is overlooked by cliff faces down which cataracts pour. We lowered the lifeboat with the pilot aboard to go ahead through the Narrows, taking soundings and measuring the current. He returned to report sufficient depth but too fast a current. The lifeboat was lowered again with more expendable crew members on board, who were given a red flag which they were to wave when the current had dropped. Meanwhile we circled in the narrow channel, itself a dangerous manoeuvre, and drifted down repeatedly on the Narrows, only to be waved away vigorously each time. The pilot on the bridge was equally cautious.

"Wait until the ducks swim through," he said.

As if in answer, a group of wildfowl started swimming gallantly through the Narrows. There was a clattering of boots on the bridge ladder, and the lanky figure of Dick Brown appeared, gesticulating excitedly.

"Hold on!" he exclaimed. "They're not ducks - they're bloody black-necked swans!"

Everyone collapsed in fits of laughter, then the three functioning engines were put full ahead and we churned through the Narrows, nearly swamping the lifeboat with our wake. Since we were being followed by a killer whale the boat crew were not amused by our efforts to sink them. Dick retired crestfallen to his former perch on monkey island, where he stood for hours at a time making ten-minute bird counts.

We picked up the lifeboat and continued into the depths of Chile. Two more channels – Canal Valdés and Golfo Almirante Montt – led us at last to the entrance of Estero Ultima Esperanza. To starboard lay a broad stretch of lowland, backed by an escarpment. Here nestles the little town of Puerto Natales. From the sea it looked lovely, with perhaps 5,000 inhabitants, a single church spire and a warm nest of small houses. We sailed past and came in to dock at Puerto Bories, about two miles further along. Puerto Bories consisted simply of a mutton freezer plant and a long wooden jetty where we tied up. The ostensible reason for our visit, as stated in a telex from the Captain to BIO, was to take on fresh water since our consumption was exceeding the production of our evaporator. The real reason was that Puerto Natales, although 150 miles north of Punta Arenas, is connected to that magical place by a dirt road.

The freezer plant was a large white-painted wooden building with the words 'Sociedad de Tierra del Fuego Frigorifico de Puerto Bories' across the front. It discharged its offal straight into the fjord, where a solid mass of birds fought and screamed in the inshore waters. A narrow gauge railway line ran down the jetty and continued along the shore to Puerto Natales. The rolling stock consisted of a dozen wagons and a single wood-burning tank locomotive of great beauty and antiquity. It was painted a bright yellow, and its brass nameplate proclaimed that it was built by Avondale Engine Works in 1920. As we docked the little engine was chugging its way down the jetty with some flat wagons loaded with wool bales, which were then unloaded by a gang of stevedores of desperate appearance.

After dinner I set off with Pete Reynell to explore Puerto Natales, while five of the ship's company departed by bus for the dubious delights of Punta Arenas. We tried to hitch a lift along the shore on the train, but the driver said with regret that he had done his final journey for the day, so we started walking along the dirt road and caught up with Claud, the French chef. Claud was normally a silent and retiring person. All day long he toiled in the galley, producing excellent food which the crew, like all sailormen, roundly abused. He slept in a tiny cabin which he shared with his assistant opposite the galley. But this evening Claud was exceptionally forthcoming. These mountains, he said, reminded him of his home in southern France where he would return one day, when he had saved enough money, and open his own restaurant. Then he could be a true artist, and no longer be forced to serve food to savages in Government ships. Claud was a gentle person, but felt strongly about food.

Soon we were picked up by a *camioneta* and given a lift into town. We passed cattle, horses and wide-horned oxen, which grazed on the saltings above a stony kelp-laden beach. The peaceful fjord was full of gulls and black-necked swans, and the rank smell of rotting algae filled the air. The first truck dropped us on the edge of town and we were immediately given a lift by a second. The friendly driver was fascinated to hear of our expedition, and treated us to a guided tour of the town. Puerto Natales had a gentle rustic peacefulness, enhanced by the magnificent scenery around it. In the centre of the town is the square, adorned with gardens, a bandstand and a bust of Admiral Prat. Prat, said our guide, is a Chilean national hero. He fought in the War of Independence against Spain and later against Peru, where he boarded and captured the enemy flagship while his own ship was sinking under him. On the square sat the church, a simple white stucco building with a red roof, and two streets of shops and cafes completed the town centre. The rest of the town is residential, made of small clean houses of wood and corrugated iron which front straight onto the street. There were a few dilapidated hotels of corrugated iron, with names like 'Victoria' and 'Colonial'. On the south side of town were a modern hospital and a construction zone where pleasant modern houses of wood and sheet aluminium were going up. The driver said that this was a co-operative venture – in return for building their own houses and promising to settle in them the people were given building materials and free title to their plot of land.

Our new friend left us in the square, and so did Claud, who had to return to the ship. Pete Reynell and I wandered into the local supermarket. A quarter of the building was given over to wine and spirits; large casks in the corner provided bulk supplies for those who brought their own bottles. Several whole sheep were hanging behind the meat counter, some dripping blood, while a big pile of intestines and sheep's heads lay on the floor. The other customers consisted of two attractive young ladies, and we sidled towards them composing a suitable opening gambit. As I was about to begin with a hackneyed Spanish phrase my quarry said in perfect BBC tones:

"I say, are you English?"

Livingstone could not have been more flabbergasted. I burbled as she told us pertly that her name was Liza Washbourn and that she came from Nelson in New Zealand. She had arrived in Punta Arenas on the Italian liner *Angelina Lauro* and she was hitch-hiking up to Canada in the company of her cousin Hugh. At the moment they were staying with a local teacher, having been prevented from hiking beyond Puerto Natales by the simple fact that there is no road. Liza and the teacher's wife (the other attractive lady) suggested that if we brought a bottle we would be welcome to call on the family later in the evening.

We selected at random a bottle of Chilean sherry, then walked round town to await a polite hour. We joined Dave English down by the shore to watch the splendour of the sunset behind the mountains. As we passed the hospital we saw the nurses gazing out of the windows at us, so Pete collapsed in the hope that they would run to our assistance. They giggled and hid. At last we made our way to the home of Señor Riquelme.

Hugo Riquelme and his wife Maria lived at the top of a rickety wooden apartment house. We were given a tremendous welcome, plied with the family booze after the sherry was denounced as vinegar, and had a share of the evening meal pressed upon us. Hugo spoke excellent English. He had just returned from a period of teaching in Santiago. He was here partly because he loved the place, and partly because the Government gave large financial incentives for teachers to come to the far south. Maria was stunningly beautiful, with wild black hair and big smiling eyes. With their baby daughter they made a happy family. Liza's cousin Hugh was a quiet person who had thrown up a job in an advertising agency. Liza was far from quiet, and quickly told us her life story. She was brought up in Bath, Somerset, and taught elocution and drama there and in New Zealand, which explained her splendid accent. Her father was a retired Rear-Admiral who had been gunnery officer in HMNZS *Achilles* at the Battle of the River Plate. Liza had started out from Punta Arenas with a thousand dollars in her pocket to last a year, and a 38-pound pack on her back. From Canada she hoped to go on to England and then return to New Zealand via the Trans Siberian Railway, recording her experiences en route for Radio New Zealand.

Some friends of Hugo appeared as we were eating, and afterwards we all went out to the house of yet another friend who owned a sheep estancia. The place was full of children and happy conversation as we drank pisco, chewed on strips of dried horseflesh and watched the farmer's slides of the nearby Eberhardt Cave. At this site in 1895 a German traveller came upon the bones and skin of an extinct giant ground sloth, *Milodon*, which had been kept domesticated in a walled-off portion of the cave. The bones were several thousand years old, and the advanced Indian tribe which practised this form of husbandry has vanished. So did the bones and skin – almost – for many light-fingered travellers passed this way before the remnants were safely removed to a museum. The farmer also showed his slides of the Towers of Paine, a stupendous set of peaks in an area of national park about 100 miles away. We resolved to visit this park, and made plans to charter a bus the next day.

The party went on until well after midnight, and then Hugo and Hugh rode out to the ship with us in our taxi to ensure that we were not over-charged. When we got aboard we found a celebration in full swing in the lounge, fuelled by several bottles of Chilean cognac. Through the alcoholic haze Brian Bary claimed to have a taxi laid on for 9 a.m. to visit Eberhardt Cave, so we arranged to charter it further to Paine.

A glorious morning broke, with the air clear and crisp like wine. Most of the *Hudson* inmates were drunk, incapable, asleep or recovering from a visit to the local brothel. The only people that assembled for the journey were Pete Reynell, Dave English, Ramón and myself. Even Brian had to withdraw, since he was in command of the ship for the day; Dr. Pickard had set off very early in a lifeboat to do some stations in Ultima Esperanza. We waited on the dock in vain; the only taxi to arrive brought a returning contingent from Punta Arenas. As we feared, Brian's arrangement was not as firm as he thought. We hitched a lift into town and located a minibus for hire at the office of the local radio station. We made rapid arrangements and eventually set off with Liza and Hugh, stopping at the ship to add Dick Brown and John Rudolph, the Fourth Mate, to our party.

The journey was by dirt road, and the bus carried a complete set of four spare wheels. The first part took us across a rolling countryside of beautiful grassland, free and open and quite different from the gloomy impenetrable coastal forest. The gentle rounded hills were covered with scattered trees and bushes. Now I could see the reason for the existence of Puerto Natales. This innermost part of Chile, in the shadow of the mountains, has a local climate which is dry and sunny like the pampas, yet warmer than the Punta Arenas area. It can support intensive sheep farming, for which Puerto Natales is the marketing centre. After 15 minutes we reached Dos Lagunas, a farmhouse in a hollow beside two placid lakes. The driver hooted in case the occupants needed anything then rattled on along a road which grew steadily worse. After 30 miles we entered the lands of the great sheep estancia of Cerro Castillo. First we passed a couple of sheep herders or *huasos*, the Chilean version of the gaucho, riding proud and erect on their superb horses, with sheepskin saddles and broad cowboy hats. Scurrying alongside were several sheepdogs. Later came a great pasture where dogs were herding about 200 sheep into one corner. Soon we reached the estancia buildings, which were similar to Rio Verde except that the shearing shed was much larger. Sheep, cattle and horses grazed in the home fields, while a police guardpost told us that we were near the Argentine border.

The terrain changed from rolling grassland to mountainous highland slashed by magnificent lakes. Trees gave way to gorse bushes and thorny scrub, and in this new world of heath and moor we encountered a profusion of wildlife. Hares darted from our path and we saw many flocks of rheas grazing on the heath. Darwin's Rhea is the South American ostrich, once plentiful on the pampas but now almost extinct. Those that we saw fled at the sight of us, spreading their grey wings to catch the wind and striding effortlessly across the land at 30 mph. The lakes were filled with strange stubby-headed Magellan Geese and handsome ibises with long slender bills. Sixty miles from Puerto Natales we entered Paine National Park and caught our first glimpse of Torres del Paine, a line of jagged teeth capped with snow and towering above the mountains that lay between us and them. The first outcrops of the mountain chain were rocky escarpments on either side of the road, with the harder strata protruding like castellated ramparts which ran in slanting folded strips around the eroded rock massifs. Fifteen miles further on we came to Laguna Azul, a huge lake which was coloured an intense dark blue by copper salts. We drove for miles between the lake and steep bare mountains, passing ponds full of geese and ducks, and swamps choked with waving reeds and tangled vegetation. The road was now nothing more than a track, weaving between the lakes and the mountains. Several times the track was eroded away at the lakeside and we had to splash through the water, with wind-blown waves breaking against the side of the bus. Helpful comments were directed at the driver.

"Close the portholes!"

"Switch on the echo sounder!"

Eventually we breasted a rise and saw the full profile of Paine Towers, rising behind Lake Sarmiento like a row of three gigantic purple decayed teeth. We followed the lake shore for several miles, gazing at this enormous stone sculpture with its overwhelming and massive presence. The track ended beside a smaller lake where we decided to picnic. Pete brought out an assortment of victuals that he had pilfered from the *Hudson*: bread, butter, Camembert and football-shaped Cheddar cheeses from the Argentine, oranges and a demijohn of rough red wine from Punta Arenas. We ate in peaceful friendship in the bright afternoon sun.

Later we followed our driver up a steep path to a pounding cataract called Salto Chico. Here Lake Sarmiento pours its glacier-fed waters through a congested rocky gap in a plunging chaos of foam down to our little lake. The noise was terrific. A cable had been slung across the cataract carrying a little two-seat metal trolley. Two by two we got into the contraption and pushed ourselves out over the centre of the waterfall where we were drenched in spray. We returned in the bus to the only building in sight, a wooden inn by Lake Sarmiento called Hostería Pehoe. Here we drank beer beneath the peaks of Paine. With Dick's glasses I scanned the great pinnacle of the middle peak, a sheer wall of polished blue rock. In 1962 this was the scene of a race to the summit by two expeditions. The French one gave up with loss of life, but the British finally succeeded in conquering the 2,670 metre peak.

At last the time came to leave. Before parting from Lake Sarmiento altogether we stopped by another great cataract, Salto Grande Paine. Here the lake plunges and leaps for several hundred metres through a wide cleft, where the sun reflected off the spray made a permanent rainbow. We turned to look once more at Paine Towers, now a misty blue with the moon already shining through a gap between the teeth, then we left this magical place. The journey home took three hours, and we were pursued by the last orange rays of the sun which crept up the rugged mountain crags. A wide sea of lights welcomed us to Puerto Natales.

Back on board we encountered the debris of a cocktail party for Chilean naval officers. We had invited our new friends from town to visit us, and an hour later they all arrived – Liza, Hugo and Maria, and various farmers. We gave them a tour of the ship, ending in the console room.

"This is the nerve centre of the ship," said Hugo solemnly, "and you have the most important job on board!"

Bowing to his flattery, we presented Hugo with a bottle of plankton for his students, then descended to the lounge for the real party to begin. Bottles of gin and cognac were produced, my guitar and Pete's accordion were fetched, and a superb night began. We sang all of our songs, and the Chileans sang theirs. Hugo and Maria did a Chilean folk dance, a beautiful and suggestive love ritual. The Chilean scientists appeared and joined in. There was a simple warmth and uninhibited gaiety that I had not known since the voyage began. Even the sight of the Captain and Doctor sidling in with guests from Punta Arenas did not put us off. The party lasted until after 4 a.m., and Pete gave a long blast on the siren as our friends finally departed. Never before or since have I met such fine people as the Chileans of these small villages.

We sailed at 6 a.m. and spent the morning doing stations in Golfo Almirante Montt, then in the early afternoon we swept out through Kirke Channel on the ebb tide. Pickard was annoyed and puzzled by the length of our stay in Puerto Natales, and could not understand the Captain's explanation for it. But it had been a joyous visit.

Next morning we passed northward up the navigable channel between the mainland and Isla Esperanza, and entered a system of fjords based on Estero Peel. Peel led into Asi which led into Calvo, plunging deeply into the centre of the Andes. We returned into Peel and went to investigate a large glacier which comes down to sea level in the south-east arm. The water was as calm as glass and was filled with small pieces of dirty ice that had broken off the glacier. As we approached the glacier snout the lumps grew bigger and thumped against the bow. At last the whole width of the snout was revealed; it comes down in a wide arc from a great inland ice sheet which stretches for 250 miles along the centre of the Andes. The cold water reflected the snowy mountains like a mirror, and the slightest disturbance showed up clearly. I could see the widening circle of ripples from a king cormorant that had just dived for fish, and the powerful wake churned up by a steamer duck (*Pato vapor*). These flightless ducks use their small wings as paddle wheels, and flap through the water with a form of butterfly stroke. Despite their plump twelve-pound bodies they can reach speeds of 14 knots, and they would sometimes keep pace with us for a short distance.

Later in the day we sailed up Estero Andreas and did a station near its head. I happened to be in the bows talking, but was forced into silence by a strange feeling that haunted the place. We were hemmed in closely by vertical rocks, bare of vegetation and terribly wrinkled. Absolute quiet reigned – there was not a bird to be seen, nor any other creature. We were probably the first ship to visit this fjord since FitzRoy, and were disturbing the ghosts. The fjord was strange in other ways. As well as a lack of bird life, there was almost no plankton in the water, probably because of its siltiness. In addition, the oceanographic structure turned out to be very complex, with two subsurface temperature minima at about 30 and 100 metres, possibly due to some cooling effect by the glacier front which descends into the fjord.

We continued northwards. For the next 120 miles our route lay along Canal Messier, a deep, straight channel only a few miles wide, obviously a geological fault, lying between great rows of mountains on the mainland and an equally impressive row of peaks on Wellington Island to the west. The scene was magnificent, lit up in brilliant sunshine. Here we saw our first ship since leaving Punta Arenas, the Swedish cargo liner *Panama* of the Johnson Line which passed us heading south. We dropped the lifeboat in the morning to investigate Seno Europa while the *Hudson* went into Seno Eyre. The next day found us still in Canal Messier, where we encountered our second ship. She was the Panamanian freighter *Capitan Leonidas*, aground on a rock to the west of the main channel with her back broken. She went aground in 1968 and was abandoned by her Greek crew with no subsequent attempts at salvage, so she sat in apparently perfect conditions and would continue thus until she broke up. Again to increase efficiency we dropped the lifeboat to do stations in Seno Iceberg (named after a glacier at its head) while the ship worked in Canal Messier.

After Canal Messier only one fjord system remained before reaching Golfo de Peñas, a wide gulf of the open Pacific which separates the cold and sometimes ice-laden fjords of the south from the more temperate fjords further north. We entered this last system through Baker Channel, from which the little Estero Nef leads off the south side. This is terminated by a wide, shallow glacier coming off the great ice sheet, which filled the fjord with rock flour and dirty ice. We returned via Baker Channel into Estero Steele, where, quite by accident, we stopped for a station opposite a tiny settlement called Caleta Buzeta. A steep glaciated valley comes down to the fjord at right angles, leaving a small piece of hilly lowland as a terminal moraine. Here ten little red-roofed houses clustered around a tiny jetty. We sent a lifeboat ashore to present our compliments and it returned with three Chilean army officers. They said that the hamlet is primarily a military settlement designed to guard the nearby border with Argentina. That night, as we lay off the settlement, Dick Brown came on deck to find the scuppers alive with Wilson's Storm Petrels, who had flown into our lights and bounced off onto the deck.

The following day we explored deeper into the complex fjord system, penetrating the remote Estero Steffen and Mitchell. While hove-to for a station we saw to our amazement a rowing boat coming towards us. The occupants were a shabbily dressed middle-aged man with a grizzled, weatherbeaten face, accompanied by his wife, four young children and a hairy dog. We crowded round the rail while the Chilean scientists talked down to him. He said that he lived in a small hut up on the hillside and that he made his living by cutting wood and occasionally shooting deer. There are wolves and pumas in the forest as well, he said. He looks for hard woods which are used for expensive furniture and selectively fells these, a trade known elsewhere as 'timber cruising'. Every month a supply boat comes along and he exchanges his wood for food and clothing. The family was dressed warmly but raggedly, and their hard life was reflected in their lean, rough appearance. They came to these parts ten years earlier from Chiloe Island to the north, and they had to be completely self reliant as the nearest settlement was Caleta Buzeta which could only be reached by a long boat journey. He had come to trade with us for soap and matches, he said, and held up a scrawny chicken for our appraisal. We were all deeply moved, and a spontaneous cascade of gifts began to rain down on the bewildered family: soap, matches, corned beef, pots of paint, two pairs of shoes, and a wardrobe of clothing including a pair of the Chief Engineer's long johns and a brand-new Arctic parka. The family seemed overwhelmed, and kept thanking us with tears streaming down their faces until they finally cast off. It was an opportunity to repay a little of the warmth and hospitality that we were receiving from the people of Chile. As Iver said, "It gives you a kind of warm feeling – even though I didn't give anything!"

CHAPTER 11

OUT OF THE CHILEAN FJORDS

In Chile now, cherries are dancing,
The dark mysterious girls are singing,
And in guitars, water is shining,
The sun is touching every door
And making wonder of the wheat.

Pablo Neruda

IN NOVEMBER 1520 FERDINAND Magellan sailed into an unknown ocean which he named *Mare Pacifico* because it was so calm. On 18 March 1970 CSS *Hudson* sailed out into the same ocean and started to roll her rail under. The Gulf of Peñas was rough, grey and cold, with a biting 50-knot wind and a lowering sky. My stomach started to churn in protest at this return to a life on the ocean wave. Luckily we were only exposed to it for 50 miles, after which we took shelter in Bahía San Quintín on the north side of the Gulf, where we did a line of stations.

Next morning we returned south and hove-to in Canal Cheap, which lies between the mainland and an island in the Gulf called Isla Javier. We dropped the lifeboat for stations in the nearby shallow Seno Jesuitas while the ship herself pushed out into the Gulf to sample in the open Pacific. These waters were the setting for an embarrassing episode in Royal Naval history. In 1741 Commodore Anson reached the Pacific with a squadron of five ships that was supposed to strike terror into the Spanish American colonies. He had suffered terribly in rounding Cape Horn, losing by scurvy most of his 'soldiers', actually Chelsea pensioners who had been forced on board at swordpoint. One of his ships was the sloop HMS *Wager*, under the incompetent Captain Cheap. After losing contact with Anson she became embayed in the Gulf of Peñas during a westerly gale and was wrecked on an island now called Wager Island near the mouth of Baker Channel. Cheap lost control of the shipwrecked mariners, and foolishly shot a drunken and insubordinate sailor. The crew mutinied, turned the *Wager's* longboat into a small schooner and miraculously sailed it through Magellan Strait to Brazil. Cheap, left on the island with 19 loyal men, tried to row north to Chiloe. Various disasters reduced his entourage to two midshipmen, Campbell and Byron. Byron, who is remembered in Byron Island to the west of Wager Island, was the grandfather of the poet and was later known as 'Foul Weather Jack' when an Admiral, because of his propensity for encountering storms. The trio were captured by Indians and after terrible privations were surrendered to the Spanish who threw them into a dungeon in Valparaiso. Eventually they were released and reached England in 1746 to a frosty reception from the Admiralty. The mutineers had already arrived, told their story and published a best-selling book. The Admiralty, instead of hanging the mutineers as Cheap demanded, quietly tried to forget the whole affair.

After picking up our lifeboat in Cheap Channel we spent an uncomfortable night in the open Pacific working our way out past Cabo Tres Montes and up the open coast of the Taitao Peninsula to the next set of fjords and inlets behind the Chonos Archipelago. The Chonos Archipelago is a fascinating and little-explored chaos of islands running up the coast for 120 miles from 46°S to 44°S. Again the place names recall its romantic history. At the southern end is Bahía Anna Pink; the *Anna* was a pink (supply ship) in Anson's squadron, manned by a civilian crew. After surviving Cape Horn she put into this bay to repair damage before keeping a rendezvous with Anson at Juan Fernández Island. Some of the Chonos Islands are named after officers of the *Beagle*, including Fitzroy Island; there is also a Darwin Bay and Darwin Channel as well as an Adventure Bay (HMS *Adventure* worked with *Beagle* on her survey) and a King Channel (Captain King started the survey, which was taken over by FitzRoy). Those were the wonderful days when an explorer could still hope to name great geographical features after himself. The *Hudson* entered the archipelago through Darwin Bay and Darwin Channel. The islands are hilly and thickly wooded to their summits with the luxuriant vegetation of a warmer climate; cypresses, laurels and magnolias replace the twisted and suffering Antarctic beeches of the far south.

Inside the island fringe we found ourselves in yet another 'inland passage', this time closed off at its southern end by the mountainous Taitao Peninsula. We started our survey at this end and sent the lifeboat up Estero Puelma while the *Hudson* surveyed Estuario Francisco. We were again amongst the snow-capped mountain peaks of the interior, and I took time from computer processing to watch the scenery and the sampling work. Each station began with the normal bottle cast or STD cast; UBC's STD or Salinity-Temperature-Depth recorder was a neater version by Bissett-Berman of our ponderous Bathysonde (today, renamed the CTD or Conductivity-Temperature-Depth recorder, it has replaced bottles completely). Then the Isaacs-Kidd mid-water trawl was streamed from the foredeck. I watched it return filled with giant 6-foot jellyfish which had to be emptied back over the side. The plankton tows came next; Dave English and Dick Brown used five small nets on a single wire, so that they fished at five depths simultaneously. Two messengers at 15-minute intervals opened and closed the nets. As they were fishing, a squall came over the mountains and dropped a solid belt of rain into the fjord; the setting sun produced a magnificent steep rainbow arc which descended into the fjord on either side of us.

We spent the next day further up the passage, in Estuario Elefantes, Estero Quitralco and Canal Costa, then we sailed into Seno Aysen. This is the outlet for a small settled area of cattle and sheep ranches around the little town of Puerto Aysen. Early next morning we came to anchor off Puerto Chacabuco, the port for Puerto Aysen. The confusion of names arises because Aysen was originally a port lying on the fjord, but became separated from it by eight miles of lowland as a result of an earthquake. Dr. Pickard announced that we were to stop for 12 hours to allow people to catch up with the backlog of station processing. Certainly this definition included me, but I had every intention of going ashore.

We were floating in the most beautiful surroundings that I have ever seen. A ring of steep hills, thickly wooded, plunged down on every side into the fjord head, creating a natural green amphitheatre whose floor was a sheet of warm glassy water. Behind these hills the distant snow-capped mountains were a shining curtain against the intense azure of a perfectly clear sky. The only break in the ring of beauty was a low wide valley coming down to the waterside, and here lay the few buildings of Puerto Chacabuco. The port is named after a battle of 1817 fought near Santiago, whereby Chile won her freedom from Spain. There were a few scattered houses, two jetties, an 'International Bonded Warehouse', and a fuelling depot with a pipeline leading to an offshore buoy. Away to the edge of the port an ancient cargo vessel lay beached; her funnel was missing but her noble straight stem and counter stern spoke of a British origin and a First World War vintage.

There was a boat ashore at 9 a.m. for officers and scientists. We landed at the jetty and set off in a bunch along a dirt road, watched with idle curiosity by a gang of labourers who were filling in potholes. The first buildings that we reached were a restaurant and a hotel-cum-bar, outside which a large fat lady was standing. Our Chilean friends engaged her in conversation and found that she was waiting for a bus to Puerto Aysen, so we all waited with her. She told us all about Aysen – that it was a big city of 5,000 people – and all about the wrecked ship. It was called the *Viña del Mar*, she said. It was an old British cargo steamer, bought by the Chilean Government and berthed here as a floating hotel to attract Argentine tourists from across the Andes. Not surprisingly, few of them favoured such rusty accommodation, and three years earlier she had broken her moorings in a gale and beached herself, where she had remained, derelict, ever since.

The bus did not appear, so Brian and I set off to explore down the road. We had not gone far when a truck came by. I stuck out my thumb, Brian stuck out his hook, and the truck stopped. Immediately the gang of Hudsonians galloped over and we all piled onto the back. From the smell and detritus underfoot we gathered that its last cargo had been sheep. We hung grimly on to the open framework as the driver set off at a furious pace down the appalling road. Our pilot had a seat inside the cab, and reported that it touched 80 m.p.h. What we could see of the scenery, between jolts and clouds of dust and spray, was incredibly lovely. We skirted the fjord, where gentle fields and woods sloped down to the water, then set off up the valley. This was cattle country; they grazed in the soft marshy fields and we often encountered small herds being driven along the road. They were reluctant to get out of our path until our maniacal driver headed straight at them. The morning sun shone warmly on the gentle countryside and the gaily painted roofs of the occasional farmhouses. Eventually we came to a suspension bridge across a river, Rio Aysen, and saw Puerto Aysen strung out along the other bank. The truck screeched to a halt and the driver alighted proudly.

"President Ibanez Bridge!" he cried. "Largest in Patagonia! Built by the Alliance for Progress! Here I stop."

We gratefully climbed down and staggered into town. Puerto Aysen was similar to Puerto Natales, a pleasant little country town with neat shacks of wood and corrugated iron. Tiny dark shops sold liquor, hardware, groceries and clothing, sometimes all in the same shop. A wooden building with a small tower and an imposing coat of arms holding up the wall proved to be the fire station. One little shed bore the impressive sign 'Van Gogh

– Boutique, Importaciones'; the boutique consisted of a few sweaters while the Importations were six briar pipes and a chromium-plated bottle opener.

After a long walk we reached a dusty square adorned with trees, flowers, neat box hedges and a bandstand. Beside the square stood a red-painted wooden church with a leaning tower. Presumably this had once contained bells, because a battery of loudspeakers at the top of the tower was now in use to send recorded peals over the town. Around the square lay public buildings – the post office, bank and a social club. The square boasted two monuments: a bronze bust of Admiral Williams to the same mass-produced pattern as the one at Puerto Williams; and a quaint statue of a fireman dressed in a pith helmet, white tropical kit and swagger stick.

I tried without success to change money at the bank, a wooden hall heated by iron stoves, lit by naked light bulbs and furnished with an ancient leather sofa. Therefore, having no escudos, I wandered around side streets where shacks lay alongside luxury villas, where a blacksmith was working in his backyard forge, and where the chief means of transport was the horse and cart. When I got back to the square everyone had disappeared except for the fearsome trio of the Chief Steward, Abe Granter the ship's writer, and Charlie Cadell, the little old English engineer with a hunched shoulder and a biting wit. They were looking for a grocery to replenish our stock of eggs. We found one on the square and I translated Bill Shaw's order for 100 dozen, which left the proprietress speechless. She let us have two cases, each containing the quaint number of 365 eggs. We loaded the eggs in a taxi and set off back to the ship, stopping at a grog shop for Charlie to buy his inevitable bottle of rum. The journey back was just as beautiful and bumpy, and when we reached Puerto Chacabuco the taxi's boot was running with raw egg.

We were ferried back to the ship where I found that further leave for the whole ship's company would be allowed in the afternoon. Thus at 1 p.m. an overcrowded lifeboat set out for the shore. When we reached the jetty the local police officer was standing importantly at the top of the landing steps and announced that we had no permission to land. When our Chileans observed that we had landed happily in his presence that morning, he replied that he was only obeying orders. To make him happy we returned to the ship, waited half an hour until we saw him depart for his siesta, then landed with no problem.

The crew set off noisily up the road looking for a bar or brothel. Pancho, Nelson, Iver and I followed the shore towards the *Viña del Mar*. In the warm afternoon sun the stony beach sloped invitingly down to the calm lapping water. Gulls grazing near the shore took off with a great whirr of wings as we approached. The beach turned to sand and we thought of swimming, but soon came across a foul floating foam and stench which told us that we had reached a sewage outfall. Upwind of this we finally reached the old ship, beached about twenty yards offshore in a few feet of water, with a list of thirty degrees away from us. The lost funnel was resting on the beach; through the rust we saw the yellow colour with red, white and blue bands of the Chilean Government shipping company. The poor vessel looked very decrepit; her rusted hull was patched in several places, her lifeboats were gone and parts of her upperworks were stripped away. But her lines revealed a nobler origin. According to Lloyd's Register she was built in 1911 on the Clyde by Caledon Shipbuilding and Engineering Company as the *Andorinha*, of 2,677 tons.

A crazy ladder made of pieces of wood nailed together ran up the ship's side. We called out but received no reply, so we untied a boat that was lying on the beach and Pancho poled us out to the ship. Iver went up the ladder first, and I gallantly took his photograph to send back to his widow. He survived, and we followed to find that the ladder was secured to the rail only by some frayed pieces of string. The deck was a shambles. Everything salvageable, including the portholes, had disappeared. Faeces littered the deck and obscene messages adorned the bulkheads. We made our way aft to a long poop which had been partly gutted by fire. Here there were the remains of a big public room and several cabins. For'ard of the poop was a large hatch, with cover missing, looking down into a rusty junk-filled hold. The upper deck was a chaos of mangled skylights and davits. We looked into the midships' superstructure and found the deck missing so that we could gaze straight down onto the engine room. The great piston block of an old Up And Downer triple-expansion steam engine, the delight of my grandfather, gazed back up at us, reduced to pure rust from its former oily glory and with a huge boiler alongside. Clyde-built, burning coal – this was the type of vessel that filled the seas of the world, that cemented Britain's hold on the globe as a maritime empire, and that is now gone for ever, as are the shipyards that built them, the people who manned them, and the nation that was worthy of them.

Under the bridge we found a lounge; the doors were padlocked, so we climbed in through one of the holes where windows used to be. The deck inside was littered with junk, including some splendid white wood panelling embellished with scrollwork. The after part of the lounge retained its varnished oak and a grand staircase with the remains of a red carpet, leading up to an empty room with a fine parquet floor. The bridge deck overhead was wide open to the sky. Beside the lounge was a smoking room, with benches and tables intact, and here we saw signs of life. Two exceedingly dirty bunks were made up in alcoves, and domestic objects such as plates and moth-eaten paperbacks were scattered around. I espied amongst some debris a binnacle and the faceplate of an engine room telegraph bearing the legend 'J.E. Chadbury, London'. I abstracted the faceplate as a souvenir, and we went out to explore the foredeck where we found a fine anchor and a hold with two big loading doors cut into the 'tween decks. At some period in her career the ship must have carried livestock.

We headed back to the ladder. It was then that we spotted a small and angry local dressed in dirty dungarees, shouting and gesticulating from the beach. We carefully descended the ladder and poled back to the beach where a heated conversation ensued with our Chilean friends. It transpired that the local slept on the ship, i.e. it was his home, and he was upset at us borrowing his boat and taking his faceplate. I readily returned the faceplate, whereupon the poor stranger and shipowner, still glowering, took the boat out to the ship and let himself into the lounge with a key. Satisfied that his possessions had not been disturbed he went ashore and sloped off towards the oil depot where he worked. Pancho and Nelson explained that he was "ill in the head".

The afternoon was beautiful. We climbed the hill behind the ship, passing through a gate into a high sheep pasture. A magnificent vista lay before us; sparkling mountains, mellow wooded hillsides, and the glassy fjord in which *Hudson* floated like a toy yacht. Trees, flowers and grassy knolls extended down from where we stood to a rocky shore lapped by gentle wavelets. We climbed further and now encountered a second, equally angry, local, who was shovelling sheep dung. Another heated argument began. It seemed that he was objecting to us being in his pasture and perhaps stealing his dung; he was the other occupant of the *Viña del Mar*. Our Chilean friends apologised profusely for these two unrepresentative citizens of their lovely country.

An hour of shore leave remained. We crossed the valley and climbed the next hill, passing a row of rude shacks with no glass in their windows but with lovingly kept gardens full of dahlias. Iver got out his movie camera whereupon a horde of children poured out of the dwellings and clustered round. According to Nelson they thought that Iver had a telescope. Then they asked to be filmed and to be given chocolate. Continuing up the hill we entered the 'Parque Nacional de los Helechos' (National Park of Ferns) according to a sign. We saw no ferns but a profusion of purple foxgloves in flower. We returned to the jetty and joined Pete, whose escudos enabled us to buy pisco in the local shop. Then we waited for the lifeboat. The returning crew were milling around two attractive girls, one with a baby, who appeared to be the local loose women, and it took a long time to prise the coxswain away from his true love and get him to take us all back to the ship.

From the amount of booze brought on board I judged that the night would be lively. Even in the lifeboat pisco was being quaffed in the traditional Newfoundland fashion – straight from the bottle. The evening brought a giant orgy of fights and destruction in the crew's mess. My evening was spent more quietly in Pete's cabin with our Chilean friends, drinking *pichunchos*, a lethal mixture of pisco and vermouth. At 8 p.m. we sailed and soon the fast rhythm of stations was under way; I crept unsteadily up to the computer to spend the night catching up with data processing.

Hudson emerged from Seno Aysen and continued up Canal Moraleda, the northward extension of the 'inland passage' up the Chilean coast. The next fjord system consisted of an island, Isla Magdalena, formed by two fjords which join at their heads. We entered the northern one, Canal Jacaf, and came out of the southern one, Canal Puyuguapi. Then we emerged from Canal Moraleda itself into the wide and beautiful Golfo Corcovado. The end of our cruise was almost in sight. Corcovado, together with the Golfo de Ancud, forms a sheltered waterway protected from the open Pacific by the 90 mile length of Chiloe Island. At the north end of Golfo de Ancud lies Puerto Montt, the beginning of urban civilisation in Chile and the end point of our survey.

It was a time for taking stock. All of us had noticed the new warmth in the air, the bright sunshine and the fragrant smell of the trees. To cruise through these northerly fjords was like cruising through Paradise. But this was reflected oceanographically in only four degrees of temperature change. Seno Aysen had a surface temperature of 13°C, compared with 9°C for the Fuegan fjords. The surface salinity in Aysen was only 4 parts per thousand, because of the fresh water influx from Rio Aysen, but at 20 metres the salinity was up to 30 and the temperature down to 10°C; it was still 10°C at the bottom. In contrast Estero Puelma, a little further south but with only a few small streams feeding it, had a surface temperature of 14°C and salinity of 20 parts per thousand, changing to 11°C and 28 parts per thousand at 20 metres. The reason why such a large change in latitude is associated with such a small change in water temperature is the fact that the whole Chilean coast is washed by the powerful, cold Humboldt Current, which sweeps north from the Antarctic where it diverts from the Antarctic Circumpolar Current to the southwest of Cape Horn. Here in these northern fjords the sun was doing its best to heat the frigid water, but in its whole passage north from Cape Horn the waters had only managed to warm by four degrees. Because the water mass is essentially the same all along the coast, the biologists aboard *Hudson* were reporting only modest changes in the range of species appearing in the plankton as we sailed north.

As we entered Golfo Corcovado I was still chained to the computer; a fault in one of the programs meant that I had to repeat many of the stations. After two solid days at the keyboard I emerged on deck, pasty-faced, and gazed around. The sea was smooth and oily, and the distant mountainous profiles of the mainland and Isla Chiloe were softened by a gentle heat haze. A small seine-net fishing boat chugged out of Canal Moraleda behind us. Along the mainland coast I could see a stately procession of three snow-capped volcanoes. The southern one, actually a ridge of three peaks seen end-on, was Mount Yanteles (2,042 metres). North of this lay the famous Corcovado itself (2,290 metres), a perfect snowy cone rising straight from the sea to a jagged peak, with smooth flanks of lava and ash, and looking identical to Mount Fuji. Further north, and far in the distance, was Mount Michinmahuida or Chayapiren (2,440 metres). All of these have been active in recent centuries, and all erupted during the great Chilean earthquake of 1960 centred on Valdivia. Darwin experienced a similar earthquake in 1835, when the towns of Valdivia and Concepción were devastated.

In the evening we sailed 50 miles out into the Pacific to sample the open ocean at this lower latitude. As the sun buried itself in a blaze of crimson behind the dark rocky coast of Chiloe Island, I turned to Darwin's description:-

> *The island is about 90 miles long, with a breadth of rather less than 30. The land is hilly . . . and is covered by one great forest, except where a few green patches have been cleared round the thatched cottages. The woods . . . are incomparably beautiful. In winter the climate is detestable and in summer it is only a little better. The winds are very boisterous, and the sky always clouded.*

The population of Chiloe at that time was 42,000 souls, mainly Indians who were extremely poor and humble:-

The lower orders cannot scrape together money sufficient to purchase even the smallest luxuries.

Next day we returned to the Corcovado Gulf and ran a line of stations up the eastern side. Towards evening this brought us through the narrow channel to the east of the low, wooded Talcan Island. The sun set over the island and lit up long sausages of cloud with a tremendous red glow. In this eerie light a small gaff-rigged sailing cutter came drifting down the channel, using sweeps as well as sail. The pilot said that this was one of a fleet of mussel boats out of Puerto Montt. As darkness fell we passed Nihuel Island, a volcanic stack (the core of an old volcano), which stood out of the water like a squat cylindrical pillar. Intoxicated with the beauty I went below and was lured into a party in Charlie Cadell's cabin. An accordion was in action, so I fetched my guitar and to the accompaniment of the gurgling of Charlie's Scotch we had a long and glorious concert. As always, the Chileans were the best singers.

The following morning was Good Friday, March 27. I fell out of bed with an extreme hangover and nausea, vowing never again to drink at sea. The feeling persisted at lunchtime when cold Hot Cross Buns were on offer. The day was spent in two fjords off the Ancud Gulf, Estero Renihue and Estero Comau. The next day was the last of the fjord survey – a sad day for everyone. The camaraderie on this stage of the cruise had been superb; we were all under the spell of the magnificent surroundings and the knowledge that we were the first to explore the oceanographic mysteries of the fjords. This was the best of "Hudson-70". I felt like spending the rest of my life in Chile, and so did many of my colleagues.

Our final fjord was Estero Reloncavi in the northern corner of Golfo de Ancud; it was full of giant jellyfish, two feet in diameter and with trailing tentacles fifteen feet long. They filled the plankton nets and draped themselves around the Knudsen bottles. The 175th and last station was completed, and we assembled for a nostalgic group photograph on the foredeck. We were all filled with sadness at the realisation that this magical shared experience was coming to an end.

On Easter Sunday *Hudson* dropped anchor off Puerto Montt. The dock was full, so we had to lay off until a Navy patrol vessel obligingly sailed out to make room for us. A fine morning mist hung over the town, which lay sprawling around an irregular range of hills. It looked like a warmer, less desolate and more affluent version of Punta Arenas. The population of 70,000 is a little larger, and it was founded in 1852 by German immigrants who still dominate the city's commercial life.

We crept in towards the dock, past the main square of the city. Far beyond the hills I could see the great snow-capped peaks of new volcanoes, Osorno (2,660 metres) and Calbuco (2,015 metres). The dock is at the west end of town near the entrance to the narrow Canal Tenglo, which winds on peacefully between a fishing harbour called Angelmo and the beautiful wooded ridge of Isla Tenglo. We berthed beyond the fine Peruvian freighter *Inca Capac Yupanqui* and in front of a small Chilean government freighter, the *Capitan Luis Alcazar,* which was preparing to offload a deck cargo of live sheep. In the fishing port beyond our dock a profusion of boats lay at anchor and drawn up on the beach. They ranged from steel draggers down through wooden seine boats to the traditional broad-beamed sailing cutters that we had seen in Corcovado Gulf.

As soon as we docked I went ashore to look at the sheep operations. The decks and hold of the *Alcazar* were packed tightly with brown, scruffy creatures. Six at a time were packed into wooden crates and lifted out by crane; they accumulated nervously at one end of the jetty. One sheep that had been crushed was carried off to a wagon where its throat was cut. A thick stream of blood ran down to form a steaming puddle on the ground. Another sheep had been slaughtered earlier and was being butchered on deck. When all the sheep had been landed a *huaso* appeared, proudly upright on a horse bedecked with polished metal trappings, and herded them off through the town, a bizarre scene as traffic stopped to make way for this Wild West carry-over.

A group of us set out from the ship to explore. The dock area was a wasteland of warehouses, shacks and muddy tracks. Huge puddles were dyed red with resin seeping from stacks of timber. Outside the dock gate we followed the shore road, lined with gaily painted fishing stores and shellfish restaurants. We passed the luxurious buildings of the Naval Officers' Club and reached a waterside market. The wooden stalls displayed big silvery fish, brown cakes of dried seaweed, four-inch diameter sea urchins, and vegetables of all kinds. The gonads of sea urchins were a staple food of the Patagonian Indians, whose womenfolk would dive for them in the cold fjords. The market bustle was already under way; trucks and buses were continually arriving, packed with grizzled peasants in thick shabby clothing carrying bundles of potatoes, tomatoes or live chickens for sale on the street. The people have swarthy, wrinkled faces and show strong Indian characteristics; the local tribe were the Araucanians, a fierce, proud and cultivated people who fought bravely against the Spaniards and the Chileans and whose last uprising occurred as recently as 1882.

Near the city centre the streets were quiet, with only a few food shops open; most of the shops bore German names, although a few were British. We soon reached the main square, facing the sea. On one side was the best hotel, the Pedro Rosales, which resembled a Bavarian mountain lodge with its carved wood balconies and steeply sloping roof. Near the sea was a bandstand where folk singers were performing to a large audience. Behind the trees, flowers and fountains there was more Teutonism in the form of the German Club (Club Alemán) and a Bavarian church with varnished wood facade and onion dome. The Germans, said Nelson, keep completely to themselves and do not intermarry with the locals. Are they liked? I asked. He shrugged eloquently. As much as the British in Punta Arenas, he said enigmatically.

We proceeded to the ramshackle railway station to find a train to Santiago for Steve Pond and Wayne Burt, who were leaving the ship here, then had a locally-brewed German beer in a cafe, which exhausted our joint escudos. All the banks were closed and nobody that we spoke to dared to offer unofficial currency exchange, for which the penalty was imprisonment, so we headed back to the ship for lunch.

Once on board, however, we met the Chief Engineer of the *Aquiles*, a Naval troop transport that was anchored off the port. He was willing, indeed anxious, to change my dollars into escudos, and provided a launch to take me out to his ship. She was a luxurious vessel, a former Danish liner built in 1953, and his quarters were palatial. The Chilean armed forces have always been a pampered elite, but at least until 1973 they had the distinction of never having interfered in politics, a proud record which they have since besmirched thoroughly. The Engineer changed my money at slightly above the official rate and dispatched me back in the same launch.

Peter Wadhams

Five of us now had the means to set out on an expedition to Puerto Varas, a little resort on the shores of Lake Llanquihue some 15 miles north of Puerto Montt. Nelson was our guide. We took a rickety bus to the town centre then another bus to Puerto Varas for two escudos (15 cents). As we reached the dilapidated outskirts of town the bus rapidly filled with peasant farmers and their enormous dumpy wives until the gangway was packed. The road led us out through rolling open countryside, mostly uncultivated, past the new provincial gaol and a terrible shanty town of shacks. By now we were turning away crowds of peasants who waited patiently with their bundles at each bus stop. Finally we reached the crest of a hill and saw the calm blue waters of the lake and the red roofs of Puerto Varas spread out below.

We wandered around the town, which was attractive but apparently uninhabited. The only living beings were small boys who dived off a wooden jetty for 10 centesimo pieces. Across the clear sparkling water of the lake stood the snow cone of Osorno and the bluff peak of Calbuco in all their majesty. Just before the 1835 earthquake Darwin saw Osorno erupt:-

> *By the aid of a glass, dark objects, in constant succession, were seen, in the midst of a great glare of red light, to be thrown up and to fall down.*

We climbed up to a hilltop park which commanded a view across the lake, and passed the sunny afternoon pleasantly before catching the bus back.

That night the same gang of us went to the cinema, intending to sample the night life afterwards. The films were American, with English soundtrack and Spanish subtitles, and I knew that my Spanish was improving when I caught myself following the subtitles and ignoring the soundtrack. We emerged after midnight to find the town apparently dead. Hearing sounds of music we found a nightclub, but it was a respectable one, i.e. one to which one takes girls, and so not our scene at all. The doorman indignantly denied that any lower establishment existed in Puerto Montt. The heavy German spirit had the place in thrall. We retired, defeated, to bed.

The next day was again warm and sunny and I spent the morning buying souvenirs. In a back street I came upon a tumbledown undertaker's parlour, outside of which was parked the most ancient hearse that I have ever seen. It was an American model of the mid-Twenties, of the type used for the victims of Al Capone, and it had a row of Gothic windows along the side. When I got back to the ship I found her surrounded by a mob of kids, clamouring for cigarettes and money.

After lunch I set out with Pete Reynell to explore the fishing port of Angelmo. The harbour is enclosed by a sea wall, against which a row of market stalls dispensed fish, fruit, vegetables, Indian ponchos and rugs. These stalls all had rear chutes which expelled detritus straight down onto the beach. Amid a chaos of colourful wooden shacks we found a wide stone ramp that led down from the sea wall to the beach, and here we perched to watch the confusion of shipping.

A small overcrowded ferry ran continuously to and from Isla Tenglo, and the harbour contained several old gaff cutters airing their sails. Many of the boats had children swarming over them and washing hanging from their booms, and it was clear that the fishermen lived on board. The wooden sailing boats were about 30 feet long by 8 feet beam, with a dark tanned mainsail and a single jib on a bowsprit, The beach itself was a rank midden composed of an intimate mixture of giant mussel shells and fish heads, laced with old boots, decaying cow horns, potato peelings, faeces and a dead rat which floated to and fro in a sewage outfall just below me. I withstood the stench long enough to sketch one of the cutters, then we retreated.

We lingered in a nearby bar to look at the carts. Horses and ancient two-wheeled carts creaked and groaned their way down the steep ramp onto the beach to handle cargo from the boats, going right into the water if necessary. The laden carts had to be conned up the ramp to the accompaniment of steady curses and whipping by the drivers. Frequently the nag would slip backwards so that the cart rammed the wall of the ramp; wild imprecations were then necessary before the horse renewed its courage. One cart took on a load of live pigs from the ferry, and had to go axle deep into the water to do so. Its way out was blocked by a lorry parked on the beach. The carter, without raising his voice or making any gestures, uttered a stream of oaths so vile as to produce a stir amongst the locals sitting on the sea wall. The lorry driver rapidly appeared. With its heavy load of squealing pigs the cart could not negotiate the ramp, and had to be nudged up from behind by another cart.

In the bar we met an American sitting with a couple of attractive girls. He said that he was a mining engineer from Abilene working in an American-owned copper mine near Santiago. He was on holiday. I hoped that he might share one of his girls with us, but he seemed attached to them both. We returned to the harbour after dinner and I sketched as the sun set over the busy scene. The boats were now the social centre of Angelmo, as families gathered on them and discussed the day's affairs.

Later we returned to the ship. Chano Chuecas had promised to activate contacts of his in Puerto Montt who would produce large numbers of beautiful girls for a party, so in great expectation we sat around in the lounge drinking steadily. Chano, however, had clearly been waylaid and never appeared. About midnight we agreed unanimously that the last night in port should not go to waste, and someone remembered that Chano had mentioned a night club called the 'Red Dragon'. Some of us had been drinking more steadily than others, and in the end only three of us were in good enough condition to set out in search of this place of entertainment. Outside the dock gate we grabbed a taxi, woke up the driver and directed him thus:

"Dragon Rojo!"

"Dragón Rojo?"

"Sí!"

"Señoritas?"

"Sí!"

He threw his ancient vehicle into gear and roared off up the hill into the sordid outskirts of town, composed of unmade roads with deep ditches. He drew up outside a wooden house which was shuttered and which did not look like a night club. He flashed his lights and hooted his horn. A door was thrown open and out came three seamen from the *Hudson* in jocular mood. In Chile the distinction between a night club and a bordello is a fine one, and clearly this establishment lay well beyond the dividing line. It was also clear that this was not the 'Red Dragon' but rather a place which had a financial arrangement with our taxi driver.

One of the girls spoke English, so we asked her the way to the 'Red Dragon'. Her directions led us nowhere in particular, so after blundering around in the mud we returned for further advice. The English-speaking girl had disappeared, so taking the line of least resistance we stayed, as the staff had presumably planned. The young ladies were sorry-looking specimens of their profession, except for one attractive girl who attached herself to the one member of our party who was wearing a tie and who therefore looked affluent. The other two of us were forced to stay to make sure our shipmate came to no harm. While our friend dallied away the hours we passed the time talking to a villainous-looking character with bulging eyes who said that he was in the German army during the War and had come out to Chile afterwards, for unspecified reasons. He bewailed the shrewishness of his wife, and informed us that he was in love with the madam of the bordello, a fat and repulsive creature with a deep bass voice. To see them dancing together was quite extraordinary: the German jerked epileptically around the massive bulk of his sweetheart, lips smacking, eyes popping from his head, arm and legs spasmodically shooting out at random angles. This was well worth watching, and the time slipped past until our shipmate, sated, cheerful, and helplessly drunk, announced that we could leave.

Supporting him between us we started off down the hill, guided by the distant lights of the *Aquiles*. Near the bottom of the hill a red light proclaimed the existence of a bar where our shipmate demanded refreshment. The interior was like a church hall festooned with Chilean flags. A duo of piano and drums played listlessly and a few girls sat slumped over the tables. It was like the Night Café in Arles in Van Gogh's painting. The barmaid was a lively girl of incorruptible morals who aroused our sated colleague's renewed desires. He began a babbling proposition which was received with courteous laughter. A few old peasants, for whom it was already morning, came in and a Chilean in the corner fell off his stool, dead drunk.

We dragged our friend away from this Hemingwayesque scene, and set off again through the rain which was damping down an early morning dust storm. The street lamps were out, but finally the dock gates were at hand and we reached the ship just before shore leave expired at 6 a.m. So ended our study of the delights of Puerto Montt.

CHAPTER 12

ROBINSON CRUSOE'S ISLAND

I am monarch of all I survey;
My right there is none to dispute;
From the centre all round to the sea
I am lord of the fowl and the brute.

William Cowper

I**T WAS A HIGHLY** inefficient *Hudson* that cast off from Puerto Montt at 9 a.m. on March 31. The able seamen at the lines were anything but able, and everyone without a vital job to do was down below sleeping off the effects of the last night in port. The ship began to come slowly alive about noon, and I emerged on deck to see us passing through the narrow Chacao Channel which separates Chiloe Island from the mainland. Fishing boats tossed on the choppy blue water as a pleasant landscape of fields and scattered farms slipped by, then some low orange cliffs marked the end of land and we were out in the wide Pacific. The temperature dropped quickly as we encountered the cold Humboldt Current and began pushing into a grey heaving swell.

The next three days took us on a dog-leg into the Pacific, in which we first headed west at 41° 40'S as far as longitude 81°W, and then turned due north to run a line of oceanographic stations up to the Juan Fernández Islands. On the westward leg the STD probe was lowered at 45-mile intervals and we did bottle stations at 77°W and 81°W. Between the two stations we crossed the outer edge of the Humboldt Current and entered warmer Pacific water, with the colour of the sea changing noticeably from turbid grey-green to a translucent cobalt blue. On the northward line we did three more bottle stations, several biological tows and STD casts every 60 miles. Conditions were far from ideal; the ship was almost empty of fuel and bounced like a cork in the unwonted grip of the open ocean. This seemed to affect the Chilenos most of all, and several of them were full-time commuters between their bunks and heads. The sea was so rough that the contents of the Isaacs-Kidd trawl were severely battered before they could be got aboard; all that remained were fishes' eyeballs.

I was running the satellite navigation system and in between times catching up on the computer analysis, so that we could present the University of Chile with a full set of our data on arrival in Valparaiso. It was also time to run up the gravimeter in preparation for the long Pacific transect to follow, but when I went down to the gravity lab I found to my horror that the gyrotable was wildly swaying and that the servo amplifiers that should have kept it in equilibrium were not working. Visions of being keel-hauled passed before my mind, but Danny and I traced the fault to blown fuses, possibly caused by surges following blackouts in Puerto Montt. The fuses were of a sand-filled type and the spares box had no replacements, so Danny began laboriously to take a fuse apart in order to reconstruct it. The next morning, to make matters worse, a steward with a water hose ruined the gravity lab's air conditioning plant by burning out the compressor, which for some inscrutable reason was mounted quite exposed in the seamen's toilets. Again a frantic patching-up operation was needed to put things right.

The biologists were excited by our forthcoming visit to Juan Fernández, because it is one of those isolated ocean islands, like the Galapagos, which has had time to develop its own species of birds and plants. There are many types of fern known only to Juan Fernández, and there is also an indigenous species of humming bird, *Eustephanus fernandensis*, which must have developed from a commoner Chilean species that was blown across from the mainland. The night before we reached land we came across a seabird which breeds only on the island, the Juan Fernández Petrel. I will let Dick Brown describe the encounter in his own words:-

> *They are fairly large, rather graceful, brown and white birds. Gadfly-petrels - they don't skim the waves like your common fulmar or shearwater, but go up, up and away, soaring off like the big dipper, and shooting down to try it again; I can't explain this exuberance, but it's a sure way to recognise them. As it happened, I had an even closer acquaintance, since one of them flew into our lights and was brought to me, ignominiously,*

in a bucket. Now, I expected that it would bite me, and indeed it did - the bloody bird has a long, thin beak with a razor-sharp tip. But what added impudence to injury was the precision with which it crapped in my camera lens.

In the early morning of April 4 a tiny purple peak appeared on the horizon – Más a Tierra, the inhabited island of the Juan Fernández group and home of that most famous castaway, Alexander Selkirk (the real Robinson Crusoe). As the island grew larger it resolved itself into a jumbled mass of volcanic rock, sweeping steeply down to the sea from an imposing flat-topped peak called El Yunque (The Anvil), 3,225 ft. high, in the centre of the island. The lower slopes are clad in patches with trees, but the upper reaches are bare rock, streaked with red volcanic veins, which the soft morning mist turned into the shape of a grey sleeping giant. We sailed round to the north side of the island and dropped anchor in Cumberland Bay, a wide indentation in the coast which offers a partially protected anchorage. Leading back from the bay is a bowl-shaped valley, where the little village of San Juan Bautista houses the island's population of about 300 souls, mainly fishermen and their families. Behind this small stretch of lowland loom the steep sides of El Yunque, and equally steep rocky points hem it in to either side. One of these is known as Selkirk's Lookout, where the unfortunate castaway had a signal fire ready in case a ship hove into view. These slopes were originally covered with sandalwood and other valuable hardwoods, but they were stripped away by visiting ships.

The Juan Fernández group consists of two major islands, called, logically enough, Más a Tierra (Closest to Land) and Más a Fuera (Furthest Out), some 100 miles to the west, but the term Juan Fernández is commonly applied just to Más a Tierra. The island has a most romantic history. The floor of the Pacific Ocean is covered with hundreds of submarine volcanoes, called seamounts, which erupt like boils from its skin. Many of them are big enough to poke their snouts above the sea surface and become the little island specks that dot the South Pacific. Millions of years ago one such rocky mass appeared 400 miles off the coast of South America, with birth-pangs of fire and lava. As it cooled down the erosion of wind, rain and waves created the beginnings of a soil so that the first seeds, carried perhaps by birds or by ocean currents, could take root. Once life appears anywhere the irresistible force of natural selection causes it to take a tenacious hold, and during the long isolation a native vegetation proliferated and developed.

But the tiny island remained undiscovered by man. Even the Polynesians, who roamed the South Pacific a thousand years ago in their great double-hulled canoes, failed to penetrate this far east. Then in 1563 a Spanish navigator called Juan Fernández discovered the island and named it after himself. As a gesture of charity to future seafarers he released pigs and goats, who in the absence of natural enemies soon multiplied. For fifty years the island was lost again; in those days sailors had no accurate means of determining longitude, and a new island could be placed on a chart far from its real position. The next visitors were Jakob Le Maire and Willem Schouten, who sailed out into the Pacific in 1616 after discovering Cape Horn. They found abundant livestock and fresh water, so that the island became frequented as an oasis of fresh meat and vegetables for the scurvy-ridden crews of trading, buccaneering and pirate ships. Commodore Anson called here in 1741 during his round-the-world voyage. On his three remaining ships were 335 exhausted and diseased survivors from the 961 original personnel of his fleet. His chaplain, Richard Walter, wrote of the first sighting of Juan Fernández:-

> Though, in its first view, it appeared to be a very mountainous place, extremely ragged and irregular, yet as it was land, and the land we sought for, it was to us a most agreeable sight; because at this place only we could hope to put a period to those terrible calamities we had so long struggled with, which had already swept away above half our crew, and which, had we continued a few days longer at sea, would inevitably have compleated our destruction.

On his return to England Anson recommended that a British settlement be made on Juan Fernández, but to forestall him the Spanish seized the island and garrisoned it in 1750. When South America was liberated from Spain the island passed to Chile, who established a penal colony for political prisoners. Later this was abandoned and the island was once again deserted until 1877 when a Chilean landowner called Alfredo de Rodt took a lease on it and brought out the first colonists to work the cray fishery. The last excitement that the island saw was in 1915 when the German cruiser *Dresden*, last survivor of Von Spee's squadron which had otherwise been destroyed at the Battle of the Falkland Islands, took refuge in Cumberland Bay. She was discovered by the British fleet and scuttled by her captain, during which the magazine exploded and many of her crew were killed.

As soon as we dropped anchor whole families of local people put out in their fishing boats to welcome the strange visitor, for a monthly supply boat from Chile is normally the only commerce that the island has with the outside world. The islanders use long double-ended boats with an eye painted on the bows to ward off evil luck. From these boats they set pots for the succulent crayfish that abound round the coast, and they also line-fish for yellowfin tuna and other game fish. These tasks, augmented by the keeping of cows, pigs and goats, furnish the people with a more than adequate living. The usual formalities with the Chilean authorities being speedily concluded we lowered a lifeboat and headed for a large welcoming committee of village children on the jetty.

We were immediately the centre of great attention, and our Chilean friends were busy explaining to everyone who we were and from where we came. The islanders are all of Chilean origin and have the normal attractive features of that nation, with the added easy-going friendliness of those who live in quiet places. We moved off in a solid phalanx through the cheerful confusion of the fishing depot, where several boats were drawn up on slipways above the stony beach amongst a clutter of pots, nets and huts. A path led through the fenced-off 'plaza', with its inevitable bust of Admiral Prat, to the village's main 'street'. Owing to the scarcity of traffic (a few trucks are the only vehicles) the dirt roadway is overgrown with stands of sweetly-scented bushes, through which pigs, chickens, dogs and goats happily sniff and root. A cinnamon-coloured humming bird, which Dick identified as the island's home-grown species, hovered delicately above the bell of a gigantic convolvulus, his wings a blur of rapid motion. Scattered irregularly along the road are the villagers' huts. Only a few have descended to neatly fencing off their territory; the majority prefer to let their huts nestle amongst myrtle trees and orchid-laced undergrowth. The Navy has a small post; there is one shop, consisting of a long counter in front of a wooden shack; and further along we found the post office, a neat purple hut. Pancho went round the back and woke the postmaster, who opened the place with great ceremony and solemnly stamped our mail with the 'Isla Robinson Crusoe' postmark.

Pancho, who had visited the island before, now led us up a bare red hill behind the village, where we came to a stone platform which is all that remains of a fort erected by the Spanish. Here a large number of children were playing football, and they escorted us further up a cliff to a row of six holes cut in the bare rock. These artificial caves were the homes of the unfortunate political exiles during the 19th century. Each cave has an entrance about 12 ft square and extends back between ten and fifty feet. Despite their magnificent view across the Pacific these cannot have been desirable residences. They are dank and moss-covered, and must have required a covering for the mouth in winter. Juan Fernández is not the tropical isle envisioned by Defoe; its climate is temperate with distinct seasons and there are certainly no palm trees to be seen.

Coming back down to the village we headed off eastwards round the Bay and came out to the beach, which is made of smooth lava blocks over which the Pacific lapped gently. To our surprise we discovered several ancient cannon, encrusted with rust, lying at random among the rocks. These must have been washed up from the many vessels which perished in sudden storms in this Bay. Behind the beach, in some undergrowth, we found an extraordinary old coastal defence gun of two-inch calibre in a domed turret, looking curiously out of place in such a peaceful setting. Green camouflage paint showed behind the rust, and it bore the nameplate 'Krupp 1898'.

Most of my colleagues now returned to the ship for lunch, but Danny and I resolved to reach a building which we had seen on our approach to the Bay; it was in an isolated cove and was said to be the island's only hotel. We followed the shore path, which petered out close to one of the steep rocky promontories that close off the valley of the village. We hailed a local boy and asked him in skeletal Spanish if there was a route round the cliff. He replied enthusiastically in the affirmative, as he was going that way himself, and he went skipping on ahead. When we reached the cliff it seemed sheer and inaccessible, but the boy was already half-way up, following an almost invisible goat track. After a while Danny gave up the ascent, pleading the effects of loose living, leaving me to soldier on. A long climb up the crumbling orange cliff, slashed by ravines and scree slopes, brought me to a gentler upland covered in scrub; Selkirk's Lookout. Below me the bay was a blue sheet of wrinkled glass and the *Hudson* a little toy; I thought of Selkirk and how his eyes must have strained into the distant haze, day after day, in the vain hope of sighting a sail.

Alexander Selkirk led a colourful life, far more so than his fictional counterpart Robinson Crusoe. Born in Fife in 1676 Selkirk grew up a rebel, for in 1695 he was summoned to appear before the kirk on charges of 'indecent behaviour in church'. The stern Church Fathers noted that he 'did not compear, being gone away to the sea'. In 1704 he was with the famous buccaneer and pirate William Dampier as sailing master of the galley *Cinque Ports* when the pirate fleet put into Juan Fernández. Here Selkirk quarrelled with Stradling, the ship's unpopular captain, and asked to be put ashore. He remained alone for over four years, until January 1709 he was rescued by Captain Woodes Rogers, another famous privateer who later became the respectable first Governor of the Bahamas. Strangely enough Woodes Rogers had Dampier aboard as pilot. Selkirk was made mate then master of *The Increase*, one of Woodes Rogers' Spanish prizes. He reached the Thames in October 1711, and it is here that he is supposed to have told his story to Daniel Defoe, who had a house near the river at Chadwell-St-Mary. Selkirk could never settle down again; his years of solitude had made him withdrawn and unhappy in a crowded world. He returned to Scotland but then went back to sea and died in 1721 while mate of HMS *Weymouth*.

Turning from the bay and my thoughts I continued my climb and at length saw a little cove beneath me, with a tiny platform of land on which a single-storey hotel was perched. There was still a deep chasm to cross, carrying a fast stream, but I espied near its head a tiny hut near a stand of trees where a woodcutter was hard at work. He called cheerily over, so I went up and exchanged greetings. He pointed out a narrow track that ran steeply down into the cleft, so I scrambled across by this and reached my goal.

I had been preceded, for three seamen were already inside being entertained by two pleasant girls. One of these turned out to be an attractive English adventuress, called Sarah, who in working her way around the world reached Juan Fernández and got a job on the staff of this newly-opened venture. Over drinks I learned that an airstrip had just been built on the other side of the island, with a flight from Santiago every three weeks. In this first season 700 visitors, mostly well-to-do Chileans, had stayed at the hotel; it could only be a matter of time, however, before the international tourist industry moved in to destroy the serenity of the surroundings. The girls treated us to a fine meal of local crayfish and the wild figs which Joshua Slocum had so praised when he visited the island in 1900 during his solo circumnavigation on the yacht *Spray*. In the lounge of the hotel are gathered many nautical relics; binnacles and spars from the island's many wrecks, and the mainmast of a balsa raft which an intrepid mariner had recently sailed here from Peru in an attempt to emulate the *Kon-Tiki*. We swam in the chilly sea from a wave-swept reef of dark red coral in front of the hotel. Apart from the goat track the only access to the hotel is by boat, so we were ferried back to the *Hudson* later in the afternoon with plans to return and hold a party later that night. Sarah would fetch some girls from the village and we would present ourselves, plus alcoholic provisions, at the hotel. Our evil plans were shattered by the bald announcement that the *Hudson* would be sailing in the early evening.

Greg and I jumped into the last boat ashore for a final look round. We walked up the shore, exchanging greetings with the inhabitants, and talked of the happiness that comes with simplicity, and of the inhuman world of frantic motion and mass communications whose tentacles will soon engulf the last of these gentle enclaves. We noticed a long procession winding down the road, and followed them just outside the village to a little fenced-off cemetery near the beach, shaded by trees. Everybody was dressed in his best clothes, and the leaders carried wreaths and flowers. In one corner of the cemetery is a monument to those who died when the *Dresden* went down; there are fresh flowers around the stone and it is capped by a lifebelt from the ship herself. The procession stopped before a nearby grave and piled flowers over it; some sort of memorial service was clearly in progress. We lingered outside, not wishing to intrude. Several of the participants smiled and beckoned us in, but just then the strident whistle of the *Hudson* sounded, summoning us back from our dream.

We jumped in the last boat as she pulled away. As soon as she was safely inboard we weighed anchor and set sail. With great regret I watched the village slip away, and when it had disappeared behind a promontory I stood at the stern and watched the island almost out of sight. The sun was now hidden behind El Yunque, and it cast great shafts of light down to either side of the peak. As the island receded the sun set behind its black jagged silhouette in a last halo of orange and red.

As I gazed at this spectacle I was joined by Dr. Pickard and asked him why we had to sail so early. He answered nonchalantly, "Well, there didn't seem much reason for staying, did there?"

My resulting passionate frustration was cooled by perusal of warnings about the anchorage in the *Admiralty Pilot* and memories of the rusty cannon. However it rose again when I discovered that we were not sailing directly into Valparaiso. Pickard had received a curt telex from the Director of BIO saying:-

> *You are not to arrive Valparaiso before 08.00 April 7. This schedule is important for the press conference by visiting dignitaries.*

We therefore dawdled eastward through the night and following day, did a final STD cast 15 miles from the coast, and then proceeded to spend the whole of April 6 swinging at anchor off Concón, a seaside resort just north of Valparaiso. This was to enable the ship to be painted and generally tarted up for the gigantic welcoming committee which we expected on our grand entrance into Valparaiso.

1. Launching the Bathysonde.

2. Preparing the piston corer; the corer is the long thin tube with a finned weight at the top.

3. Arrival at Rio de Janeiro, our first port of call.

4. Iceberg in the South Atlantic.

5. The wrecked Chilean base at Deception Island – the main hut and radio mast covered in volcanic ash.

6. Puerto Percy, Tierra del Fuego – Bob Hessler and assistants for his beach survey.

7. Punta Arenas – the monument to Magellan.

8. Staff of the Chilean fjord survey. Back row (l. to r.): Captain Butler; B D Uccelletti; Dr Nelson Silva; Dr Lisandro Chuecas; David English; Dr Steve Pond; Dr Ramón Ahumada. Front row (l. to r.): Prof Brian Bary; Peter Wadhams; Dr Iver Duedall; Dr Richard Brown; Prof George Pickard (chief scientist); Murray Storm; Dr Hector Inostroza; Riccardo Montaner; Prof Wayne Burt. Photograph taken by Francisco Rey.

9. Canal Kirke and waterfall.

10. The peaks of Torre del Paine from Lake Sarmiento.

11. A fjord near Puerto Natales.

12. The ice-filled Estero Peel

13. Estero Peel and its glaciers.

14. A fjord near Puerto Aysen.

15. *Hudson* in Puerto Chacabuco.

16. Puerto Aysen – local transport and the wooden church tower.

17. The visit from the woodcutter family.

18. Puerto Montt – unloading fish.

19. Juan Fernández Island – cannon on the beach from a wrecked ship.

20. Leaving Juan Fernández Island. The peak is El Yunque, with Selkirk's Lookout.

21. Valparaiso – Allende's election headquarters.

22. Machu Picchu – sitting on Intihuatana, the Hitching Place of the Sun.

23. A flying fish from the tropical Pacific (sketch by author).

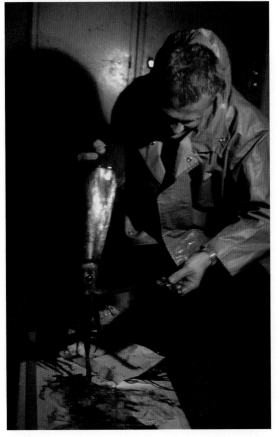

24. Ken Freeman with a squid that he caught in the tropical Pacific.

25. Coming in to dock in Vancouver.

26. The Queen Charlottes survey – putting out marker buoys for seismic shooting.

27. The Queen Charlottes survey – rendezvous with CNAV *Endeavour*.

28. British Columbia – Pete Reynell and myself crossing the Great Divide.

29. Sunset over pack ice during the Beaufort Sea survey.

30. In the Northwest Passage with *Baffin* ahead of us. Rock drill is on the foredeck.

31. CCGS *John A. Macdonald* coming to rescue us.

32. Footprints of a polar bear on freshly fallen snow.

33. Lancaster Sound – *Baffin* and the icebreaker *John A. Macdonald*.

34. A misty evening on the Grand Banks, and our last day at sea.

35. Entry into Halifax, October 16 1970.

CHAPTER 13

SPLENDOUR IN THE HIGH ANDES

They could not say who had made them, only that they had heard from their forebears that everything to be seen appeared suddenly in the course of a single night.

Pedro de Cieza de León,
on the ruins of Tiahuanaco.

A COLD FOGGY DAWN found us creeping into Valparaiso Bay where we anchored in a silent white circle of sea to await customs clearance. At 9 a.m. we raised anchor, edged in past a floating dock and tied up amongst crowds of fishing boats at one of the many jetties that push their long fingers into the bay. The lifting fog revealed an attractive city of steep hills, each capped by a huddle of buildings served by its own funicular railway or *ascensor.* It also revealed our welcoming committee, which had expanded by rumour to include Joe Greene and half the Government of Canada, the entire staff of the Canadian Broadcasting Corporation and the President of Chile. In fact the bedraggled knot of people on the jetty consisted of two junior Chilean naval officers; a bullet-headed politician called Bud Orange who was M.P. for the Northwest Territories; Russ Melanson, still sporting his beard from the Atlantic; and a darkly beautiful pregnant lady whom Nelson joyfully identified as his wife.

As soon as the ship was cleared I went ashore with Iver Duedall and Pancho Rey. The dock gates were flanked by rows of souvenir stalls selling wood carvings from Easter Island, and opened on to a large busy square with the normal monument in the centre. On one side lay the railway station and post office; on the second the grand stone façade of the *Intendencia* or municipal building; on the third the yellow peeling front of the decaying Hotel Reina Victoria; and on the fourth the entire female staff of 'Maria

Teresa's'. I blinked. Could this be real, or had "Hudson-70" finally driven me insane? It was all too real. An attractive brunette detached herself from the throng, hailed us with joyous words and asked us the way to the ship. Close behind her was Hugh Henderson's special girlfriend, and on her heels the Captain's favourite girl.

"We have closed down for the week," she said. "We came up here because you are our special friends! Come!"

Well, the *Hudson* had certainly been successful in cementing international relations, I thought. Joe Greene should be proud of us. However, instead of coming I went, for I had a serious purpose in mind for these few days in Valparaiso. I yearned to see the Inca city of Machu Picchu in the Peruvian Andes, and the far more ancient city of Tiahuanaco on the shores of Lake Titicaca. Valparaiso was the nearest that I would ever get to these fabled places and I was determined to take this opportunity. With Pancho to help me I dived into a travel agency.

It was not as easy as I thought to become an international tourist in South America. The lady in the agency told me that I could not book a flight without having a Chilean visitor's card, for which I would have to go to police headquarters. She directed me onto a bus called the 'Wild Baron' which for five cents took me across the city to a dusty and decrepit building. Inside a solitary policeman was dealing with a drunk, and told me that the immigration section would not open until 3:30 as it was now siesta time. After much pleading and grovelling he finally consented to make me out the vital card. I rushed back across the city and met the patient agent who had meanwhile obtained for me a Bolivian tourist card and had booked me a flight for the same day. However, she now told me to go to the Peruvian consulate for a Peruvian tourist card. By the time I had obtained this it was too late to get to Santiago in time to catch the plane. I staggered wearily to the travel agency for the third time and asked her to book the next flight, which turned out to be two days away.

It was now late afternoon and time for the *Hudson's* press conference. A planeload of Canadian reporters had been flown down at Government expense in a military aircraft via a pleasant beach stopover in Jamaica, all to interview the gallant scientists of the *Hudson*. However, if we thought that we would actually be allowed to say anything, we were soon disillusioned. We stood around in the dining saloon dressed up in our suits, while Dr. William Cameron, who had flown down with the reporters, held forth. Bill Cameron, a senior government oceanographer, had helped to organise "Hudson-70" but as yet had not been on any part of it. We were astonished, therefore, when he undertook to answer all of the questions put by the gang of flowery-tied Pancho Villa-mustachioed reporters.

"What was the weather like off Cape Horn?" asked one.

"I'm going to answer that climatologically," said Cameron briskly, as Pickard was opening his mouth to reply. "The Drake Passage has the worst weather of anywhere in the world!"

Cameron now became more expansive.

"These men around you have their pulse on the aorta of the world's oceans!"

Bud Orange took notes happily.

"You can always recognise an oceanographer by the salt on his shoes and the distant look in his eyes!"

And so it went on for an hour and a half, during which we oceanographers shuffled our salty shoes in embarrassment while the room got hotter and hotter. At last came the blessed relief of a reception in the lounge.

The guests were the normal collection of Chilean dignitaries and Canadian embassy staff, and the food included crayfish from Juan Fernández which the Chief Steward had been hoarding. Most of the scientists for the next leg turned up. They included old familiar faces – Pete Wangersky, John Sharpe, George Gill and Art Coote. Then there were Dick Haworth and Mike Hughes from the Marine Geophysics Group at BIO, on board to run the gravimeter on the long Pacific section; Bruno Greifeneder, to help run the bottle casts; and the noble figure of Bill von Arx, who had finally joined us. I chatted to them all before turning my attention to the most beautiful girl present, whose name was as lovely as her silk polka-dot minidress, Maria Cecilia Villablanca Silva. She was a law student, and I discovered to my delight that next year she was to come to the University of Essex for a graduate course.

The party was going famously when Cameron stomped into the middle of the room and announced in a scarcely diplomatic way,

"My men are tired!"

This man wasn't but the guests took the heavy hint and left. Fortunately Pancho came to our rescue, and invited some of us round to his house for a party. The incomparable Maria Cecilia disappeared before I could invite her too. We grabbed a taxi which took us round the Bay of Valparaiso and up a hill behind Viña del Mar, a seaside resort just north of the city. From

Pancho's eyrie the twinkling lights of the city lay like the Milky Way before us. Inside we met his father, then a large contingent of girls arrived, the fruit of an expedition by Pancho's brother. A lively party soon developed with plenty of dancing, and lasted until the small hours.

The next morning I visited the travel agency again and then explored the city, which had a pleasant Mediterranean feel with squares full of palm trees, winding narrow thoroughfares and steep hills lined with baroque apartment buildings. The election campaign was rising to a crescendo, and posters disfigured most vertical surfaces. I passed the Allende party headquarters, adorned with a large hammer and sickle and the slogan 'For a popular government let us build socialism'. After lunch I was confined to the ship for an open house, but had the pleasure of being visited by large numbers of ladies. First came the incomparable Maria Cecilia, whom I showed round the ship and then entertained to drinks until she had to leave for a lecture. Then no fewer than five girls from the previous night's party arrived, sending word that they were held up at the dock gates and required an escort. I happily provided this, and much to the envy of the officers and scientists spent a delightful afternoon squiring them around the ship and entertaining them to a party in my cabin.

Unfortunately I had already promised the evening to Riccardo and his wife, who had invited me round to their house, so instead of continuing in this pleasant feminine company I had to leave them to the dubious care of some colleagues. I set out with Riccardo and Pete Reynell in Riccardo's large American car. Riccardo was high up in the Chilean oceanographic hierarchy, and had just returned from a year with the US Naval Oceanographic Office in Suitland, Maryland. The car was one fruit of this trip. Riccardo's house was also high up in the hills behind Viña del Mar, and once again we were overwhelmed by Chilean hospitality, with food, liquor and lovely girls who magically appeared. The evening was spent singing songs to Riccardo's accordion, Pete's squeezebox and my guitar. Once again it was the early hours when the party broke up. Riccardo drove us back through the still-active streets, and found a taxi driver near the dock with whom he negotiated at length. He told me that the driver had agreed to pick me up at 5 a.m. and take me to Santiago airport to catch my flight to La Paz.

After two hours of fitful sleep I emerged to find the driver waiting, and we set off in his large American cab. There was still a surprising amount of traffic in Valparaiso, but when we reached the main highway, a two-lane road that wound up into the hills behind the city, the traffic diminished to a steady succession of heavy lorries rumbling through the night. After an hour or so, in the grey light of dawn, we began to descend a steep escarpment by a terrifying road full of hairpin bends. There spread out in front of me lay the great Central Valley of Chile, the only large stretch of flat fertile land in the country. It contains most of Chile's agriculture and population, and Santiago sits in its centre. The road became a straight line pointing eastward towards the distant Andes. Soon an increasing concentration of billboards and factories showed that the city was near. After passing the industrial suburb of Maipu the road turned off towards the International Airport. I checked in with Lufthansa, and after a terrible breakfast of ham sandwiches and instant coffee I boarded a 707 along with only a dozen other passengers.

My journey to La Paz and then across Lake Titicaca to Cuzco and Machu Picchu was a seminal experience for me, since I had spent my childhood utterly fascinated by South American archaeology and the mysteries of the Incas. It was a rare privilege to follow this route in those days, but today it is on a standard tourist route so I shall be brief in describing the trip.

The flight landed at La Paz airport, which stands on the Bolivian altiplano at 13,358 feet above sea level and is the highest commercial airport in the world. The jet runway had only recently been completed. It was four miles long and sloped at two degrees, both of these being necessary to allow jets to take off in the rarefied air. As we left the plane the efficient Teutonic hostesses sprayed us with oxygen from a cylinder. Even in the airport terminal the strangeness of this new world was striking. Expressionless Indian peasant women drifted through the crowds, swathed in layer upon layer of full-skirted long-sleeved dresses topped by aprons and multi-coloured shawls. Some carried babies hitched up in the shawls, others heavy loads. Their lank black hair was tightly drawn back in braids and covered by a black bowler hat, tipped at a jaunty angle, a copy of the hats worn by early Spanish colonial ladies. Seventy percent of Bolivia's population is Indian, made up of two distinct peoples, the Quechua and Aymara, with different languages. The Aymara are the more ancient, and are responsible for the vanished civilisation of Tiahuanaco, while the Quechua were planted here by the Incas to strengthen their hold on the country. Both peoples have been oppressed since the Spanish Conquest, first by the Spanish and then by the native-born Spanish *criollos*; they are grindingly poor and have little say in the running of the country, maintaining a quiet sullen dignity through which they seem to mourn for lost glories.

I shared a taxi into the city, gasping at the breathtaking spectacle of the city spread out beneath us in a huge bowl, two thousand feet deep and several miles across, scooped out of the altiplano by the River Choquepyapu, a tributary of the Amazon. The city filled the bowl; in the centre lay the hub, with a handful of tall modern buildings; then up the sides stretched a vast expanse of rambling adobe huts, with the sun glinting off their tin roofs. We descended the walls of the bowl by a winding switchback road, passing through a labyrinth of poverty stricken shacks. The adobe bricks of each lean-to were not even mortared together; in heavy rains whole districts were washed down the slopes. Where tin was unavailable as a roofing material, straw took its place. Through this maze hordes of multi-coloured peasants and children picked their way, while llamas, chickens and dogs scratched in the hot dust. There were no roads except our own, only dusty paths traversed by men and beasts. In little plazas, marking the confluence of the paths, women sat patiently in the sun with a few wares spread out for sale, sometimes fruit and vegetables, sometimes packaged groceries and ballpoint pens. An oppressive silence hung over the scene.

We finally plunged into the city centre, a shabby agglomeration of narrow streets thronged with jostling humanity, decrepit tenement buildings, and ill-stocked shops capped with vast neon signs. I found a room for $1.25 in the 'Gran Hotel Torino', created from a once gracious but now decrepit Spanish colonial residence. It presented a blank, peeling façade to the street, but inside lay a cool cloister with colonnades above. The lintels of the stone cloister arches were carved with baronial crests and the date 1804. My room was spartan but clean, with light fixtures that hung in ribbons of uninsulated wiring. I even managed to locate a toilet, and after extensive searching by two of the hotel staff some toilet paper was procured as well.

After overcoming a headache caused by the thin air, I visited the Tiahuanaco Museum. This was a fine building in mock-Aymara style, adorned with copies of reliefs from the city. Inside the display showed real pride in the country's Indian heritage. The eastern half of Bolivia is tropical jungle, which is now being cleared and settled. Down the centre run the Andes, leaving only the relatively small area of altiplano in the west as the traditional centre of population and civilisation. The jungle Indians were represented by the shrunken heads of the Jivaro tribe. They are the size of tennis balls, but with perfectly preserved facial features. The process involves removing the eyes and pouring molten sand through the eye sockets and mouth. This gouges out the interior of the head, allowing the remainder to be shrunk. The eyes are reinserted and the hair trimmed. I passed from these grisly exhibits to the more fascinating and mysterious history of the Highland Indians who rose to such immense heights of civilisation. The Aymara have lived around Lake Titicaca for thousands of years, and their earliest relics have much in common with the Patagonians – feather headdresses, cloaks of llama hide, tooth necklaces and Pan pipes. Their ancient burials, preserved by the dry soil, show bodies which were placed in the foetal position and tightly bound up in a basket arrangement of ropes and reeds. Many of their skulls show evidence of trepanning, an operation carried out either for religious reasons or as a supposed cure for brain diseases. A small metal axe or pick was used to excavate a hole the size of a shilling in the back of the skull. This was surrounded by a groove, incised to hold a metal plate which covered the hole. If the patient survived, new bone grew round the hole and smoothed its contours. If not, the victims' skulls showed jagged holes with cracks radiating from them. Many skulls were deformed, usually into an egg-like shape with a flattened forehead. This was done in early childhood by binding tight bandages round the head and tying a board against the forehead.

The exhibits from Tiahuanaco itself included bead necklaces, bronze tools and jewellery, bronze statues, and pottery ranging from rough brown utilitarian ware to beautiful black and ochre decorated pottery of the 'classical' period (A.D. 300-1,000) adorned with swastikas, condors, snakes and pumas. The city of Tiahuanaco was built about 600 B.C. by an Aymara culture which controlled all of the altiplano and much of Peru down to the coastal Nazca valley. Nobody knows how this culture developed the advanced building techniques which sprang fully-grown into existence at Tiahuanaco. By 1,000 A.D. the civilisation was declining and in the 15th Century the Incas conquered it. By the time the Spaniards had conquered the Incas in their turn, the city was abandoned and nobody could tell the wondering chroniclers who built it, or why. I talked to the Director of the National Archaeological Research Institute, an enthusiastic and devoted man who said that at present he was trying to restore one of the temples at Tiahuanaco, but was held up by total lack of funds.

As I left the museum, I ran into a *manifestación* or demonstration. It was unusual in that it consisted of schoolgirls and was led by their teachers. A mass of earnest young girls in white pinafores surged into the road and, after much shouting by the teachers, a partial sit-in was achieved, blocking the carriageway. A large blackboard carrying their list of demands was placed in the midst of them; they wanted more money for schools, more classroom space, better facilities and better play areas. The girls, whose ages ranged from 8 to 14, now began chanting slogans in a cheerful and well-organised way. They all carried blankets to sit on, and a large crowd gathered to cheer them on. At first a huge queue of honking cars piled up, but when the drivers saw the determination of the schoolgirls most of them backed up and headed away by a detour set up by the traffic police. Those that remained were rocked to and fro by the demonstrators until they changed their minds. The police made no attempt to interfere.

Wandering through the Indian markets I came to a record shop with the grandiose name of 'Compañía Panamericana de Discos', from which music was blaring forth. A record of charango music by Jaime Torres caught my eye; it was something that I had heard in Dottie's flat in Buenos Aires so long ago (all of ten weeks). I went in and bought it from the beautiful dark-eyed assistant, who threw in an Indian bamboo flute. She was very friendly and I asked her where it was possible to hear folk music in La Paz. She replied that in the evening there are informal guitar sessions in the studios of the local radio station, where you can go to play or listen. She agreed to go there with me at eight, and I emerged walking on rarefied air.

Altitude sickness, the dreaded *sorojche*, dictated another lie down in the hotel, made less comfortable by the fact that the room became extremely cold as soon as the sun went down. Gamely I set out again at 8, to find that the city in the evening was almost deserted, quite unlike Valparaiso. The record shop was still open, and my new friend Lydia was demonstrating discs to a couple of Indian boys who clearly had no money to buy. Leaving her brother to close the shop she set off with me to the radio station, in an unmarked building near Plaza Murillo. The station consisted of a few rooms filled with banks of antiquated transmitting equipment manned by one man, who said that there would be no folk music session tonight. I suggested a good restaurant instead. She led me to a subterranean imitation Bavarian place with mock mediaeval furniture, coats of arms and waitresses dressed as serving wenches. This was not quite the ambience that I had in mind but the food was good, a hotly spiced chicken dish which Lydia said was genuinely Bolivian. We lingered over wine. I tried to learn something about Lydia and her life in La Paz but she was quite shy. She was born and raised locally, and had spent two years in secretarial school during which she had learned English. She looked almost pure Spanish so I presumed that she came from middle-class parents. Next year, she said, she hoped to visit friends in the U.S.A. to learn better English. After the meal I took her out by taxi to her parents' house, halfway up the bowl in a neighbourhood that seemed poor but not as poor as the adobe huts nearer the top. I chastely kissed her good night, and had to hammer on the door of the hotel for admission, with a raging headache.

Next morning I was heading down a steep winding street when an army jeep roared up. Three armed soldiers piled out and began walking deliberately down the street behind me. There was nobody in the street except them and me, and they kept perfect pace in my wake. Horrible visions of arrest and disappearance rose before me. Searching for sanctuary I spied the yellow stone facade of the English Catholic College. I mounted the porch and rang the bell. A tiny window opened and behind the barred grill the shining face of a 12-year-old girl appeared. This was soon replaced by the chubby features of an elderly Scottish nun. I told her of my military followers.

"Oh yes, they often arrest foreigners," she said serenely, "It gives them a chance to rob you."

We waited until the soldiers had swaggered safely past, then I took my leave with her parting blessing ringing in my ears.

Plaza de San Francisco is the biggest square in the city. It was a large open space thronged with ancient buses and cattle trucks arriving from the altiplano. On one side stands the imposing brown façade of the church and convent of San Francisco, built in 1634 and one of the oldest buildings in La Paz. The church has a stumpy bell-tower capped by a square-based dome. I went through the elaborately carved Moorish entrance into the dark interior. It was lined by no fewer than twelve altars. The first, facing the entrance, was a huge gold baroque triptych of saints and martyrs encrusted with gilded whorls and scrolls. An ancient ragged peasant, with a long thin wrinkled brown face, shuffled in and kneeled at the altar rail to pray. When he had finished he dropped a coin in the offertory box which sat under a wax figurine of the Virgin Mary decked out in satin and lace. The label on the box read 'For my new altar'. I looked around. The walls were lined with other altars, all protected by tall iron railings. Some were of gold, others of native silver; all were decorated with baroque excess and featured elaborately dressed statues of the Virgin, Child and various saints. Halfway along one wall was a space where workmen were busy excavating an alcove for yet another altar – hence the collecting box. I was filled with sudden anger. Here was a church in one of the poorest countries in the world, overstuffed with gaudy riches acquired by sharing in the loot of the Conquistadors – the silver, for instance, would have been mined from the silver mountain of Potosi by Indian slaves. And it was actually engaged in building a new altar with the pittance of the poor! For shame! The church was filling with Indian men and women, who were engaged in devout and impassioned prayer at the altars. They wrung their hands, they raised them to the Virgin, they crossed themselves continually and prayed aloud in rapid voices. It was impossible not to be moved. The Church here, I realised, plays the same role as the Church in mediaeval Europe; it offers the peasant the hope that, however vile and hopeless his lot on earth, there is a better life beyond the grave where there will be no more landowner and serf. Soon a group of very fat priests came in from the convent next door and began to say Mass. I watched for a while from near a wooden pulpit, richly carved by an Indian artist with animals and plants in vigorous primitive style, then moved on.

It was time to seek Tiahuanaco. I rushed to the record shop to say goodbye to Lydia, then started out in an old American car with an English-speaking guide. We weaved our way laboriously up through the adobe barrios and out of the city bowl, two thousand feet upwards onto the altiplano. We paused on the lip of the bowl for a last look at the enormous vista of this shining city of poverty. Perched beside us was a tiny shack, ten feet by six, boasting a fine wooden door, a small hole for a window, and a corrugated iron roof held on by bits of wood. An adobe brick rampart, covered by grass to prevent rain erosion, was all that stopped the hut from sliding down into the ravine. Yet, despite his squalor, the *campesino* had a view unrivalled by that of the greatest mansion. We soon came to a small town which the guide said was a satellite town for La Paz, a way station where peasants from the altiplano change from long distance buses (whose roofs were piled high with produce) to cattle trucks for the descent into the city. Passing the airport we struck out across country, but soon came to a tiny village with an enormous colonial church. This is Laja, said the guide, the original site of La Paz. The city was founded here in 1548 by the Spanish, purely as a stopping place on the road from Lima to Potosi. The bitter exposed position of the site caused them to move quickly down into the deep ravine of the Choquepyapu. All that was left was this mission church, an imposing stone building with two widely spaced colonnaded bell towers flanking the entrance.

Now we were out on the lonely treeless altiplano itself, 14,000 feet above sea level. It is not absolutely flat, but gently undulates. But it is bleak and barren beyond belief. It seems at first an endless expanse of untended grassland, but then we would come upon small groups of farmers laboriously digging in the earth miles from anywhere, with no fence, hedge or dwelling in sight. There was no machinery; in some places ox-drawn ploughs were in use, while in others to my amazement the earth was being turned over by the ancient Inca foot plough, a sort of giant wooden shovel wielded by two men while a third turns over the earth dug out at each stroke. The ox plough is for grain, said the guide, while the foot plough is for potatoes and other tubers, of which 300 varieties were domesticated in ancient America (including the original of our common potato). We passed small flocks of sheep, llamas and cattle, and isolated villages each of a few thatched huts. On the horizon loomed two great mountains, Illimani which we were leaving behind us, and Huayna Potosi, which shone ahead of us in snow-clad ridges rising to 22,000 feet. The altitude causes severe problems for the peasants, said the guide. Water boils at 80°C, so cooking takes longer; in the absence of firewood they must burn dung for fuel. But there are few accidental fires, because of the lack of oxygen, and few germs to cause pulmonary diseases, although the highlanders are very susceptible if they move down to sea level.

At last, after sixty miles, came Tiahuanaco. From the top of a low ridge I could see in the distance the shimmering silver of Lake Titicaca, the world's highest lake and the cradle of South American civilisation. Below us lay a huddle of buildings hemmed in by adobe walls, with a railway line running prosaically alongside. This was Tiahuanaco village. And there, out on the bare deserted altiplano a mile from the village lay the ruins of the most mysterious ancient city in the world.

There were no other tourists present, just a small group of Indians digging a trench in a desultory way in the middle of vast ruins. I immediately recognised the famous Gateway of the Sun, a massive monolithic stone gateway surrounded by the relief figure of a winged god-head, bearing a staff in each hand. Rows of smaller winged gods surround the central figure, each god being slightly different from his neighbour. The gateway is carved out of a single block of basalt 15 feet high, of a type that is found only at the northern end of Lake Titicaca from which it must have been brought by raft. Today the gateway stands isolated, protected by iron railings. But on its back side near the top there are four niches by which stone blocks once connected the Gate to a temple. These recesses were lined with gold, which was stripped out by the Spaniards with the aid of gunpowder, sending a massive crack through the Gateway. A similar structure, but devoid of reliefs, stands nearby and is known as the Gateway of the Moon. Three stylised monolithic figures sit nearby, each about ten feet high, carved out of basalt and representing seated gods whose hooded eyes stare out mysteriously across the bare plain. Incised on their bodies are the ancient religious symbols of snake, puma, staircase, swastika and curling tongue.

The two most impressive parts of the ruins are a massive megalithic wall and a restored semi-subterranean temple. The temple is the size of a large swimming pool and is entered by descending a flight of stone steps. The floor lies about eight feet below ground level, and the walls are made out of dressed stone blocks in which stone heads are embedded in the lower courses at regular intervals. Around the base of the walls runs a raised stone pavement. In the centre of the courtyard stand three more monolithic stone figures, one with a carved snake running up its side. The nature of the worship or ritual carried out here is unknown, and it may not have been a temple at all but a games court of the same kind as the Mayan ball courts excavated in Yucatán.

The megalithic wall is immense, about 200 yards long and ten feet high, constructed of Stonehenge-style basalt uprights with the gaps between filled in by carefully dressed sandstone blocks, and the whole wall finished off neatly with a straight top. This may have been the wall of the city or of a fortress within it, for at one end stands a triumphal entrance comprising a wide stone staircase, with very worn steps, leading to a recently restored portico flanked by stone uprights. This is known as the Puerta de Kallasasaya; although the flight of steps is 25 feet wide, pairs of steps, each taking up the full width of the entrance, are carved out of single blocks of stone.

Just as mysterious was another row of separated megalithic columns with small rooms behind them, of which the lower courses remain. It looks like a row of shops, with the massive columns marking off each shop front. The excavated chambers of the 'shops' are most strange, for their walls are superbly finished in smooth square blocks, which have little square recesses and indentations like an unfinished Lego building. Other recesses are more like carefully carved channels with right-angle bends; perhaps they were water conduits. One of the megalithic uprights had a groove carved down the side, and in the part normally below ground level I spotted carved designs resembling a Christian cross resting on an ellipse. These may have been carved by the Spanish, but they could also have been masons' or architects' signatures, reminiscent of the Mycenaean dagger symbol found on one of the columns of Stonehenge.

I skirted a llama, who stood reflectively chewing the cud, and walked over to where the trench-digging was going on. Half a dozen Indians were at work, on behalf of the Archaeological Institute at La Paz, and the earth that they were removing was being loaded into the back of a truck for careful sifting elsewhere. They immediately abandoned work and rushed up to me, pulling out sacks full of pottery that they had dug up. I was appalled at this willingness to despoil an archaeological site. I was also appalled at myself when I found myself buying a decorated pot, an earthenware puma and a small bronze figure of the winged god, all heavily encased in red soil and so presumably genuine.

We drove on to Guaqui where the car dumped me to catch the ferry across Lake Titicaca. Guaqui was a miserable village, possessing little except a single jetty where the railway line from La Paz ended, and one big warehouse. Waiting at the jetty was a splendidly ancient vessel called the *Ollanta*, one of a pair of antiques built in Scotland which maintained the service. They were built on Clydeside in 1912, sailed to Peru and taken apart there, brought up to Lake Titicaca by rail in pieces, and re-erected on the lake, an extraordinary feat. *Ollanta* was a fine looking ship, with straight stem, tall funnel, teak-panelled wheelhouse and awnings spread out on deck. She was also flying the Blue Peter, but when I tried to board her I was prevented on the grounds that nobody could get on board until the train from La Paz arrived. Indian stevedores were loading huge sacks of zinc concentrate on board out of the warehouse, working to a steady rhythm, carrying one sack at a time up a plank gangway and dumping it in the forehold. The warehouse looked completely full of sacks and I wondered when we would be able to sail. All the stevedores were chewing coca, the leaves of which anaesthetise the stomach muscles dulling the pangs of hunger and giving endurance for the backbreaking toil. Their only form of relaxation was to go down to the shore, squat down and excrete, which they seemed to do very often. The shore was lined with *totora* reeds, and moored in a bank of these I saw a reed boat. These famous boats, made in the ancient Egyptian fashion out of bundles of reeds tied together to make a cigar-shaped platform, are used by Aymara fishermen.

After an hour's wait the train pulled in, its single passenger carriage disgorging a small knot of obvious tourists. I joined the group and was finally allowed on board. My new colleagues included a couple of American Peace Corps workers, on holiday from town planning duties in Santiago; the inevitable wandering Australian girl; a student from Vancouver Island; a pair of English nurses; and a couple of French geophysicists, one of them Deputy Director of the Ecole Normale Supérieure, who had been measuring the propagation of infrasonic waves on the altiplano. In this interesting company I had a fine formal dinner in the ship's 'smoking room', a superb Edwardian chamber panelled in mahogany with brass fittings and frosted glass windows. Meanwhile the stevedores kept on at their toil under flood-lights, and did not finish until 11 p.m. when we finally sailed.

We were shown to our cabins, mine being a stark box of white painted wood which I shared with the two Americans and the Canadian. I fell asleep under the reassuring thumping sound of the old triple-expansion engine as the elderly vessel (since replaced by a hydrofoil) began the 125 mile voyage to the Peruvian end of the lake. I rose early to find us pounding along in bright sunshine beside a bare shoreline of orange rocks, lapped by the dark blue water of the lake. Fishermen were at work, most of them in modern rowing boats, although we soon came upon a fringe of reed bed where a group of Indians were at work making a reed boat. Several of them were holding a large bundle together while the master shipwright was binding them. Behind lay a group of wigwams made of woven reed, the homes of the lake fishermen, while a few cattle slept in clearings among the reeds. Soon the small port of Puno came into sight. As we came alongside the jetty in a proper nautical manner it was difficult to believe that we were two and a half miles above sea level.

We disembarked and spent an hour passing through a chaotic customs examination at a pair of rickety benches on the jetty, where our bags were minutely searched. Then we were allowed to board the train that was waiting, where we sat for some hours alongside a little natural harbour scooped out of the reeds. Here several reed boats lay alongside small cultivated patches of barley and maize. The boats were perfectly formed with raised bow and stern, and some had straddling masts made of two spars joined at the top. Reed boats survive in only a few, strangely scattered places – Egypt, Chad, Sardinia and Peru – and Thor Heyerdahl used Aymara Indians to build the second and more successful of his transatlantic reed boats, *Ra II,* to prove that the ancient Egyptians could have reached South America.

We finally jerked into motion, for a lengthy and spectacular journey to Cuzco. The line was magnificent, built in 1895 by the inevitable Scottish engineers, and rising to the greatest elevation of any railway line on earth. It follows the valley of the Vilcanota River through the midst of the Andes, plunging through tunnels, steep gorges and wild mountain defiles, then emerging into fertile enclosed valleys with intense cultivation. In places old Inca terraces, now overgrown, could still be seen on the sides of the mountains. At every stop a crowd of Indian women would besiege the train, dressed in the same colourful dresses and shawls but with brown bowler hats, and would try to sell alpaca ponchos and sweaters to the passengers.

Beggars would swarm on board as well, running down the corridor crying for money before being chased off by the guard. Some were terribly sad creatures, with deformed or missing limbs. One was a dwarf with foreshortened arms and legs, who scurried along the train on all fours like a dachshund. The poverty and misery exceeded even that of Bolivia, and my feeling of helpless pity was mixed with overwhelming guilt for being so privileged myself. The greatest elevation of the journey was reached at La Raya, at 14,172 feet. Then we began to descend towards Cuzco, passing Peru's only vicuña farm which was attempting to domesticate this wild species of llama, hunted almost to extinction for its exceptionally fine wool. Near Cuzco the power failed, and we sat in eerie silence and darkness for an hour before continuing. Eventually, late in the evening, we reached Cuzco.

We checked in at a hotel by the station for a dollar a night each, then set off to explore the centre of the greatest and best organised civilisation on the American continent. From here the Incas ruled half of South America. It was here that Francisco Pizarro came in 1532, kidnapped the Emperor Atahuallpa, ransomed him for a roomful of gold then treacherously murdered him. Then the bestial Spanish took apart this empire, murdering and plundering, destroying its art, enslaving its citizens or decimating them by disease, sword or the fires of the Inquisition. Today the highlands of Peru are more thinly populated and infinitely poorer than five hundred years ago. By night the city wore a mysterious air, seeming to steal back into its past. From ground to head height Cuzco is still Inca; the chief houses, churches and palaces have lower courses of Inca masonry, which survived Pizarro's destruction and became the foundations for the new Spanish city. Many of the streets are also Inca, running uphill in long gentle cobbled steps, suitable for llamas and people but not wheeled vehicles. The snake symbol is carved in relief on some of the stones in the walls, and over stone lintels which still remain as the entrances to Spanish houses. From the dark narrow streets I emerged into the wide Plaza de Armas which is flanked by the baroque façades of the Cathedral and the Church of the Company of Jesus, built on the site of Inca Huayna Capac's palace. The square was almost deserted; under the Spanish Cuzco became a mere provincial town, and it still seems to be sleeping the sleep of ages.

Next morning I rose before dawn to catch the train for Machu Picchu from the small Santa Ana Station on the far side of town. The city was even more mysterious in the half-light and morning mist. Indians were about, burdened as always with heavy loads or else leading llamas. I passed the

Church of Santo Domingo, formerly the Temple of the Sun where a gigantic gold sun disc was kept, amid gardens filled with gold and silver imitations of plants and animals. Now it is a gloomy monastery, but at one end a tall semi-circular bastion, made of perfectly fitting diorite blocks, remains to show how imposing the temple once was. Ironically, an earthquake in 1950 severely damaged the monastery but left its Inca foundations untouched. Between this monastery and the Jesuit Church runs a very narrow street, with high walls entirely made of Inca masonry. Here the Emperor could cross from his palace to the temple where the Chosen Women, priestesses of the Sun, were quartered.

The station was in a square where a busy Indian market was in full swing. Sweet potatoes, peppers, gourds and peas were the staples on sale, although one vendor was selling local medicines, including shrivelled llama foetuses and shredded items in paper bags. At the station I joined forces with the French geophysicists for the 70 mile journey to Machu Picchu by diesel railcar.

The scenery was awe-inspiring. First we passed through rolling hills of increasing steepness. Here we crossed and recrossed portions of the Royal Highway of the Sun, the great Inca paved road that ran north-south through the kingdom, with rest stations at intervals for travellers and for the *chasquis*, the runners who maintained official communications between cities. We would emerge around a hill and find an embankment carrying a paved road running alongside us. The portion of road would be so perfect, and seemed so normal with Indians leading llamas along it, that we would assume that it was modern. Then after a few hundred yards it would end in a yawning gap over a chasm, where a rope suspension bridge would have stood in Inca times. A modest modern track would run down from the Inca road into the gap and up the other side.

Soon the hills gave way to steep mountains and tropical jungle vegetation. We were following the bottom of the Vilcanota gorge, which led into the equally precipitous Urubamba gorge. The mountain peaks were out of sight above our heads, while exotic flowers and giant cacti flourished along the banks of the rushing rocky river. Abandoned Inca terraces clung to the steep walls of the gorge, and once we passed the ruins of an Inca stone bridge. From a stop at a small village we could gaze up the mountainside at the massive walls of the Inca fortress of Ollantaytambo, guarding the valley approach to Cuzco. As we neared our goal, the gorge became narrower and its walls steeper, almost vertical faces 2,000 feet high. There was just room along the floor for our single track line and the Urubamba itself, which plunged through a series of rapids over huge boulders, throwing brown spray high in the air. Eventually we reached a station from which a switchback road led up into the clouds. There was no evidence whatever of the presence of a city. The Spanish never discovered Machu Picchu: they fought their way along the gorge bottom, the route that we had travelled, but saw no sign of the inaccessible mountaintop city. Here, for 50 years after the Conquest, tattered remnants of the Inca hierarchy lived on, until they either died out or moved to some yet undiscovered site.

A minibus took us up the road to the city, and deposited us at the foot of the ruins. Prepared as I was by endless photographs, I was still overwhelmed by the tremendous impact of the city. The whole mountaintop was clothed in great stone buildings, all open to the sky where their thatched roofs have long since disappeared. Instead of roads, a multitude of stone stairways connect the buildings. The life support system for the city lay all around, in the stone terraces that cover the upper slopes of the mountain and where the food for a population of 2,000 was grown. Behind the city, like a backdrop, rose the higher sugarloaf peak of Huayna Picchu, with a winding Inca path leading up to a lookout post on the summit. Two thousand feet of vertical jungle-clad wall descend on every side to the brown ribbon of the Urubamba River which looped round below us like a moat. To the north and east, row upon row of jungle-covered peaks stretched to the horizon, concealing who knows what other cities. What an experience it must have been for Hiram Bingham in 1911 as he slogged up here on behalf of Yale University and 'discovered' this city, following the directions of Indians whom he had befriended and who knew all along of its existence.

The ordinary houses of the city are single-storey structures, well built of stone blocks but without the perfect finish of the palaces and temples. Each house has a raised stone platform for a bed, niches around the walls where household articles were kept, and holes in the top of the walls where wooden beams for the steeply sloping roof would once have rested. In some houses the entrance still retains its lintels of hardwood. There is an industrial district, with remains of foundries, mills and stonemasons' yards. Everything is laid out in rectagular blocks with military precision, and llamas keep the grass between the buildings well cropped.

All the staircases lead up to a large fortress and temple complex at the top of the city. The buildings here include a strange circular temple, made of the finest fitting masonry, which curls around to enclose a cleft in a protruding rock. This is variously described as a ruler's tomb and an observatory, but its real purpose is unknown. Dominating the complex is the finest temple of all, the House of the Three Windows. Perfect megalithic masonry is used to outline three trapezoidal windows. According to Inca history, the founder of the dynasty, Manco Capac, set out from a house with three windows in his native village to embark on the conquest of Peru, so the shape of the build-ing is probably a tribute to him, just as Christian churches have the shape of a cross. On an open plaza near this temple sits the strange stone called Intihuatana, the Hitching Place of the Sun. Similar stones form the core of many Inca temples. It is a lump of granite about six feet high, carved with a small vertical pillar and protruding horizontal arm like a piece of modern sculpture. The archaeologists' explanation it that the stone was the centre of a ceremony at midsummer and midwinter, when the sun's elevation at noon, marked by the shadow of the pillar, stopped increasing or decreasing: the priests carried out a ritual to 'bind' the sun and prevent it magically from continuing on its trend.

From the city itself I followed a path past a cemetery where the mummies of women, children and old men have been found (but no young men); and on past the quarry where the stones for the city were cut. The path then led to Huayna Picchu, which I tried to climb. The Inca pathway still exists, cut from stone with a single block sometimes carved into five or six steps. I got a third of the way up, but then it began to rain heavily. The pathway became a conduit for the runoff and I was literally swept back down to the bottom by the flood.

There was so much to explore in Machu Picchu that I yearned to stay longer, but the train and the distant *Hudson* were waiting, so I could not linger or even hope to stay in the small hotel below the city. As the bus took us down to the station a young Indian boy amazed us by running full tilt straight down the mountainside, appearing smiling in front of the bus at each turn of the switchback, then coming shyly but triumphantly up to us at the end for his well-deserved reward.

Back in Cuzco I explored the Jesuit Church and the Cathedral, both grossly magnificent inside, with intricately carved and gilded altars and pulpits and naive paintings of doll-like Virgins and saints in gaudy clothes, all the work of Indian craftsmen. Having destroyed the Inca culture the Spaniards thought it a fine idea to teach the Quechua to carve and paint in the baroque style, to the glory of Spain's murderous god. I also found the famous stone of 12 angles. This forms part of the wall of Inca Roca's palace, of which the foundations were used to build the Archibishop's Palace. The stone is about five feet square. It is carefully cut to fit exactly the smaller stones around it. Archaeologists have managed to reproduce the perfect fit of square Inca stonework by pounding away at the blocks with small stone hammers, but the technique of achieving such a complex fit with such a large stone has been completely lost. I ended the evening by going with my American friends from the train to visit a Peace Corps colleague who was running a school at Cuzco. My hopes of learning about life in the city from him were dashed, since he was sprawled on the sofa with his girlfriend in a glassy-eyed giggling state while the sweet smell of marijuana hung in the air.

I had to leave early the next morning to fly back to my ship. The first step was a local hop to Lima by an aircraft of Faucett Airlines, the Peruvian internal company. The plane whisked me through cloud, finally swooping low over the guano islands - whitened by the droppings of millions of seabirds which are mined for fertiliser - before landing on the flat desert shorelines of Lima airport.

I had three hours before the Santiago flight, so I took a rapid taxi tour. First we visited the very centre of the city, the Plaza de Armas. This square had been famous, or notorious, since Pizarro founded Lima in 1535 as the capital of Spanish Peru. For the whole colonial period it was the site of the *autos-da-fé* of the Inquisition, where thousands of 'heretics', mostly Indians, were tortured and burned to death in public. The leader of the last Indian revolt in 1780, Tupac Amaru, was torn apart by horses here. The greatest building in the square is the baroque cathedral. Inside is a glass coffin containing the body of Pizarro, who was murdered by a colleague in 1541. It is somewhat inappropriate that one of history's vilest persons should be buried in a cathedral, but here he is, naked, with brown cracked skin from which odd ends of bone protrude. The coffin rests in a black granite monument under a statue of a sleeping lion. Encased in the outer wall of the cathedral is the foundation stone laid by Pizarro shortly before his demise. On the flanking side of the square is the Presidential Palace, with wrought iron gates guarded by Indian soldiers who were sweating away in fancy white uniforms with riding boots, plumed helmets and red epaulettes.

Next I sought the Archaeological Museum, but as this was closed the driver took me to the Rafael Larco Herrera Museum, a vast private collection of Mochica and Chimu relics. The Mochicas were the first civilisation of Peru, beginning several hundred years BC at the same time as the Tiahuanacans. The Mochicas settled the coastal desert, making it bloom with an elaborate irrigation system fed by the rivers that run down at intervals out of the Andes. Their social system, a benevolent despotic welfare state, was a precursor of the Inca system. Each farmer owed work to the state but also owned land of his own and enjoyed welfare benefits at times of famine. The Mochicas originated most of the technological advances later adopted by the Incas, including recording information on knotted cords (*quipus*), building with adobe bricks, and the construction of great pyramids and temple plazas. The glory of the Mochicas was their pottery, of which a vast quantity still remains to be dug up from their shallow desert graves. Their pots are fashioned into the shapes of people and animals in scenes from their daily lives, so that they convey a vigorous impression of an attractive culture. There is a room full of erotica, with vases showing intercourse in a wide variety of positions, and pots with pubic spouts. The same symbols as in Tiahuanaco appear everywhere – staircases, snakes and curled tongues. The Chimu, who carried on the Mochica tradition until their absorption by the Incas in 1,400 AD, had more restrained pottery of black ware. In the museum were some Mochica burials, mummies that were consigned to hot dry sand with pots and household goods, their heads bound with rope and covered with golden masks. There were exquisite textiles, finely woven of wool and cotton with bold patterns, and feather cloaks of blue and yellow check. Jewellery included brooches, pins, rings and necklaces of gold, silver, amethyst, turquoise and pearl. Once again the hand of Spain destroyed all. The Spanish marched up and down the coast destroying the canals as part of an extermination operation against the resisting Indians, so the fertile land reverted to the uninhabited desert of today.

I rushed back to the airport just in time to catch the plane. After a long flight and a bus journey from Santiago to Valparaiso I arrived back at the *Hudson* in the late evening. I hoped that she might be delayed, as on so many previous occasions in Chile. But it was not to be. We were sailing on time. There would be no more chance to see my many Chilean friends, or to pursue the incomparable Maria Cecilia. The endless continent of South America was finally coming to an end.

CHAPTER 14

ACROSS THE SOUTH PACIFIC

... my purpose holds
To sail beyond the sunset, and the baths
Of all the Western stars, until I die.

Alfred Tennyson

W E SLIPPED OUR MOORINGS early in the morning and sailed across Valparaiso Bay to Las Salinas, a stretch of beach running north from Viña del Mar to the resort of Reñaca. Here the golden shoreline is disfigured by an Esso oil depot, where we anchored and hooked on to an underwater pipeline. The long process of taking on 800 tons of fuel oil began, and to our great disappointment the Captain announced that there would be no shore leave. I sat gloomily in the hot afternoon sun, talking to Greg who was stationed on the quarterdeck to smell out leaks in the oil coupling. It was frustrating to see the attractive apartments of Viña del Mar shimmering in the heat haze and to know that the girls of Chile were out of reach. I gazed out across the Bay, which was filled with a mass of diving birds. Looking down into the water I could see silvery flashes from the bodies of thousands of tiny anchovies which swarmed in the bay. Huge flocks of black guanay birds were on patrol, like low-flying bombers. As soon as they sighted a school of anchovies they would retract their wings and plunge vertically into the sea from a height of fifty feet or more, emerging to swallow their victims. They would dive again and again until the school was broken and dispersed. Gawkier but more majestic were the pelicans, huge black birds which fly awkwardly with crooked wings, like pterodactyls. The famous fold of skin under the bill bloats out only when the bird scoops up a mouthful of fish and water, and in normal flight the bill appears long and narrow, but because of its heavy weight the bird has to hold his head back in a curious crooked fashion. This brought to mind so well the way that pelicans are depicted on Mochica pottery.

The pumping took all day and all night, and early in the morning of April 15 we crept back into Valparaiso port to clear Customs and to send off our last letters with the agents. At noon on a cool and misty day we weighed anchor and finally put to sea. I stood for a long time watching the city, the harbour, and finally the last point of land, as they were swallowed in the mist. South America was gone. The four months that we had spent in and around this vast continent had been, for me, the experience of a lifetime. Never before had I seen such extremes of wealth and poverty, such diversity of cultures and such magnificent intensity of living.

Ahead stretched the Pacific, the inexhaustible ocean that occupies half of the globe. We had thirteen thousand miles to sail upon her before we reached Vancouver, with only one pause for breath in Tahiti. An hour out of port the magnetometer was streamed and the console room was fully in action, with the magnetometer, echo sounder, beam gravimeter and Bill von Arx's string gravimeter all operating and with the satellite navigation receiver chattering away. It had been all of three months since the place had been as busy as this, but now the old familiar pattern was back again. Roger in the cabin, Orest and George with their explosions, four-hour watches on the console, XBTs at midnight and long chats with Pete Reynell during the middle watch. South America soon began to recede in my mind, with only Peruvian diarrhoea remaining for a while as a reminder, its rhythm blending with the eternal rhythm of the sea.

On these two long Pacific legs the most important work was concerned with the gravimeter. We were heading for the point 65°S, 150°W, from which we would follow the 150°W meridian up as far as the Gulf of Alaska, the longest meridional transect ever carried out by a survey ship. By accurately recording gravity along this line, using both our beam gravimeter and the revolutionary little vibrating string device brought along by von Arx, we would obtain a reference line from which the shape of the geoid could be deduced. The 'geoid' is the name given to the true shape of the Earth, which differs noticeably from a perfect sphere. It is in fact pill-shaped, with a flattening at each pole equal to about one three-hundredth of its diameter. What is more, the flattening is slightly different at the two poles (1/298.5 at the North, 1/297.3 at the South), and there is a variety of bumps and depressions over the globe, amounting to tens of metres in height. This entirely neglects continents, of course, and is simply the 'bumpiness' of undisturbed sea level.

Wherever bumps occur they have a slight but measurable effect on gravity, which we would record. Our long transect was going to be of special value because of plans to launch an oceanographic satellite equipped with a radar altimeter, which would orbit the earth over the poles and hence sample the whole globe as the earth turns underneath it. Large bumps on the geoid, such as the polar flattening, affect the motion of satellites, but small-scale bumps do not, and therefore they can be detected by the radar altimeter. What is important is to separate the permanent bumps, caused by the structure of the earth, from temporary bumps caused by the heaping-up of ocean water by currents, tides and changes in barometric pressure. Every time that the satellite crossed 150°W, our results would be used to calibrate it so that it could detect seawater heaping and hence measure ocean currents. In fact our results were not needed for several years. After many delays the Seasat satellite was launched in 1978 but failed after three months. However, a European satellite called ERS-1 was launched in 1991 with the same type of instrument on board, and the results of *Hudson's* long survey finally came into their own after more than twenty years.

To strengthen the gravimeter crew we had Mike Hughes and Dick Haworth aboard, old colleagues from the shakedown cruise, as well as the great Bill von Arx himself. The presence of Bill on board was a joyous intellectual experience for everyone. Of the oceanographers that served on "Hudson-70", Bill alone possessed all of the characteristics of nobility. His manner was quiet, shy and the opposite of overbearing, yet in discussions in the lounge and coffee room he was always ready to share with us his vast breadth of knowledge on oceans, atmospheres, astronomy, literature, philosophy and common sense. On deck he showed us how to find Jupiter in the daytime sky by measuring over the zenith using the angle between thumb and forefinger, and he loved to explain unusual atmospheric phenomena such as the green flash, the burst of green sometimes seen as the last of the sun sinks below the horizon. He was a refreshing change from most scientists, who are so busy with their own specialisation as to be quite ignorant of science as a whole, let alone culture in general. Bill was the complete Renaissance man.

The weather grew steadily worse as we sailed westward and southward towards the imaginary point on the globe that was our goal. On the second day out an unusual roll carried away my last remaining bottle of Chilean wine, making the cabin smell as if a wild orgy had been held there. The sea became livelier, and on the 18th the sun disappeared, to be replaced by a low leaden sky hanging over a grey heaving sea laced with rain. By now we were down at 46°S, well into the Roaring Forties, and it was clear that we were in for a long spell of dirty weather. A wind gusting to 60 knots came up from the west, raising a swell that caused the gravimeter's gyrotable to bang several times against its stops, indicating a roll of at least 20 degrees.

By the 21st we had reached 56°S and the air temperature was down to 6°C. The weather had stayed steady, if bad, but now the barometer dropped further to 975 millibars and we began to run into squalls. During the night watch I could see them on the radar screen sweeping in towards us, the falling rain from the squall producing a pattern of splodges on the screen that moved surprisingly quickly. Looking out from the bridge windows I could see each squall as it passed; between the showers the moon lit up the sea in a hard grey light. Our course was taking us steadily down into colder water, first pushing against the Peru Current then meeting the great Antarctic Circumpolar Current from which the Peru Current splits off to the northeast. The sea was chilly and the autumn weather chillier.

I was now sharing the watchkeeping with three other people, so that I did not do a standard watch. I found this confusing and much more tiring than the normal 4-on-8-off system, especially with the persistence of my Peruvian stomach. There was time, however, for the occasional guitar session in the hangar with Ron Shaw, Greg and his new cabinmate Harvey Heaton, a diesel mechanic fresh out from Halifax. We found that our equipment tended to fly round the hangar, and in the end we gave up. The ship was moving in a very peculiar way, giving sudden lurches which would tear telephones from their sockets and fling lounge-dwellers out of their armchairs. The engineers said that the flume tanks were not working.

It was during this long haul to the southwest that the discovery was made which put our name on the charts. Every oceanographic expedition hopes to achieve this, but few succeed these days because the ocean is so well explored. On April 20, in a region of the seabed previously thought to be fairly uniform, we ran into a zone of rough mountainous bottom. At 54° 19'S, 94° 33'W we crossed a great peak which stood 1,500 metres above its fellows, rising to a mere 2,920 metres from the surface. Then, only 60 km later, at 54° 38'S, 95° 12'W, we crossed a very deep trough extending down deeper than 6,103 metres. The temptation was irresistible to call them Hudson Peak and Hudson Deep. And so they appear on the new charts of the Pacific. The discovery was not an immediate one, nor was the observation a perfect success. Dick Haworth was processing the gravity and magnetic data tapes several days after they were recorded, and it was not until May 3 that he noticed the massive positive and negative gravity anomalies which could only be caused by a great peak and deep. When he went to the echo sounder rolls he found that the watchkeeper at the time (fortunately not me) had neglected to change the scale on the echo sounder as the bottom plunged down towards the floor of the Deep. All he could say was that the depth was somewhere between 6,103 metres and 6,575 metres (3,600 fathoms on the chart). And he was somewhat crestfallen when he burst into the lounge with the news.

"I've discovered a new peak and deep!"

"Fantastic, Dick! How long ago did we pass it?"

"Er, thirteen days."

The features are thought to be part of a fracture zone, where one of the Earth's tectonic plates is being ripped sideways by shear.

Meanwhile we reached the iceberg zone. During the afternoon of April 24 a small growler, looking very forlorn and half-melted, drifted past a few yards to port. It was only about six feet long and stood barely three feet out of the water, but the radar showed a larger berg a few miles away from which it must have calved. This warning was enough to bring action from the Captain. Remembering the near-disaster in the South Atlantic he altered course to 269°, almost due west, and decided that we would only go as far as 63°S instead of 65°. This meant that we would lose 120 miles from our meridional transect, which annoyed Bill immensely. That night I kept the middle watch from midnight to 4 a.m., with the weather worsening again and the barometer down to 968 millibars. Part of the watchkeeper's duty was to launch an XBT every two hours, and I was fortunate in that mine corresponded with the crossing of the Antarctic Convergence. We were at 59°S, and the surface water temperature fell from 4°C to zero between two casts. It is likely that the previous day's iceberg was breaking up because it had just crossed the Antarctic Convergence into warmer water.

The next afternoon Russ Melanson, senior scientist for this leg, held a meeting in the lounge to plan the sequence of operations for the stations which would begin as soon as we reached 63°S. The meeting was accompanied by the continual crashing of spray against the front of the lounge, and we could see water forcing its way up through the anchor chain tunnels and erupting from the foredeck like a geyser. The foredeck crane began to ice up as the spray coated its rigging. It was decided that each station would begin with a Niskin bottle cast by Pete Wangersky, back on board to continue his study of organic carbon in the sea, assisted by Ted Yoshinari, a Japanese graduate student from Dalhousie. Then would come the Knudsen cast, to be done by myself and Bruno Greifeneder, an Austrian who had recently joined Bedford Institute. Meanwhile Orest and George would be doing reverberations. Each station would take longer because it was absolutely necessary to wait for a satellite fix before setting off again; this was so that we would not stray from our 150°W line.

As we approached 63°S the icing continued, and the air became so cold that spray breaking over the bows froze before it hit the bridge front, so that it rattled on the windows like grapeshot. Snow came in fits on a freezing wind. We came onto station at 10 p.m. on April 26th, finding that this was to be called station 227; our station list had been swelled by the vast number carried out by Pickard in the Chilean fjords. This was the furthest south that *Hudson* was to reach in the Pacific. The Niskin cast and reverberations took four hours, so it was at the ungodly time of 2 a.m. that I found myself being woken by Bruno and turning out into a foul night.

I emerged dressed in six layers of clothing and stared grimly at the scene from the Chains. The ship was rolling heavily and a black sea, heard rather than seen, rose and fell below me. By a new and sensible order of Roy Gould, I was constrained to struggle into a safety harness which meant that I could not properly reach the hydrographic wire so that I had to work one-handed. Our first task was to lower the Bathysonde but we found that the pressure-measuring circuits in the instrument would not work, probably because it had not been used for weeks. Next came the shallow cast, which included ten extra Niskin bottles for Pete Wangersky as well as thirteen Knudsen bottles. It was bitterly cold, and my fingers froze while loading the first bottle. The wire angle varied alarmingly, with ominous scrapings of the wire against the hull as the ship rolled, but all went well. We had to guess a water depth for the deep cast, because the echo sounder in the winch house was not working so that we could not follow the progress of the pinger. However, this also went off safely and I gratefully descended to thaw out over breakfast.

The next station was 180 miles further north, at 60°S, and again we reached it in the middle of the night. I was woken at 2.30 a.m. by a succession of enormous rolls, which threw every loose object onto the deck. We were on station but seemed to be lying beam-on to the sea. I turned over for a couple of hours' more sleep, but had scarcely rejoined a particularly pleasant erotic dream when I was woken again with the news that Orest and

George had lost their cone. This is the large sheet-metal contraption which hangs on the same cable as the hydrophone and which serves to damp down the vertical motion of the hydrophone as the ship rolls. To do this it depends on the elasticity of the supporting cable, and in the violent rolling the cable had just snapped. Bruno and I went straight ahead with the bottle cast, since the Bathysonde was still out of action. Conditions were awful again, with a fierce wind carrying sleet and hail into the winch house. One of the bottles failed to reverse, but a rapid computer check showed that the others had recorded correctly, so we did not have to repeat the cast. The loss of the cone inspired another outburst of George's amazing ingenuity. From the hold he procured some steel sheets which he welded together himself into a passable imitation of the original cone. Three days later Orest and George were back in business as though nothing had happened.

The first two stations were our final contact with true Antarctic waters. The third station was at 55°S, north of the Antarctic Convergence and in conditions that seemed almost tropical. The sea temperature was all of 3.6°C instead of zero, the sun was shining and the waves were lower. Bottle casts were a pleasure again. The rich smell of life that had pervaded the Antarctic waters of the Atlantic had been missing out here in the Pacific, probably because we were now well into the southern autumn with the plankton bloom long past. However, the water had still been rich in the nutrients which fertilise the ocean 'soil', for as we crossed the Convergence the chemists found the concentrations of phosphate, nitrate and silicate at all depths dropping to a fraction of their Antarctic values.

After the third station I went round to Greg's cabin to borrow a book and found it filled with a sweet-smelling fug. Greg and Harvey were sitting with beatific expressions, puffing away at a cigarette which they solemnly passed back and forth between them. I was enjoined to come in and 'get off'. Being a complete innocent, I had no idea what was involved. Harvey showed me their supplies, consisting of a large plastic bag full of ground-up herb and a block, like a meat loaf, made of a solid brown substance.

"That's grass," he said, pointing at the bag, "and the other's hash." He patiently explained that grass is the leaves and flowering tops of the cannabis plant, while hash is a much more concentrated resinous extract. The block that I saw was a vast amount.

"There's enough here for everyone on the ship to stay stoned from here to Vancouver," he said. "That's what we're going to do, anyway."

"Where did you get it?"

"Mike Crimp got the hash. He got it in exchange for a pair of jeans. He passed it on to us."

Now began the serious ritual of rolling the joint. As an innocent science student in Cambridge, the 1960s' world of drugs had passed me by and I was entirely ignorant of the terminology as well as the technique. However, I was shown how to inhale, and Greg and Harvey waited in holy anticipation for me to 'get off'.

The smoke was sweet and acrid; the effect was pleasant but very mild. I waited in vain for vision and deep spiritual insight. It felt similar to the effect of three pints of beer without the accompanying discomfort in the bladder. Then suddenly I realised that for the last half-hour Harvey had been describing in minute detail a simple event of the recent past, a motor cycle crash at 60 mph from which he had emerged miraculously unscathed. He was re-living the event with total recall and I was re-living it with him, held completely enthralled by the narrative. I realised that both he and I were really 'off' and that this is what it meant, as least as far as my system was concerned. The evening passed in such simple pleasures and I suffered no after-effects except for a difficulty in sleeping for a few hours afterwards.

Harvey and Greg lived up to their promise of remaining stoned through-out the voyage, along with various other members of the crew. If I did not join them, it was not because of moral qualms but simply because I have never smoked and disliked the feeling of inhaling hot fumes into my lungs. The only other drug that I tried on the voyage was *maté,* a mildly narcotic tea used by the gauchos of Argentina and Chile. Mike Crimp brought some round, together with the apparatus for drinking it. It is made from the shred-ded leaves of the *yerba* plant, which are placed in a hollowed gourd. Boiling water is poured over them and the resulting brew sucked up through a long metal tubular filter. It tasted spicy and bitter, like railway tea that has been in the urn too long. I found out afterwards that the first brew is always like this, and that the polite host sucks up the contents of the gourd, spits it out and then pours on fresh boiling water for his guests.

Meanwhile, with stations five degrees apart we were passing rapidly from bitter cold into sub-tropical heat, seeing our climate change radically day by day. On the fourth station, at 50°S, we were still surrounded by giant petrels and three species of albatross (wandering, sooty and black-browed), but the surface water temperature was up to 10°C so that we had to put new thermometers with a wider range on the Knudsen bottles. By the sixth station (40°S) the Antarctic birds had disappeared and warm-water life began to appear in the sea. The bottle cast was done at night, and several squid swam in and out of the bright pool cast by the searchlight on the water, together with some tiny silvery fish that darted around at an immense rate, leaping half out of the water in their agitation. These creatures reappeared at the eighth station and proved to be baby squid, shooting themselves bodily out of the sea to escape the myriad dangers of a watery youth.

Roger took a core at this station, and pulled out a 28 foot sample of sediment. At the top there were two black metallic pebbles which turned out to be manganese nodules. There are vast fields of these nodules on the sea floor, especially in the sub-tropical Pacific. They form around a nucleus which may be a shark's tooth or a dead foraminifera lying on the seabed. Manganese from sea water then precipitates out to form a skin over the nucleus, by some chemical process not yet understood. There have been proposals to mine this valuable source of manganese using a deep-sea dredge or suction tube, and Howard Hughes designed the first ship for this purpose, the *Glomar Explorer*. However, the ship was borrowed by the CIA to recover a sunken Russian submarine using manganese mining as a cover story, and this gave manganese mining a bad name from which it has never recovered. There has also been considerable disagreement about who owns the resources of the seabed, which was only resolved recently by the Law of the Sea Treaty. The fact that two nodules were found in our core suggested that there was a thick covering of manganese nodules over the seabed in this area, and that this would be a fruitful zone for mining.

Next day I wandered into the after laboratory and found Pete Wangersky gazing fiercely down a microscope, his rotund face red with anger.

"Shit again!" he cried. "Damn the human race! Look at that!"

I gazed down the microscope at a mess of randomly shaped fragments which included a couple of long narrow fibres.

"Where's the shit?"

"Those fibres are pine fibres, from toilet paper. All over the globe, people are wiping their arses and flushing the toilet paper down into the sewers. Where does it end up? The ocean!"

"But doesn't it disintegrate?"

"It does as far as the eye is concerned. But all the microscopic pine fibres that make up the paper stay in suspension, and the ocean is full of them, even here a million miles from anywhere! The trouble is, they mess up all my calculations. Here am I, trying to find the mass of particulate organic carbon in the ocean – that's all those fragments you see, dead bodies and so on – while all the time Man is adding to it with his crap!"

Pete warmed to his subject.

"Organic carbon is fascinating stuff. We're also measuring dissolved organic carbon, that's all the chemicals secreted into the water by living animals. Some of them are really complex molecules, with molecular weights of up to 100,000. And it's not just waste products. Some of it has a purpose. You know about 'red tides', those enormous blooms of dinoflagellates which poison the sea and kill fish? Well, the dinoflagellates secrete carbohydrates which provide food for bacteria which produce vitamin B12 which is absorbed by the dinoflagellate to help it grow. It can't produce the vitamin itself, so it fertilises the sea around it so that bacteria can do the job for it! And there's another species of plankton that sinks down into the lower layers during daylight, and secretes a carbohydrate which reduces the viscosity of the water around it so that it sinks faster. Isn't the ocean fascinating!"

His anger forgotten, Pete was beaming with enthusiasm, and returned to his exacting work with fresh energy.

On May 9 we crossed the Tropic of Capricorn in hazy sunshine, while we rolled in a long lazy swell. At noon a small hummock appeared on the horizon to starboard, the first land in 24 days and our first sight of the South Sea Islands. I rushed to the chartroom to see which it was, out of the thousands splattered at random over the chart, and found it to be Tubuai, at 23°S, 149°W. It gives its name to the Tubuai Islands, the southernmost island group of French Polynesia. It quickly sank over the horizon, but not before our imaginations had been thoroughly aroused with dreams of palm trees and hula girls. We counted the days to Tahiti – only three to go! It seemed impossible that ten days earlier we had been shivering in Antarctic waters.

We did the tenth and last station that evening at 20°S. Our old friends the sharks were back, with four of them simultaneously nosing around the hydrographic wire. Squid were also plentiful, and between casts I tried fishing with a squid jigger that I had inherited from Bob Hessler. The technique is to drop it just below water level and to gently dance it up and down so that the squid thinks that it is a fish. I had no success and passed the jigger on to Madhu Paranjape, an engaging Indian biologist from Bedford Institute. He immediately caught a fine squid, nearly a foot long. After the cast we went down to the pantry for a squid orgy, to be conducted by Ted Yoshinari, an expert squid chef. Ted was born in Manchuria and learned squid cookery while doing his degree at Tokyo University. First he squeezed the head off, then thrust his hand into the body cavity to draw out the stomach, liver, intestines and springy transparent backbone, all in a single movement. This left the cylinder of muscles that produce the contractions, the tail fins, and the thin iridescent skin with its thousands of photophores, which peeled off easily. Ted cut the body muscles into rings and fried them quickly in butter, serving them garnished with soy sauce. The taste was of exceptionally fine rubber.

I collected the entrails of the squid for my museum of nautical monstrosities, together with a sample of the brown ink, drawn from the sac at the top of its head. At the end of the station a shark was caught from the stern; Ted claimed the eyeballs and preserved them in methanol. I had a look at them after the protein had hardened. They were the size of gobstoppers. The retina was blue-grey and extremely tough, with a small hole for the blood vessels to enter. Ted withdrew some of the clear aqueous humour from the eyeball using a syringe, and I added this to my increasingly bizarre collection.

The next morning brought us in sight of Tahiti and its sister island Moorea, which appeared as hazy grey humps on the horizon, capped by orographic cloud. We could have reached the island the same afternoon, but we learned to our dismay that Dick Haworth wanted to take our gravity line up to 16° 30'S before turning for Tahiti. We cursed him for his thoroughness, and we cursed the Captain for his pathological desire never to arrive anywhere early. After reaching the required latitude we spent the rest of the day on a core and plankton tow while the islands lay tantalisingly close, each a mountainous mass of jumbled brown rock with the lower slopes blending into the intense deep green of tropical foliage. Palm trees were just visible along the white strip of shoreline. It looked like a paradise built especially for sailors. In the evening, at long last, we commenced steaming dead slow towards Papeete, queen of the South Seas and perhaps the most romantic sounding port in the world.

CHAPTER 15

THE SOUTH SEAS PARADISE

The palm-tree shall grow,
The coral shall spread,
But man shall cease.

Tahitian prophecy

I ROSE BEFORE DAWN to see Tahiti looming up ahead, dark grey and mysterious and swathed in cloud and mist. We were approaching from the northwest, so that Tahiti lay to port and her sister island Moorea to starboard. Moorea was smaller but more impressive, a steep jumble of rocks rising from a dense jungle base to the majestic 4,000-foot peak of Mount Cook (or *Tohivea* in Polynesian). As always in the tropics, dawn came suddenly and soon the whole scene was bathed in brilliant clean sunlight. We passed through the nine mile wide channel between the two islands and approached the coral reef which fringes Tahiti. It was marked by a long line of foam where a lazy swell was breaking over the coral; behind lay a few hundred yards of calm shallow water and then the yellow line of beach, backed by palm trees.

Then Papeete came into sight, capital of Tahiti and of the whole colony of French Polynesia. It first appeared as a long and unimpressive straggle of white buildings fringing the shore, overhung by a blanket of morning mist. When we were about a mile from shore a pilot boat came out and disgorged a very fat Polynesian who guided us into the narrow channel through the reef, marked off by buoys. To starboard I could see the runway of the International Airport, built in 1961 on land reclaimed from the lagoon. Before then the island was served only by ships – mainly schooners – and by a slow but comfortable flying boat service. Now the jet age had turned Tahiti into a trendy extension of the Mediterranean, complete with Club Méditerranée and similar French abominations. To port lay another horror inflicted by the French, a new harbour and naval base completed recently through the efforts of 9,000 Foreign Legionnaires who had been drafted to the island. Their social behaviour had sown a legacy of resentment and hate amongst Polynesians, especially the menfolk, which we were to reap. In harbour were French freighters and a tangle of grey-hulled naval tankers and minesweepers. Beyond these twin monstrosities the town itself grew prettier as we approached it, snuggling behind a long white curving sea wall amid a forest of yacht masts.

We came in to moor at an oil dock outside the town, tying up near a little boatyard containing a picturesque inter-island schooner. A knot of gendarmes was waiting on the jetty and swarmed on board officiously. Also waiting were new arrivals joining from BIO: the micropalaeontologist Charlie Schafer, and two biologists, Anand Prakash and Ken Freeman. They brought the mail, which we greedily devoured. But a long delay ensued before the local bureaucrats would allow us ashore. I spent the time impatiently on deck, scanning the wide sweep of Papeete with glasses: at one end was a new hotel with palm-thatched chalets; then came the waterfront where yachts and powerboats mingled with schooners including the magnificent old inter-island trader *Tiare Taporo* dating from 1913; behind this was the long white colonnade of the Customs House and then a white stucco church with a red steeple.

It was nearly noon when we were finally cleared to land, and I set off immediately with a group of shipmates. We skirted the naval barracks and reached the outskirts of the town. Papeete is only a few streets deep, and most of the activity is concentrated on the busy road and promenade that run the length of the waterfront. Beautiful Polynesian and French girls in flowery cotton *pareos* roared past on mopeds, and the promenade was thronged with plump olive-skinned Polynesian men, diminutive Chinese and tourists of every description. Bars were everywhere, and the first one that we came across was Quinn's. Made famous by writers from Pierre Loti to James Michener, we expected it to be the romantic haunt of gin-soaked beachcombers, copra traders and men who had fled from unspeakable pasts. Instead it was almost empty and quite tame, a simple square building like a thatched bandstand with walls filled in to waist height with woven palm matting, the upper part open to the balmy breeze and car exhausts. We sat down and had a local Hinaro beer, then wandered on.

The waterfront was lined with yachts from every nation under the sun, with ports of registry ranging from Port Angeles and Santa Barbara in the USA to Victoria, Canada, and Melbourne, Australia, and there was even a little sloop called *Suka* from Maldon in Essex. The town which lay behind was a combination of tourist trap, busy French provincial centre and run-down Chinese ghetto. Most of the shops were Chinese, dark mysterious emporia selling groceries and every kind of hardware, piled up willy-nilly in the gloom. Each row of Chinese shops had an upper storey with a balcony, where the family lived behind slatted blinds and under a corrugated iron roof. The public buildings and churches were pure French, while the outdoor life of tiny stalls selling coconuts and soft drinks, and of the great vegetable market filled with enormous piles of water melons, was pure Tahitian. At last we came to the key to Tahiti, Robert's Cycle Hire stall, where for seven dollars a day we were able to hire mopeds. Now we were free to explore. I paused to buy swim fins, snorkel and mask and then set off with Roger and John Sharpe to see the island.

Tahiti is shaped like a figure of eight, dominated by two great volcanoes from which lush jungle sweeps down to the sea. The higher, Mount Orohena, rises to about 7,000 feet. All of the villages and the cultivated land lie on the narrow fringe of coastal lowland, and are connected by a single road. Therefore a tour of Tahiti involves an eighty mile ride around the outside of the island either clockwise or anticlockwise. We chose the latter, and were soon bowling out of town past the airport, along a busy country road. The road was lined with neat huts, of which the traditional design consists of a wooden platform raised above ground level on stilts, forming a 'ground floor' held up by wooden posts and open to the breeze, capped by a steeply pitched thatched roof. Rolled-up blinds of pandanus palm can be let down to provide privacy where necessary. In amongst the huts were groves of coconut palms, each tree having a zinc band around its trunk to prevent access to the fruit by rats and land crabs. The only people around seemed to be very plump middle-aged Tahitian ladies, swathed in pareos, who sat together talking in the shade.

After a few miles we came to a modern hotel called the Maera Beach, occupying the land between the road and the beach. This was a phenom-enon that we were to find right around Tahiti. The village houses, fields and plantations are on the landward side of the coastal road. On the seaward side there used to be just a fringe of palm trees and an idyllic beach where the villagers drew up their boats and kept their fishing gear. But now the beach was denied them. Around almost the entire coast of the island the shoreline had been bought up by a string of hotels, who thus effectively appropriated the beach for themselves and their clients, leaving the island-ers no access to their own sea. We decided to ignore the hotel's 'keep out' signs, parked on the beach, and entered the inviting blue water which lapped against the sand.

I was in paradise immediately. I had never dived on a tropical reef before and was unprepared for the unbelievable and indescribable beauty of the scene: the clear, bright, intense blue of the water; the flashing clouds of reef fish of myriad colours and shapes; the great outcrops of coral like crazy rock sculptures or piles of outsized brains; the giant clams which lay in wait with serrated blue jaws; the waving fronds of orange and red seaweed. I swam and swam, out from the beach across the shallows, then out onto the reef itself, a mighty ridge of yellow and dark red where the marine life is full of a frantic intensity, and then out beyond the reef where waves tossed me to and fro and the coral fell away steeply to hazy, dark depths in which larger and more menacing fish lurked. It was an overwhelming experience.

I lost all count of time, and it seemed like hours later when I finally noticed my own exhaustion and staggered ashore to find my colleagues busily chatting to two young Tahitian maidens. I joined them in this task. The girls were called Germaine and Andrea, and were both very young, about fourteen. They were clearly of mixed blood, and Germaine proudly announced that her grandfather came from Banff in Scotland. She spoke French and a little English to us, which she said she had learned in school where the Polynesian language is not allowed. There was dancing in the hotel that evening, they said, and why didn't we join them later? We eagerly agreed.

Sunset arrived quite suddenly as we talked. Tahiti is an isle of perpetual summer, and this misleads the visitor from temperate lands into expecting long light evenings. In fact the sun disappears into the sea at 6 p.m. and rises at 6 a.m. year-round. In our case the sun sank in a fiery red behind the dream-like peaks of Moorea, a scene of perfect beauty spoiled only by a crane excavating a hole for a new hotel on a particularly lovely point of land.

We headed back to Papeete, planning to get changed for the dance. On our way we overtook the moped of Mike Crimp, who had paid a shipmate 40 dollars to get three days off duty. In the event, we ran into more ship-mates, milled around town, visited souvenir shops, ate smoked kebab and coconut milk at a roadside stand, and ended up not returning to our young friends. Late in the evening I returned to the ship and ran into Pete Reynell, condemned to be duty watchkeeper. His morbid task had been to patch up a string of returning Hudsonian crewmen who had been worsted in battles with beefy Tahitian males. The crew didn't know much about Tahiti, but they had been told that the girls were free with their favours; being straightforward

Newfies, and drunk as well, they responded to this idea by grabbing at girls in the street, including those accompanied by their husbands. In the resulting combats Ron Shaw, son of the Chief Steward, had received a broken arm. The Captain had also come aboard muttering. He had been in Quinn's when the scene there hotted up during the evening, and had spent a lot of time and money working on a particularly attractive girl, who turned out after further investigation to be a male transvestite.

Next morning I got up early with the intention of wasting no further time on Papeete but exploring the whole island. I set off with Roger, Mike Crimp and John Sharpe to do a clockwise circuit of the island. The road led us first through some very ordinary French suburbs, no doubt the abodes of civil servants, then we came to a large modern building with flagpoles outside and the title 'Centre des Expérimentations du Pacifique' on the wall. I took it to be a research laboratory, and ventured into the foyer to announce myself as a genuine Cambridge physicist seeking a guided tour. The receptionist said not a word, but with a gesture summoned two burly Legionnaire guards, who literally Frog-marched me out of the door. It was a laboratory all right, but not the sort that I had imagined; it was the centre of the organisation running the French H-bomb testing programme in the South Pacific.

Dusting myself down, and casting some Anglo-Saxon epithets at the departing Normans, I rejoined my comrades and we put the last vestiges of Papeete behind us. Out in the countryside everything was transformed. To our right an intensely lush jungle rose up the steep rocky sides of the central volcano, enlaced with violently beautiful blossoms of hibiscus, frangipani, bougainvillea and the delicate *tiare* flower. Beside the road were shady groves of coconut palms, with occasional thatched huts almost invisible amongst them. The beach to our left fulfilled perfectly the conventional idea of Paradise, an endless expanse of clean white sand, backed by gently waving palms and fringed by placid waters of clearest azure. We stopped at intervals to swim, and to help Roger in his self-imposed task of taking core samples of sand at different distances from the beach to take home to his professor in Canada.

Soon we came to our first goal, Matavai Bay. This was the historic landing place of Captain James Cook when he first reached Tahiti in 1769 to observe the Transit of Venus for the Admiralty. The bay was a beautiful crescent of black volcanic sand, ending in a headland where Cook had built a fort which he called Point Venus. The site is now a park, and contains a tall white lighthouse and a monument to Cook in the form of a globe on a stone plinth, with a plaque which says:-

This monument erected by Captain James Cook to commemorate the observation of the Transit of Venus June 3rd 1769 was restored and fenced round and this plate was placed here by the Royal Society and the Royal Geographical Society in 1901.

I gazed out from the monument to the palm trees and the sea, and thought of how this island must have seemed to the first British mariners to land here. Tahiti was the centre of Polynesian culture in the Pacific. When it was discovered by Samuel Wallis in 1767 it had a population of 40,000. The life of the people was in many ways idyllic. The climate is perfect and they did not have to work to live; coconut and breadfruit groves surrounded their huts, the reefs teemed with fish, and mountain torrents provided plentiful fresh water. The people lived in palm-leaf huts and dressed in togas made of bark cloth or *tapa*. Marital customs were quite strict, but it was considered normal for young unmarried girls to indulge in unrestrained sex, and this led the first European visitors to consider Tahiti a paradise of free love, home of the Noble Savage untainted by Adam's fall. There was a dark side: internecine wars were frequent and bloody, and the religion, which showed itself physically in the great stone ceremonial *marae,* or platforms which supported statues of the gods, was disfigured by human sacrifice. But the life was far better than what came afterwards. Wallis's visit was followed by that of Bougainville in 1768, and then in 1769 by Cook himself. Already the islanders had contracted venereal disease from the visiting sailors, and this later rose to epidemic proportions. Cook's men found that the island girls would give their all in exchange for a nail, which nearly caused his ship to fall apart, but this was in fact not a sign of wanton morals. A steel nail was a valuable item, for it could be fashioned into a fish-hook and used to feed a family. In 1788 Captain Bligh anchored in Matavai Bay in HMS *Bounty,* with the task of taking on board seedlings of breadfruit to be transplanted to the West Indies for the feeding of slaves. The charms of the island girls were a major cause of the subsequent mutiny, since the crew were less than anxious to leave again when the ship was loaded.

The news of the discovery of Tahiti led to an influx of the scum of the ocean, such as Yankee whalers. The islanders soon lost the art of making tools, which they could easily gain by trading their favours with visiting sailors, and they acquired a taste for rum, worthless trinkets and fire-arms, causing internecine wars to become much bloodier. Then the missionaries came, and imposed morality at the cost of destroying the religious and social traditions of the Polynesians. Finally the French grabbed the island in 1842 by a wanton act of aggressive colonialism, and it has since been absorbed into the French colonial system. At a time when other colonies were being set free, French Polynesia was being turned into a cross between a tourist paradise and a dumping ground for all the filthy nuclear experiments that the French would rather not carry on at home. Thus it remains today, a Department of France, represented by a member in the National Assembly.

I wandered down to the beach, where fishermen were at work wading through the shallows with a net stretched out between them. Their outrigger canoes were drawn up on the shore, where their catch hung from the branches of a tree. I plunged into the inviting water and snorkelled out to the reef, where I again entered paradise. There is so much to see in the busy community of a coral reef that hours of drifting above this fascinating world cannot dull its novelty. Firstly there are the clumps of the coral itself, in delicate shades of brown, yellow and pink and with shapes ranging from the convoluted cranium of brain coral to tree-like fronds or large rocky masses. Then there are the fish, a riot of colour like nothing that I had seen before. The beautiful yellow butterfly-fish, with a long probing nose to reach into coral crevices; the Moorish idol, with a black, red and yellow striped body and a long trailing streamer like the scarf of a bicycling student; the large green and blue parrot-fish, with a perpetual smile on his face and a vicious-looking beak which allows him to actually eat coral; the extraordinarily ugly cowfish, with a globular blue-spotted pink body and two horns protruding in front of his bulbous eyes; the long tubular trumpet-fish, gliding calmly among the fronds of weed; and the tiny pipefish, hanging from the surface by their mouths; I followed them all and marvelled at their exotic shapes and colours. Konrad Lorenz found that this coloration is not a defence mechanism against predators, but rather serves to keep away other members of the same species, so that a given fish can feed undisturbed in its own little area of reef on its own particular form of prey. The tiniest fish were royal blue in colour and swam unafraid among the stinging fronds of sea anemones, cleaning off the detritus from the anemone's last meal.

Once again it was hard to emerge into the terrestrial world, but I finally set off again with my colleagues. We were now heading across the north side of the island, where white sand beaches are interspersed with vast expanses of exposed coral. A storm was brewing out at sea, and the absence of a protective reef here meant that the great rollers were breaking over the nearshore coral formations, sending spray sweeping across the coast road. Soon it began to rain, an intense downpour which lasted for half an hour and left the road steaming.

We passed small villages where women were washing clothes in the mountain streams, beating them against rocks. Local buses passed us, open vehicles with wooden benches for the travellers. We dived again from a breakwater near an Anglican church. This time the sandy sea bed was strewn with sea cucumbers, disgusting looking creatures shaped like diseased sausages, with brown pustules over their grey-black skins. They draw in sea water through a hole at one end, and when attacked repel the aggressor by expelling their own intestines through the same hole. They were said to be good to eat, but it is only recently that I have tried one in Japan. They are not good to eat.

We stopped for lunch at a supermarket-café, where we bought baguettes, crabmeat and ice cream, which we ate sitting on a river bank consumed by ants. We carried on until dusk once again unexpectedly engulfed us while we were at the eastern end of the island, beneath the lesser of the two volcanoes. As darkness fell we came across the Gauguin Museum, but found it closed. Next door was a restaurant, however, where we stopped to dine. The meal was magnificent, cooked by a Chinese girl who was the restaurant's sole staff member. The main course was curried freshwater shrimps, which live high up in the mountain streams. They were accompanied by papaya fruit punch, French white wine and coffee. We were the only guests, and ate outside under the canopy of a million brilliant stars. The night sounds of the jungle, insects and crashing animals of unknown kinds, were the accompaniment to an evening of utter contentment. Afterwards we wandered out onto a nearby jetty, and made out the dorsal fin of a shark cruising offshore, revealed by the luminous flash of the displaced water. A meteor shot across the firmament above our heads. The beauty was beyond all description, making me feel inexpressibly sad at the brevity of life.

Finally we set out for the long journey home in the darkness. The unlit road was made dangerous by fallen coconuts, which in their fibre husks were formidable obstacles. Out at sea islanders were reef fishing by the light of pressure lamps. The scent of flowers and warm damp jungle was overwhelming, and I saw how easy it would be to fall under the spell of the South Seas and to spend the rest of my life here.

The next day was my twenty-second birthday. I set off early to visit the post office, and on passing the *Suka* saw signs of life and hailed her. I was invited on board by the couple who owned her. They had left England in

1966 and had sailed first to the USA, then through Panama and on to the Marquesas and Tahiti. Both the boat and the couple looked rather shabby, but they were obviously very happy with their footloose life. Then I met up with Rog, Mike and Ted Yoshinari, and we caught the little ferry *Keke II* for the ten-mile trip to Moorea.

We passed through the gap in the reef between two lines of breaking surf, and headed on out to sea, where flying fish took off in shoals from our bows. The powerful boat soon reached the edge of the Moorea reef, which we followed until we came to a wide sandy bay backed by the enormous dark green thumb-shaped peak of Mount Cook. Moorea is much more of a random, rocky island than the simple double cone of Tahiti, and the jungle-clad razor ridges which surrounded us were magnificent in the fragrant morning sunshine. The bay contained the Bali Hai Hotel, built over the water in palm-thatched chalet style, and we could see blue and yellow angel fish swimming amongst the pilings as the boat unloaded freight and some of her passengers. We went on to land in the next bay, Paopao Bay, alongside the Hotel Aimeo. Here Mike found that we could hire a Mini-Moke jeep with a stripped clutch, in which we set off to explore the island.

We found Moorea more varied than Tahiti, because the coast consists of a sequence of bays instead of being straight. Some of the bays were very beautiful, more lovely than any dream image of the South Seas. Imagine an absolutely placid basin of perfect azure, fringed by tall-stemmed palm trees which lean their heads over the water as if to view their own reflections in a mirror. At the narrow entrance of the basin a seine net is strung across the water. Beyond lies a white line where a lazy swell is breaking over the distant reef, then the blue of the sea merges into the blue of the sky, where a few fluffy cumulus clouds float suspended. This is Moorea.

We swam from deserted beaches, finding huge concentrations of black sea cucumbers and blue-spined sea urchins near the beach, and isolated coral clumps in which giant clams were embedded. I spotted a single very large conch shell, which I retrieved. We bought a bread and cheese lunch at a Chinese store, then stalled the car as we climbed a steep hill dividing two bays. We had to leap out and shove coral rocks under the rear wheel to stop the Moke from running backwards over the precipice, as it had no brakes as well as no clutch. Then we coasted down into a village where an old two-masted schooner was loading copra from a shed on a jetty. Copra, the dried meat of the coconut, is the chief product of the plantations in Tahiti and Moorea, and is exported for use in soap and margarine. Behind the jetty rose a neat white church, dating from the time of King Pomare II, who began to rule in 1815 when the London Missionary Society was converting the islanders and building churches everywhere.

Beyond this village the coast road plunged into jungle again, in the midst of which we came across an isolated hut of traditional construction, set back from the road, but bearing on a nearby tree trunk the sign 'Visitors Most Welcome'. Intrigued, we drove up to it and were met by a figure straight out of a thousand romantic novels, the Elderly English Chap Gone Native. He introduced himself as Peter Brooke. "Cousin of Rupert Brooke, the poet, y'know, and grandson of Stopford Augustus Brooke, who wrote all those boring hymns." He was an erect white-haired figure with a noble bearing, offset by his costume of baggy long shorts, cotton shirt and sandals. He shook us firmly by the hand and welcomed us into his abode.

It was furnished in Robert Louis Stevenson style, with a few basket chairs, some rattan and cane tables, a chest or two and a hammock. The walls were of rolled-up blinds, and prints of Gauguin paintings were pinned precariously to the posts which supported the roof.

"A spot of tea?" he asked, inevitably. An attractively plump Tahitian lady appeared, smiling, from the inner room and then disappeared again to put the kettle on.

"I have two of them," he said. "They do everything for me."

We settled in the chairs, and he extracted our life stories quickly, then started on his own. He was a writer, he said, pointing to a battered typewriter, and had been in Tahiti on and off for 21 years. Why had he come here? It was a long story, involving the corruption of the British political system and a little personal difficulty concerned with smuggling.

"It started at Oxford. I was at Balliol and President of the Union. I was very left wing, and was determined to have a political career. I was up there with Quintin Hogg, Michael Stewart, Randolph Churchill – it was an exciting time. I remember once Winston came along as guest speaker. I gave a speech which made Churchill very angry at first. But then he laughed and said 'Perfect radical speech – off the point – calculated to insult – jokes were already well established so the audience knew when to laugh'. Then a Duchess came to dinner afterwards. She made an insulting remark about my moustache and my politics. I told her, 'You're not likely to come in contact with either!' Happy days!"

He laughed heartily.

"Then the politics got serious. I stood as the Independent National candidate for Guildford. That was at the time of the National Government, the appeasers. They offered me a safe seat if I would stand for them, but of course I refused. But then I really got something on them. I met an ex-whore called Thelma in a second-hand bookshop, and got to know her very well. In fact I lived with her for three years. It turned out that during her professional career she'd had two distinguished clients. Both of them only wanted to be jerked off. The first was the chief of propaganda at Conservative Central Office. The second was Stanley Baldwin himself. He used to pay her £3,000 a year, and came round to see her after every major speech. Once when he was attacked by Lloyd George he couldn't get a hard-on afterwards. The papers next day said 'Lloyd George castigates Prime Minister'!"

He guffawed. We sat fascinated. Could all this be true? Ted broke the spell to remind us that the last plane back to Tahiti was about to leave and that we had already missed the last boat. We reluctantly took our leave.

"Come back if you get a chance," he said cheerily. "Oh, and before you go, come and have a look at this."

He took us behind his house and along a narrow path which led up to a vertical rock face. He pulled out a ladder which was hidden in the under-growth and bade us go up one at a time. There in a tiny cleft in the rock, completely hidden from below, was an ancient Polynesian burial place. On a bed of straw stood three wooden models of double-hulled canoes, complete with masts. On each stood a dusty skull, while other bones were arranged carefully around the boats.

"My Tahitian wife told me about it," he said. "Normally white men are never told where the holy places are - we've destroyed so much. The natives keep the place up - they bring fresh straw and repair the canoes. I sent one of the bones to the British Museum for carbon dating. It came out at 600 A.D., that's the very beginning of Polynesian colonisation of Tahiti. These bones must be some of the first settlers, or even the discoverers."

We bade farewell and drove on a few miles to the rough airstrip, where we saw the last plane of the day taking off. Luckily the local island bus, called 'Le Truc', was standing by, and the amiable driver, who boasted an enormous shiny olive paunch, offered us his own house on the beach for the night, for the minor consideration of twelve dollars. The house was actually a wooden shack, but it stood in an idyllic bay where we watched a stupendous sunset whilst being eaten by sand flies. Nearby stood a Chinese store which was just closing, but we persuaded the proprietor to stay open and sell us noodles, steaks, ham, eggs, bacon and oranges. We cooked up a huge meal which we ate on the verandah beside two worn wooden *tikis* (posts carved with a god's head) which the owner had erected to guard his entrance. Ted, our cook, had thrown the peel of the oranges out onto the beach, and now in the moonlight we saw to our surprise the coils of peel moving around as if animated. Was this a haunting? The surroundings were so romantic and mysterious that it could easily have been. But then we heard scuttling sounds and saw pairs of evil red eyes; huge land crabs had emerged from holes in the coral rocks and were making off with the orange peel.

The enforced stay gave me a chance to take up Peter Brooke on his offer, so while the others turned in to sleep, Mike and I returned in the Moke and revisited this extraordinary person. He welcomed us warmly, we settled back in the chairs, and he carried on his narrative at the point where he had left off. His tale held us transfixed for most of the night.

"Where was I? Oh yes, I was living with Thelma. I introduced her to my father. He was a Unitarian minister, very distant and very innocent. When I said that she was a good friend, all he said was 'It's always good to have friends'. On my 21st birthday he gave me three pieces of advice, which were the sum of his life's wisdom. Firstly, if injured in a road accident don't make a statement but get in touch with your lawyer. Secondly, you're too young to have contact with the ladies, but when you do, always communicate with them by telephone. Thirdly, avoid doing business with members of your family. Thelma was a good girl. Whores are really honest, professional people, like Polynesians. To a Tahitian girl sex is like going to the lavatory, a perfectly straightforward activity. The really corrupt type of woman is the nice girl next door, where you spend a fortune on taking her out and she still only allows you a kiss on the way home.

"What finished me with politics was the Abdication. I couldn't stand the moral hypocrisy of everyone, especially Baldwin when I knew what he had been getting up to. When the war came I joined the Navy and was a Lieutenant-Commander on convoy escorts to West Africa – Bathurst, Freetown, Dakar. It was in Dakar that I got into smuggling; I started running diamonds there in '43. My contact was a whore in a brothel that had been shelled by the *Rodney* in '42! Then I became confidential secretary to Mountbatten when he was C. in C. in the Far East and then Viceroy of India. He was a hard man to work for, but always stood by me when I was threatened with expulsion for – er – difficulties. The people there hated us because we were in a position to give orders to our superior officers.

"I left the Navy after India. I was disgusted with England by then. I bought a decommissioned 110-foot Fairmile subchaser, with twin Thorneycroft engines, a lovely fast ship. I advertised for a Wren crew, and got 365 replies. They're less liable to get drunk than men, and you can sleep with them as well. I made one of them Chief Engineer. I wanted to get my money out of England, so I borrowed 20 passports from members of a cricket club that I got drunk, and used them to get round the foreign currency regulations. Then when we sailed for France we had 400 tons of cocoa, a Ming vase, a Persian carpet and two letters by Keats on board. Customs didn't find any of it!

"We went on to Barcelona and started running cigarettes and liquor across from Tangier for the Barcelona Chief of Police. He was caught and sent to Valencia, where he carried on the same thing. I went to Gibraltar and sold the boat for £10,000 to an ex-RN type who said that he wanted to start smuggling. I did warn him against it but he went ahead and got caught. Committed suicide, poor chap. Then I went to the USA where I had a sister in New Hampshire. I got my mistress over too – she was South African – by forging a letter from the University of Chicago inviting her to resume her pre-war studies. Then I met Watson of IBM, who offered me a job. In those days everyone had to use the IBM tailor. I told him that I had my own tailor, John Gordon of Albemarle Street who was tailor to Captain Bligh, and that was good enough for me. It wasn't good enough for him, so he fired me. That brought me to Tahiti.

"This is a very cheap place to live. I've worked showing tourists round, but mainly I write. I'm just finishing a biography of Mary Shelley. And I've got 70 acres of oranges and coffee, which someone looks after for me. I got them through Joanna, my Tahitian wife. We're separated now but still good friends. These two girls here now - they're good friends as well!"

And so it went on. Here was an exceptional man who had never compromised with life, the sort of extraordinary Englishman who seems to end up in the most distant and obscure corners of the planet. And, almost at the end of his life, a happy man. It was nearly dawn when we finally left his hut.

Later I found out that indeed a certain Somerset Stopford Brooke of Balliol had been President of the Oxford Union in 1928 and had stood unsuccessfully as a parliamentary candidate in 1929 and 1935. Then the trail went dead; he had left the embrace of the British establishment. I wondered when he had changed his Christian name, but it is clear that in the real world being called 'Somerset Stopford' has some disadvantages.

The rest of my time in Tahiti was prosaic by comparison. We awoke, bitten all over by sand flies, to find ants in the sugar, land crabs stealing grapefruit

rind from the kitchen, and my snorkelling gear stolen from the back of the
Moke. Having made arrangements to return the car we caught the small plane
which runs a shuttle across to Tahiti, and gazed down from it upon the maze
of reefs which showed up darkly against the sand through the perfectly clear
water. Back in Papeete I replaced my diving gear and set off again with Rog in
a rented Fiat to spend the day sampling and diving around the reefs.

In the southwest of the island we came across the great restored *marae*
of Arahurahu, which we reached as the sun was setting, enhancing its sense
of mystery. The *marae* were great ceremonial enclosures of Tahiti, built of
worked stone and representing the public religious centre for a complete clan
or tribe. All of the *marae* were destroyed by the missionaries, but Arahurahu
has been restored to match descriptions by the early explorers. It is a rectan-
gular enclosure about two hundred yards long, surrounded by a thick stone
wall eight feet high to prevent lesser beings (e.g. women) from viewing the
ceremonies. At one end is an *ahu*, a stepped stone pyramid in three layers
rising to about thirty feet. On this platform stood the idols of the clan and
here the priests carried out the rituals, viewed by the clan males who each
had his own stone to sit on within the enclosure. Here humans were sacrificed
before important actions such as war were undertaken; taboos were set and
raised; the changes of season were celebrated; and using invocations handed
down from ancient times the spiritual power of nature, or *mana*, was called
forth in aid of the clan's needs. Even today Tahitians keep clear of the ruins of
marae after dark, and we were happy to move on after looking at the massive
stonework.

We spent the last evening at the Miss Tahiti contest in a Papeete hotel, a
colourful occasion where the winner was a half-caste girl from Moorea in a
pareo-printed bikini. Next morning I got up very early and had a final walk
around Papeete, wandering through the water melon market and getting my
hair cut by a Chinese barber. At nine o'clock we sailed with curiously few
regrets. The lush tropical beauty of Tahiti is, of course, superb, but in a way
it was a let-down because Tahiti is so famous that we were prepared for
what we saw. And the human atmosphere had been strangely unfriendly.
Unlike Chile, people did not go out of their way to make human contact
with us. And the islanders seemed to bear a sullen resentment towards their
French masters, with both groups disliking the inscrutable Chinese who run
everything. The visit reminded me that there is no such thing as an earthly
paradise, and so I turned my face more happily to the north and a few thousand more miles of ocean.

CHAPTER 16

A WESTERN HOMECOMING

Through the great fogbound Straits
Where the cedars stand watching
I'll be far off and gone
Like Summer Wages.

Ian and Sylvia Tyson

THE DARK GREEN PEAKS of Tahiti's mountains dropped slowly into the misty line that separates deep blue from deeper blue, leaving a heap of orographic cloud as a final marker. Station work began straight away. The first station was number 237, and took place at 15°S, 150°W. From here we were to continue the 150°W transect, stopping at 5 degree intervals (i.e. every 300 nautical miles), right up into the Gulf of Alaska. Darkness had fallen when I went up to the winch-house to run the bottle station, and the stars were burning with a brilliant intensity. It was a joy to work with the caress of soft breezes on my body. I found that the sea surface temperature was nearly 29°C, with the surface salinity at the very high value of 36 parts per thousand; at these latitudes the high rate of evaporation increases the brine concentration in the surface waters.

I soon fell back into the pleasant routine of bottle casts, computing and satellite watches, with interludes of partying and of browbeating the marine biologists to get a look at their fascinating specimens. Our second station, on May 18, was done at 10°S, only 15 miles from Caroline Island, a British colony of the Christmas Island Group. This is one of the 'low islands' of Polynesia, an atoll rising only a few feet above the sea and revealing its presence by a fringe of palm trees. Atolls are a triumph of the urge for life that pervades the earth. They are built up by corals in a race against the slow sinking of the submerged volcano that forms their base. The coral that breaks the surface is pounded up by waves into a coarse gravel which provides a lodging for wind-blown dust and water-borne coconuts. Against all the odds a vegetation grows, a soil of sorts forms and eventually the island is colonised by adventurous Polynesian mariners. But life on an atoll, far from being a tropical idyll, was never anything but hard for the first settlers, with a restricted diet of fish, coconuts and taro and a need for warfare or emigration when human numbers exceeded the carrying capacity of the scrap of land.

We were now under the influence of the South Equatorial Current, flowing westward at two knots, and it was hard to hold the ship on station against this warm stream. We reached the Equator just before noon on May 21. Since November 30 1969, a date which seemed to lie in the impossible past, I had been continuously in the southern hemisphere. Looking back at my old diary entries I remembered how new and exciting everything about being at sea was then, and how inexperienced I was. Now I felt like the Ancient Mariner. I had been given the opportunity to explore the most exotic and remote regions of the globe, an unforgettable and unrepeatable experience, and we still had the Arctic to look forward to. I wondered how I would cope with life when this magical voyage was over; how could anything again match up to this?

These reflections were caused not just by Crossing the Line (again there was no ceremony) but also by a telegram that I had just received from Sir Edward Bullard in Cambridge, offering me a research studentship at the Geophysics Department. Cambridge again! The dangerous emotion of nostalgia welled up, and I wallowed in memories of mellow brickwork, old friends, good times and first love, forgetting how much I had hated the smug arrogance of the place and how glad I had been to escape. I had already discussed with Bill von Arx the possibility of joining the Woods Hole-MIT graduate programme, and I had sent off an application from Tahiti. Besides, I felt that I had no real interest in marine geophysics. It was not the rocks beneath the sea that fascinated me but the sea itself and the myriad mysteries of the life that it contains. After two days of agonising I turned down Bullard, with some regret since it was thanks to his influence that I was aboard *Hudson*.

Meanwhile a message came from BIO asking us to divert and do two cores off the Queen Charlotte Islands on our way in to Vancouver from the Gulf of Alaska, as a prelude to the survey which was to form our next leg. Our arrival date in Vancouver was sacrosanct because of news coverage and publicity arrangements, so the only way to fit in this extra work was to delete some stations from our vital long section. Our chief scientist on this leg was Bill Cameron, perpetrator of the farcical press conference in Valparaiso. He now held a scientific meeting at which he suggested spacing our stations beyond 10°N at 6 degrees apart instead of 5, and deleting two stations. The proposal was agreed with much grumbling and dissent, and enquiries as to whether BIO had any idea of real scientific priorities.

The station at 5°N was done in the middle of the night, and I was treated to an extraordinary spectacle in the bright circle thrown on the sea round the wire by the floodlights. A huge swarm of squid – at least 100 of them – appeared on the surface, swimming around in a concerted crowd like a coach party. They varied from a few inches to two feet in length, and the larger ones were orange with a bright spot on their backs. There were also several tiny silvery squid of the sort that jet themselves out of the water, and the larger squid appeared to be feeding on these. I would see a flash of spray as the tiny squid took off, and then a larger orange squid would thrust himself swiftly through the water to the landing point of the smaller animal, whereupon he would quickly consume it. Later on came the even more amazing spectacle of a huge mass of small silver fish, making the water boil with their desperate motion. They were quickly joined by the orange squid, who began browsing on them. Then along came a small yellow-brown shark who, amazed at his good fortune, began swimming gently through the gathering, grazing at random on the silver swarm. The shark at one stage attacked one of the orange squid, and was met by a dark cloud of ink. The ink formed a brown impenetrable curtain occupying a volume of several cubic yards and allowing the escape of the squid. This complex drama of life and death was all played out under the floodlights as if in a theatre.

Next evening Rog and I took some cashew nuts round to Orest and George's cabin and blackmailed Orest with them to open up the last of his Chilean wine. A wine and cashew orgy ensued, during which the prosaically efficient George described his methods of shark fishing, which he had now raised to an art, though not a fine art. A squid was used as bait on a hook suspended by a pulley from a boom on the quarterdeck. The shark, once hooked, was hauled from the water, shot in the head by the Doctor, decapitated, and the head retained for the sake of the jaws. The body was allowed to fall in the sea, the squid was extracted from the jaws and the hook rebaited. Since Tahiti George had caught six sharks, and was now planning to establish a shark jaw retailing business on his return to Musquodoboit Harbour.

By 10°N we were in the North Equatorial Current, having crossed three current systems in the space of three stations. The Pacific, like the Atlantic, contains two great surface gyres or circulating systems of currents. In the South Pacific the gyre is anticlockwise, with the Antarctic Circumpolar Current forming its southern, eastward-flowing portion and the South Equatorial Current its northern, westward-flowing portion just south of the Equator. The flow is completed by the Peru Current (northward) and the East Australian Current (southward). In the North Pacific the great gyre is clockwise: the North Pacific Current flows eastward at high latitudes; it turns southward down the American coast as the California Current, then westward as the North Equatorial Current, running just north of the Equator. The Kuroshio Current off the coast of Japan completes the cycle. Thus, near the Equator there are two westward-flowing currents, from different origins. To complicate matters, however, they are separated by a narrow but fast flowing eastward current jet, lying directly on the Equator and called the Equatorial Counter Current. As a further complication, a narrow eastward jet also underlies the South Equatorial Current at only about 100 metres depth; this is called the Cromwell Current and, astonishingly, it was not discovered until 1952.

The North Equatorial Current has a sharp boundary with the colder, denser water which lies underneath it. At the 10°N station, Bruno found the Bathysonde chart recorder pen shooting from one side of the paper to the other. He suspected a fault, but then found that the Bathysonde was hovering at 150 metres depth, exactly in the middle of the very steep thermocline that marks the bottom boundary of the Current. As the ship heaved up and down in the lazy swell the temperature shot from high to low and back again. The surface temperature was a mere 27°C now, still hot but a reminder that nothing but worse awaited us. All that day we were accompanied by several flights of Blue-faced Boobies, a bird of the same family as the gannet. They are large and white, with a black trailing edge to the wings, blue heads and a peculiarly mechanical way of flying which makes them look as if they are powered by clockwork. We suspected that they must have a breeding colony on a nearby island, for we had never seen them before and we never saw them again.

That evening I had some leisure to watch the amateur fishermen on the after deck during a station. Three casting nets were being enthusiastically wielded, to the sound of the eerie cries of the boobies out in the darkness. The most interesting catch were three puffer or porcupine fish, *Arothron*, of which one was still alive in a bucket. This is one of the most extraordinary creatures of the sea. In his normal state he is a pudgy fish, about 7 inches long, tapering towards the tail and wider than he is high. He has a royal blue back and white belly, and is covered with black markings. His fins, which look too delicate to power such a stout body, are filmy and frail. The upper and lower anal fins move in unison from side to side like twin rudders, aiding the propulsive power of the tail fin, while two fanlike fins behind the head perform an oscillatory motion. It is when attacked that the puffer fish reveals his unique defence mechanism. By ingesting huge quantities of water he blows himself up into a ball, with only his head and tail sticking out. Simultaneously a mass of sharp spines, each about an inch long, rise from the black markings to give the apparition a fearsome and indigestible appearance. In the bucket this could be done by grabbing his tail. However, while blowing himself up, he also ejected, no doubt in fear, a heap of granular excrement. This is another special feature of the fish. Along with a few other species they perform the important function of working down coarse coral into fine-grained sand in the lagoons of coral reefs and atolls. They browse on the coral tops in search of polyps, worms and algae, and swallow lumps of the coral as well, which are digested and then excreted as fine grains. A scientist in Bermuda found that coral-browsing fish were producing a ton of sand per hectare per year. The final feature of the puffer fish, of which we were not aware, is that his liver is extremely poisonous. Puffer fish, or *fugu*, is a delicacy in Japan where it can only be served by licensed restaurants with specially trained (and heavily insured) chefs, while in Haiti puffer fish poison is thought to be the paralysing agent used by witch doctors for turning victims into zombies.

The other catch of the evening were three beautiful flying fish, all unfortunately dead. Ted Yoshinari took the largest, about a foot long, skinned it and extracted the meat, which I fried in butter (fortunately I did not fry the puffer fish as well). It was a soft white meat with a delicate and delicious taste. The other two fish seemed to be of different species. Both were long and slim with appealing moon-like eyes. The larger had opaque wings changing colour from blue to yellow to black to yellow moving towards the tips. His body was of smooth ultramarine with a white belly. The smaller had translucent filmy wings with pink veins. The tail fin was in the form of a V with an extended lower arm, which acts as a rudder or hydrofoil while in flight. His body was a shining royal blue, changing to purple, pink and silver underneath. I held the creature out to the wind. The main flying fins flexed naturally so as to maintain the best angle of attack for gliding. They were exquisite creatures, perfectly adapted for their function.

Next day I finally saw the elusive green flash at sunset. Von Arx had talked about it a few days earlier and we had all been on the lookout, but without success. The flash occurs as the last edge of the sun sinks below the horizon under very calm conditions; the final flash of sun is green. Since looking at the sun as it sets gives you spots before the eyes it is difficult to see the flash even when it occurs, and its very existence was doubted until the Vatican Observatory photographed it in colour early in the century. On this occasion it was very clear, lasting for about half a second. The explanation is straightforward. When the sun is low in the sky its rays come to us through a long column of atmosphere, whose density increases towards the Earth's surface. This bends the rays towards the Earth, and the degree of bending (or 'refractive index') for blue light is greater than for red. The combined rays which make up the normal white light of the sun are therefore split, with the blue disc seeming to be slightly higher in the sky than the red disc. The result is a white solar disc with a red fringe at the bottom and a blue fringe at the top. The scattering effect of molecules in the air upon this light dilutes the blue somewhat and it ends up as green. There are stories of crew in old sailing ships keeping the green flash in sight for several seconds by running up the rigging as the sun set.

On May 28 we crossed the Tropic of Cancer and were once again in real northern waters. The evening was calm and sunny, so a crowd assembled on the upper deck to watch for the green flash, which obligingly appeared again. Von Arx stood amongst them making strange motions with his hand. He explained that the angle between thumb and forefinger is just right as an elevation from the setting sun to the planet Venus, which sure enough appeared as a tiny pinpoint of light when I looked in the right direction. Later this extraordinary man showed me how to find Jupiter at sunset by measuring 110 degrees over the azimuth.

By May 31 we had reached 36°N and the surface water temperature was down to 17°C. The life around us changed to more temperate forms. Albatrosses reappeared in quantity, all black browed. Although albatrosses are mainly Southern Ocean birds there are three species found in the North Pacific, breeding on Wake Island and other Hawaiian islands. They impressed us again with their long glides hugging the crest of the swell. George Gill, oblivious as always to the poetry of life, caught three in his casting net, all of which died from rough handling, a threefold promise of disaster if Coleridge is to be believed. Hawaii had been making its nearness felt in other ways, mainly by the trashy music and advertisements of its principal radio stations, relayed to the lounge and coffee room over the ship's loudspeakers by courtesy of Sparky.

Other mysterious creatures appeared. During the cast five unidentifiable fish swam by, five feet long, pale green in colour and looking like immature sharks, but without dorsal fins. When the cast came up an enormous salp was draped over one of the bottles, brown and slimy. Meanwhile Ken Freeman (a biology student who joined at Tahiti) had caught a large squid with his casting net. It was no less than 32 inches long, the biggest yet caught. We dissected it and I kept various pieces for my museum, including the skin. I was able to look under a microscope at the chromatophores, or pigment cells, which produce the remarkable colour changes in a squid's skin. Each chromatophore contains a tiny sac filled with red, blue or yellow pigment. Each sac is attached to a strand of muscle, which can be contracted to spread the sac out in a patch of colour, or relaxed to make the sac shrink to a pinpoint. By differentially contracting different muscles any combination of colours can be produced by the squid, including sending waves of colour over its body. And these colour changes can be done in less than a second.

The chemistry group on this leg was strengthened by C S Wong, a bulky but gentle Chinaman who worked for the Pacific Oceanographic Group in Nanaimo, British Columbia. C S was studying closely the first drafts of our temperature, salinity, oxygen and nutrient sections across the Tropics. Although this was the first section done at 150°W there were other partial sections done by Japanese and US ships at 130°, 155° and 170°W, and by comparing these very carefully C S had discovered an anomaly. Deep in the tropical Pacific, at 5°S and 10°N and at a depth of 4,000-5,000 metres he found two regions of water with anomalously low temperature and high dissolved oxygen. High oxygen meant that we were dealing with a 'young' water mass, which had recently been at or near the surface. Much of the water in the deep ocean is 'old'; it has not been near the surface for several hundred years and its oxygen has become very depleted. C S found these same anomalies in the other sections, and deduced that they represent two deep eastward-flowing currents, coming from different source areas in the western Pacific. This was an important discovery, because the surface circulation is in the opposite direction. After further observations it now seems that the deep circulation of most of the Pacific mimics the surface circulation but in the opposite sense, although the deep flow is greatly complicated by the presence of underwater ridge systems.

Soon it really began to get cold. The station at 43°N had a sea surface temperature of only 11°C, as bad as the English Channel. We sighted our first Alaskan fur seals: unfortunately the seals did not realise that we had a pathological murderer on board. Five friendly fur seals came swimming by the ship during the station, coming right up to the rail. The Doctor could not resist the temptation to destroy life, so out came one of his rifles and a seal died. The poor creature was too far off to recover, so the killing was completely pointless. Besides this, as Madhu pointed out forcefully to the Doctor, it was illegal. The fur seals of Alaska, which breed mostly on the Pribilof Islands in the Bering Sea, were hunted almost to extinction last century by the Russians and Americans until the Alaska Fur Seal Convention of 1882 strictly regulated hunting so that the stocks could recover. This was the first example of an agreement between Russia and the USA, and it has been observed for over 100 years. Madhu threatened to have the Doctor prosecuted, and he slunk below in a temporarily crestfallen state.

By June 5, twenty days out of Tahiti, we were in the cold and mist of the Gulf of Alaska. For an ancient mariner like me, twenty days were nothing, but for others it was long enough for tempers to become shorter. Our station that evening was due to be done at 55°N, but at 54°30'N we passed over a seamount and Charlie Schafer decided unilaterally to stop the ship in order to do a core. However, cores can only be done in daylight, so this meant doing the bottle station and then waiting around until dawn. Further, the seamount generated a strong positive gravity anomaly, which would make it difficult to pick up the gravity line again accurately when broken by the station stop. The normally gentle Bill von Arx was enraged, and when Charlie told him that he had consulted the First and Second Mates Bill retorted:

"The First and Second Mates have nothing to do with science, and neither do you!"

The real problem was the absence of the Chief Scientist. Bill Cameron had taken to his cabin shortly after the first and only scientific meeting, and was scarcely seen for the rest of the voyage.

As the night wore on, things got worse. After our station Orest decided to do a reverberation measurement to fill in the time until dawn. He piped up to the bridge:

"Can I start?"

"Ready when you are," replied Pete Reynell.

Orest lowered his hydrophone, which immediately became entangled in a ship's propeller, still slowly turning after the last manoeuvre. The hydrophone was lost, and hours were spent untangling the cable from the propeller by running it slowly forwards and backwards. It was a bad night, but at least the dawn core was successful, a 20 foot specimen containing foraminifera alternating with volcanic rock fragments. Roger claimed to have found a new species of *Globorotalia* amongst the foraminifera; to my unpractised eye it was impossible to differentiate among the chaos of shells of different shapes and sizes. The experienced 'foram' specialist can tell these tiny skeletons apart by the shapes and numbers of chambers in their shells. When food is caught in the spines small strands of protoplasm stream out from tiny holes in the shell, surrounding the food fragment and digesting it outside the shell. Then they stream back into the shell. The shells of dead forams sink to the seabed and form the huge deposits of globigerina ooze which coat much of the bottom of the world ocean. When compressed and uplifted they form the familiar chalk strata such as the White Cliffs of Dover.

At the bottle station Iver sent down a couple of eggs, attached to the pinger, to 2,700 metres. They came up whole, but an analysis of the contents showed that seawater had been absorbed by the shell, which became porous under the enormous pressure.

On June 7 we reached the northern limit of our long section, at 57°30'N. The northward run from the Antarctic ice edge had been over 7,000 miles, the longest oceanographic section ever attempted, and indeed the longest that it is possible to attempt. Unfortunately, according to von Arx, it was just a little too short. When we stopped we were over the Aleutian Trench, and a few more miles would have taken us up onto the Alaskan continental shelf where the gravity field has been accurately surveyed by the United States Geological Survey. This would have given us a tie point for the end of the gravity line. But public relations could not be allowed to take second place to mere science; the arrival time in Vancouver was sacred, so we had to turn.

The end of the survey was marked by a party in the lounge, in which long-hoarded bottles of champagne were uncorked. I celebrated in short bursts during watchkeeping, and at 3 a.m. had the pleasure of watching the sun rise over the Gulf of Alaska through a narrow strip of clear sky between the grey sea and the ever-present rolling cloudbanks. At this time of year it never became completely dark, and a red strip stayed on the horizon throughout the night.

Next evening, to continue the celebration we had a squid orgy, the subject being Ken's fine specimen which had been preserved in the freezer. Ken and I cut it up while Ted Yoshinari did the cooking. We tried it fried in butter and soy sauce, and boiled in water, soy sauce and lemon juice. Either way it tasted fine, without any trace of a rubbery texture. C S Wong drank the liquid from the boiling as a soup, and told us of his other favourite squid dishes such as squid eye soup, boiled squid ink, and raw squid meat marinated for a few days in chopped-up innards. We declined to test these recipes.

The run in to Vancouver took three days. Clocks went on by an hour and the weather became gradually warmer. On the third day land appeared to the east in the form of a distant skyline of hills covered in a blanket of dark green forest. It was the wild rainy west coast of Vancouver Island, and a deeply moving moment for the crew. Here was the first sight of their native land for seven months. Sparky connected the P.A. system to the local radio station, to reveal the clear voice of Anne Murray singing 'The Snowbird'. There was scarcely a dry eye in the ship.

During the afternoon we entered the Strait of Juan de Fuca, with the great snow-capped ranges of the Olympic Mountains in Washington State to the south of us. We skirted the southern tip of Vancouver Island and then edged in to the outer harbour of Victoria, where we dropped anchor for a couple of hours while some engine room spares were ferried out to us. The capital of British Columbia looked extremely inviting on this sparkling summer afternoon, in contrast to the grimmer skyline of Halifax. Everything was in Technicolor, from the blue ruffled wavelets in the harbour to the attractive buildings behind.

"Just wait till you see it properly," enthused Pete Reynell, whose parents lived on the island. "It's like everything that England could have been but isn't."

As evening drew on we raised anchor and threaded our way through the Gulf of Georgia towards Vancouver. The Gulf is studded with hilly wooded islands which looked romantic in the red glow of sunset.

"That one's Saltspring Island," said Pete, pointing out a large island with a conical hill at the centre, "and there's Galiano Island in front of it and Pender Island to the right. Some day I'm going to buy land on one of those and settle down. By the way, make sure you're up early to see the entrance to Vancouver Harbour."

Early rising was difficult, because Pete and I spent a long boozy evening while he talked reverently of the lovely village of Deep Cove north of Victoria where his parents lived, and of the relaxed 'west coast' feel of Vancouver Island which makes it a different world from the puritanism of Nova Scotia. However, I managed to emerge into the pine-scented clarity of a perfect morning just in time to see an enormous suspension bridge floating above me. It ran between two high bluffs covered with apparently uninhabited forest. This was Lion's Gate Bridge, guarding the entrance to Vancouver. But where was the city? The wooded wilderness to the right of the bridge is in fact an urban park, Stanley Park, which hides the city from those who approach by sea. As we passed under the bridge an immense harbour opened up to my gaze. On the south side was a big cluster of skyscraper office blocks marking downtown Vancouver. And, miraculously, the docks for which we were heading lay at the foot of this thicket of towers, in the very centre of town.

Waiting on the dock were three figures; one I recognised immediately as George Pickard, while the other two were Iver Duedall's wife and the Captain's wife. We tied up at 8:10 a.m. on June 12 and felt ourselves home again. For me the homely sensation was curiously strong, and I sensed that the West Coast of Canada was going to play a part in my future life.

CHAPTER 17

BRITISH COLUMBIA AND THE ROCKIES

And through the night, behind the wheel, the mileage clicking west;
I think upon Mackenzie, David Thompson and the rest
Who cracked the mountain ramparts and did make a path for me,
To race the roaring Fraser to the sea.

The Northwest Passage
Stan Rogers

V ANCOUVER WAS A GLORIOUS city in that summer of 1970. It was still the era of 'flower power' and rock music, and the city glowed with light, colour and warmth. For the first time I realised what a massive, unbridgeable gulf there is between the east and west coasts of the North American continent. Youth and vibrant strength seemed to shine out of Vancouver. I spent the first morning ashore wandering the downtown streets, mingling with the noisy, colourful crowds and marvelling at the street life. Long-haired freaks stood on street corners selling the *Georgia Straight* underground newspaper. 'Head' shops sold the approved paraphernalia for smoking marijuana, as well as the orthodox uniform of beads, Indian dresses, flowery shirts and smelly Afghan shoulder bags. Everything was so wonderfully innocent, and life seemed to hold infinite possibilities. Halifax was never like this.

After lunch a bus picked up the scientific staff from the ship and whisked us westward out through the suburbs to the wooded peninsula on which the University of British Columbia (UBC) is perched. Here we were treated to a reception at the Faculty Club at which all the old faces of the Chilean survey reappeared – George Pickard, Brian Bary waving his hook at me, Dave, Murray and the rest. Drink and reminiscences flowed freely. I was entranced by the beautiful setting of the university. The buildings nestle in a fragrant resinous forest on a magnificent peninsula of reserved land, with views out across water in three directions. To the north lay snow-capped mountains and fjords as spectacular as any in Chile.

In the evening Roger and I headed into the former skid row district of the city, called Gastown, which had been recently renovated as a trendy area of shops, bars and restaurants. The harmless drunks and derelicts had been tidied away out of sight. We were, of course, girl hunting, but found that in this respect Vancouver did not live up to the Chilean example. Or perhaps Canadian girls just didn't seem exotic enough. At all events we were forced to retire, pure in body if not in mind, to our virginal bunks.

Next morning I went out to UBC by myself, talked to Brian Bary and George Pickard, and arranged to come and work for them for a while as a research assistant. *Hudson* was due to go over to Esquimalt (the naval dockyard suburb of Victoria) to be drydocked for repairs, a job that might take four weeks. BIO had raised the awkward question of whether they should keep paying me for this period if I was doing nothing. My offer to go and work at UBC satisfied the BIO management that I would be gainfully employed, while UBC viewed the arrangement as a casual one. It was decided that I would travel with *Hudson* over to Esquimalt then return with a UBC gang who were coming over by truck to unload some equipment from *Hudson*.

With my immediate future settled, I caught a bus to the Maritime Museum, which also looks out over the sea and mountains. My visit was a pilgrimage to view the Royal Canadian Mounted Police schooner *St. Roch*, the first ship to sail both ways through the Northwest Passage in 1940-2 (eastbound) and 1944 (westbound). Her captain was the famous Inspector Henry Larsen, a traditional maritime hero of Scandinavian origin who was known and loved throughout the Arctic. The motor schooner was a tiny wooden vessel, in a poor state of repair (she has since been completely renovated) and looking impossibly frail. If she could do it, so could *Hudson*.

That evening *Hudson* returned UBC's hospitality by giving a cocktail party on board for them and for local dignitaries. Afterwards I escaped with Rog, Pete Reynell, and Pete's attractive sister Vicky, who had come over from Victoria to meet him. We returned to Gastown where we sat in a smoky den, drank apple juice at exorbitant prices, and listened to a folk guitarist.

The next day was a Sunday, and an open house had been organised and heavily advertised in the Vancouver press. We were all conscripted to man positions along a tour route through the ship. My job was to demonstrate the computer. Two hours before the ship was open, a massive queue had gathered on the dock. Chaos ensued when they surged on board. Six thousand glossy brochures had been printed, which soon disappeared. More than ten thousand people tramped through the vessel. I bathed in the admiration of local maidens, to whom I demonstrated the flashing lights whilst talking of the perils of Cape Horn. But dalliance was not possible, for we were sailing that night for Esquimalt.

We slipped through the Straits of Georgia as I slept, and first light found us at the Esquimalt fuelling jetty. Esquimalt harbour is a large, peaceful expanse indented with rocky points and promontories, one of which bears a white weatherboarded lighthouse dating from the early days of settlement in the 1840s. The actual naval base, the main centre for Canada's Pacific fleet, takes up only a small part of the outer harbour, and only three frigates lay alongside as we passed. When it was founded, however, Esquimalt was a major British base; Captain Scott was stationed here as a young man, and had a romance with a local girl called Kathleen O'Reilly. The fuelling jetty was deep in the neglected inner part of the harbour, where quiet waters lapped against rotting pilings.

I learned that the UBC gang would not arrive until the next day, so I disappeared and caught a bus for Victoria where I spent the rest of the day. It was an extraordinarily attractive town. It is the capital of the province because it was by far the largest city when British Columbia acquired provincial status. Since that time, however, history has passed Victoria by; Vancouver, on the mainland, at the mouth of a great river, and at the end of the Canadian Pacific and Canadian National Railways, developed into a mighty city, while Victoria dreamed away the years as a backwater populated mainly by retired prairie farmers and genteel emigrants from England. As a result it resembles a blend of Bournemouth and Dodge City. The Dodge City part comes from the architecture of the inner city, which dates from the late 19th Century, with false fronts and shaded sidewalks like any Hollywood cowboy town. The Bournemouth part comes from the ponderous Victorian civic architecture of the Parliament Buildings and, most of all, the Empress Hotel. This splendid brick pile stands beside the inner harbour and is renowned for its English afternoon teas. Fish and chip shops and other establishments, authentic or otherwise, underlined the fact that, for the purposes of tourists from the USA, we were in Olde Englande.

Next morning the truck from UBC arrived with Murray Storm and Dave English. I helped them load up some sampling gear from *Hudson's* hold, then we set off together northwards for the Vancouver ferry. The road led for 18 miles out of the city and into the pleasant rolling countryside of the Saanich Peninsula. Again, it was much like England and quite unlike the rough scrubby woods of Nova Scotia. The land was cleared a century ago for farming, and now consisted of neat English-style fields, with hedgerows, mock-Tudor houses and winding country lanes. At the northern tip of the peninsula we entered the Swartz Bay ferry terminal and ran the truck into one of the big BC Ferries which maintain the link with the mainland. The route is impressive because the vessel has to traverse a narrow passage between two islands, making an awkward right angle turn in the narrowest part of the channel, called Active Pass, where there are strong tidal currents. The turn is made more dangerous by the fishing and pleasure boats which hang around in the Pass, a good fishing area. Just a month later, one of these great ferries was cut in two by a Russian freighter attempting to enter the Pass, with the loss of four lives. After two hours we landed at Tsawwassen, a small village near the Canadian-US border. A piece of the USA lay just a few hundred yards to our right as we drove ashore, but amusingly it was only a tiny peninsula called Point Roberts, completely cut off from the rest of the USA by Canadian territory thanks to an error by the boundary commission.

Back at UBC we unloaded, and I found that the university had arranged a room for me in a student residence. Next day I started work, and was set to helping Tom Osborn, a physical oceanographer, in the construction of a free-falling microstructure probe of his own design. It had been recently discovered that in the upper ocean the temperature and salinity often do not change steadily with increasing depth (as assumed from the results of Knudsen bottle casts) but rather in a series of steps. Each step is only a few metres deep, so the structure is a series of thin uniform layers of water and slightly different properties, like pages of a book. This structure is very delicate, and easily destroyed by wind-induced turbulence. Tom designed a probe which falls through the water, revolving as it goes, with a temperature sensor to map the microstructure. At some preset depth it drops a weight and rises again to the surface.

I worked happily away on this project for the rest of the week, visiting the small UBC research ship *Vector* and being initiated into the mysteries of American football by my room-mate in the residence. Then on the Saturday I accepted an invitation from Pete to come over to the Island and visit his family. They lived in Deep Cove, a small village on a beautiful fjord called Saanich Inlet near the Swartz Bay ferry terminal. The houses of the village were sunk in a dense forest of fir, spruce and cedar, surrounding a tiny cove where sailing boats rode at anchor. Pete's father, John Reynell, had owned a coastal shipping company in Borneo and had led an adventurous life. His stepmother, Tilly, was a beautiful Eurasian who had been a stewardess on Cathay Pacific Airways when they still flew flying boats. They were a happy and welcoming family. I talked away the hours with John, and went flying on a free lesson from the nearby Victoria Airport above the emerald mosaic of Gulf Islands. Next day we explored the islands properly in the family's old wooden boat. It was on that day that I decided that this was where I wanted to live. Amongst the Gulf Islands I was surrounded by the most beautiful scenery that I have ever encountered, outside of Chile, and even after a life-time of further travels I have seen nothing to match it. The sun glowed in a perfectly blue sky. The calm water was a deep transparent indigo. The maze of islands rose in forest-clad hills and ridges, occasionally erupting into bare brown rock, with clearings for meadows, fields and farmhouses. The smell was of pine resin, seaweed and the richness of high summer. We picnicked on Pender Island, then moored in a deserted cove near Bedwell Harbour to try swimming in the chilly water.

I stayed on for Monday as well, visiting Victoria again and going to a party given by a neighbouring family called the Copelands, where I got to know their attractive daughter Anita. On Monday, too, Pete and I hatched a holiday scheme. His friend had a Volkswagen minibus that he was willing to lend us; this would be a perfect opportunity to tour the Rocky Mountains and to try to get to Calgary for the annual Stampede. We planned to leave on the Thursday. I returned to UBC on Tuesday, resumed my duties for a nominal two days, and obtained Tom's blessing for my disappearance.

Pete arrived in the VW bus in the morning and we drove first into Vancouver to buy camping equipment, then set off eastwards through interminable suburbs, heading for the Trans-Canada Highway and the Rockies. Out in the countryside at last we drove along the wide flat valley of the lower Fraser River, which contains most of the arable land in the province. Great mountains were visible initially in the misty distance on either side of us, then gradually they closed in and the wide corridor of farmland became narrower. Finally the mountains formed a continuous barrier, clad in forest on their lower slopes but with bare rocky tops. The road followed the river up into the mountains, and here we came to the town of Hope, a neat little place with quiet intersecting streets.

It was here that I learned to drive. Up to now Peter had done all the driving, but I needed to do my share, so Pete spent a couple of hours nursing me round the backstreets as I crashed the gears and fumbled for the clutch. Luckily my motorcycling experience served me in good stead, and Pete finally announced that I had passed my driving 'test'. By now evening was drawing on, and only the mountaintops were still bathed in sunlight. We drove on east out of Hope, passing a dreadful scar in the mountain wall that was the site of the Hope Slide. An earth tremor in 1955 caused a massive landslide which inundated the Trans-Canada Highway, burying several cars with their occupants. The earth carried down by the slide still lies in great heaps on the valley floor, and the road has been rebuilt over the top.

Just past the slide we reached a provincial campground, and pulled wearily in. These campsites are always set in deep woods, with showers, toilets and secluded pitches for each vehicle, equipped with a fireplace, a stack of firewood, and a table, all for only (in 1970) three dollars a night. It was a haven of peace. We hauled out our camping gear, lit a fire and cooked steaks for our supper as night fell. Then in the fragrant atmosphere of woodsmoke we talked about life until we could stay awake no longer. Pete pitched his tent, while I slept on the bunk in the bus.

A glorious morning broke, and I discovered that one of life's greatest experiences is breakfast in the open air in the mountains. We set off again with me at the wheel. The road was now winding and dangerous, with a rock wall on one side and a steep drop on the other. The Fraser was narrowing down towards the Fraser Canyon. Almost immediately, by way of warning, we came upon a burning truck in the middle of the highway, surrounded by police cars and ambulances.

Soon we came to the most awesome sight of our journey. The Fraser River narrows into a raging torrent as it pours through a gap that it has worn through the mountain barrier. In the Fraser Canyon there is no level land. Its rock walls are sheer. Clinging to it, in fact excavated from it by explosives, are no fewer than three thoroughfares; the Trans-Canada Highway, the Canadian Pacific Railway, and the Canadian National Railway. At Hell's Gate, where the torrent is wildest, concrete weirs control the flow, with fish ladders (a series of concrete channels) built along one side to enable migrating salmon to get up the river past the works of man. The water was green-brown and turbid with its load of rock flour carried down from the glaciers of the distant Rockies. The canyon went in this fashion for twenty miles. The western backbone of Canada is so wild that man is hopelessly dwarfed and diminished in its presence. No great poems or paintings have been created about British Columbia; its primaeval quality exceeds the reach of man's mind.

The days that followed produced a succession of such wonderful experiences. We drove up the Yellowhead Highway towards Jasper National Park at the northern entrance to the Rockies. After 400 miles on the road we camped under Mount Robson, at 12,972 feet the highest point in the Canadian Rockies Our campsite was a convivial place. Two tug o'war teams were meeting here for an encounter to celebrate the opening of the new highway. One was from Kamloops, the other from faraway Prince Rupert on the northwest coast of the province. The jovial master of ceremonies invited us over to his camper for beer and steaks. The beer-drinking was held to be a training exercise for the athletes, and went on happily until late in the evening.

We crossed the Yellowhead Pass, at 3,760 feet, which took us out of British Columbia and into Jasper National Park in Alberta. Here we spent days driving out to admire glaciers, lakes and mountains. I realized that my own (adopted) country had scenery and natural magnificence every bit as great as that of Chile and the Andes. Wildlife was prolific and tame. Groups of deer would wander across the road, chipmunks would scuttle from the rocks to beg food, and tame squirrels descend on us from the trees. One evening, our campsite was invaded by a flock of Rocky Mountain Dall sheep, with tightly curved horns. They wandered quite boldly up to us, and Pete found that they enjoyed eating cornflakes. Eventually one of them started choking – he had eaten his way down to the free plastic spaceman.

We drove on down the 170 mile Icefield Highway which links Jasper to Banff along the spine of the Rockies. It was a drive through stupendous scenery. We came upon the Columbia Icefield, a very large ice cap (the largest in continental North America) which has an outlet glacier running down almost to the road. In fact in the past it straddled the valley where the road now runs; successive stages of its retreat as the climate grew milder since the Ice Age ended are marked by terminal moraines, ridges of sediment a few yards high and a few hundred yards apart. It was a dramatic demonstration of climatic change and what it can do to the world; since 1970 it has continued to retreat and when I visited it again in 2008 the snout was more than half a mile from the road.

We continued southward, the VW bus labouring over the Bow Pass at 6,785 feet, and coasted down towards one of the world's loveliest sights, Lake Louise in the Banff National Park. A perfect amphitheatre of grey rock and white shining glacier enclosed a lake of limpid emerald blue. After camping at the lake we pressed on and came to Banff, the townsite for the Banff National Park, a neat little town on the Bow River. It originated in 1882 as 'Siding 29' of the CPR, a stopping place which allowed visitors to climb to some recently discovered sulphur hot springs. To prevent rapacious exploitation of the springs by squabbling pioneers who claimed rights over it, the Canadian Government established the first nucleus of a national park in 1885. This tiny 10 square mile area, called Rocky Mountain Park, was the beginning of the enormous national park system of today.

After camping and exploring the beauties of Banff we moved on to the big city of Calgary. The Rockies came to an end very suddenly. In twenty miles we were out of the National Park, and the terrain changed rapidly from tall peaks to modest foothills and then to prairie. Great square fields of ripe wheat stretched to the horizon, bereft of hedgerows, trees or anything to soften their harshness. Soon the city of Calgary came into view, a ragged suburban sprawl enclosing a small downtown district of high office blocks. We headed for the city campsite, a great disappointment after the unspoilt beauty of the mountains. It was situated on a small island in the middle of the Bow River. by now wider and more sluggish than when it passed through Banff. The island was sparsely wooded, crowded with tents, and infested with vicious mosquitoes. We made haste to pitch our tent and explored the city, a hot, dusty cow town now being transformed into a glossy centre for the oil industry. We were more used to wild nature, so we headed back to Banff. Here we continued our search for feminine company. We found a cellar club full of delightful girls, and I became friends with an archaeological student from the University of Saskatchewan. I took her up another mountain ski lift the next day; this was Sulphur Mountain, where the University of Calgary has a cosmic ray station at the top. We hiked over to the station, knocked on the door and were welcomed by a friendly Dutchman who was in charge of the place, and who behaved as if he knew us, or was expecting us. He showed us round the stacks of cosmic ray counters, and invited us round to his house for the evening. We were mystified and assumed that he had mistaken us for somebody else. However, we spent a pleasant day boating on the river and picnicking, then went round to his house for drinks. He then insisted on taking us out to dinner at the Rimrock Hotel, which lay on a ridge overlooking the town. We effusively thanked our friendly host, but never solved the problem of who he thought we were.

Pete now telephoned home and found to his disappointment that his grandmother had appeared without warning from England, and that he was required to pay respects to this elderly and apparently formidable lady. We regretfully had to take leave of our new friends, and set off westward. We decided to take a more southerly road home, so as not to reproduce our outward route. Just past Lake Louise, therefore, we turned southwest to cross the spine of the Rockies through the Kicking Horse Pass. This again was a magnificent sight, mainly because of the engineering skill by which the CPR was driven through the mountains. The railroad spirals downwards through the centre of a mountain, emerging in a series of viaduct loops between the tunnels. As we gazed down on this sight from the road, we saw a freight train of more than a hundred wagons negotiate the Pass, filling three of the loops at once like a long worm curling its way through an apple.

On we drove into British Columbia along Highway 1. Again I was driving, when I glanced briefly out of the side window at a garbage dump in a clearing, from which smoke was spiralling. Suddenly I saw a movement near it. A bear! We stopped, leaped out of the car and advanced upon the bear with our cameras at the ready. The creature was snuffling around the dump, looking for titbits. It was a black bear, a large but apparently harmless creature which shambled around on all fours. At first he seemed unconcerned by our presence. Then as we drew nearer he edged away. We came on further. Suddenly we realised that he was edging around us in order to cut off our retreat to the road. We fled slowly in a dignified British manner.

We camped for the night at Sicamous, a typical small town among the forests and mountains of central BC. A deep cold mountain stream, called Yard Creek, ran through the campsite. It was to be our last night in the mountains. By now I was burned to a deep brown, and was used to the routine of sleeping out in the wine-like air of the mountain nights, with the Milky Way shining overhead and a lingering smell of woodsmoke in the wind. I was used to cooking steaks over a wood fire and discussing the philosophy of life with Pete. It was a pity that, like all the good things in life, it had to end.

We set off early the next morning, with Vancouver our goal. The road took us through the Okanagan Valley, a parched desert region which has been irrigated for fruit growing. Amid the orchards we found several vineyards, making authentically bad British Columbian wine. We stopped at Penticton at the southern end of the lake, where the Dominion Astrophysical Observatory maintains a large radio telescope. On the strength of my Cambridge background we were given a complete tour of the facilities. On we drove, coming at last to Hope via the southern road which avoids the excitement of the Fraser Canyon. From here it was but a 100 mile drive to the sprawling suburbs of Vancouver, where we eventually located the house where Vicky, Pete's sister, was staying. Here we wearily bedded down for the night.

It was now July 7th, and *Hudson* was due to sail on the 12th for her geophysical cruise to the Queen Charlotte Islands, off northern British Columbia. I thought that I should report back to UBC, so I drove out there and met Tom Osborn. Far from being annoyed at my long absence, he promptly offered me a place as a graduate student at UBC. This was a serious offer and an attractive opportunity. I decided to stay on at UBC to think about it. Again I was put in a student residence, sharing a room with a student from Sarawak. Apart from a brief trip to Stanley Park Aquarium to see the performing killer whales, I stayed on the campus for three days, talking to scientists about possible research projects and receiving a formal offer from Bob Stewart, the head of department.

Still undecided, I caught the ferry over to the Island, where I was met by Pete and accommodated in his parents' house. A round of parties with family and friends followed, and I put off my decision until the end of the geophysical cruise, which now loomed bleakly before me. But I renewed my personal vow that, whatever life might bring, I would return one day to live on Vancouver Island.

CHAPTER 18

A GEOPHYSICAL INTERLUDE

"Xhaaidlagha Gwaayaai"
Islands at the boundary of the World
Haida name for Queen Charlotte Islands

AFTER THE WONDERFUL EXPERIENCE of western Canada, the prospect of spending three weeks at sea on a marine geophysical cruise did not appeal. But there was nothing to be done about it, if I wanted to stay on the payroll of the Bedford Institute. Besides, this would be a final chance to see if marine geophysics could be interesting enough for me to make it my career.

In many ways this leg, Phase VII of "Hudson-70", would involve some fascinating science. We were not going anywhere exotic, in fact we were operating in well-known waters, but we would be striving to put in place another piece of the jigsaw puzzle that is the pattern of plates over the Earth's crust. The Sixties had been an exciting decade for marine geophysics, in which the theory of seafloor spreading, or continental drift, had suddenly taken over as the new orthodoxy after being ridiculed and ignored since Alfred Wegener proposed it in 1912. Now everyone believed that the Earth's crust is made of plates which move at a speed of a few centimetres per year, and which spread apart from mid-ocean ridges where new crust is created. These new pieces of crust grind past each other or collide at faults where earthquakes and the upthrusting of fold mountains are palpable signs of the mighty forces at work. But the actual pattern of plates was not yet firmly established over the whole world, due to the shortage of scientists and ships to do the necessary survey work. Here off the west coast of Canada three plates meet (the American, Juan de Fuca and Pacific Plates) in what is known as a 'triple point', a zone of

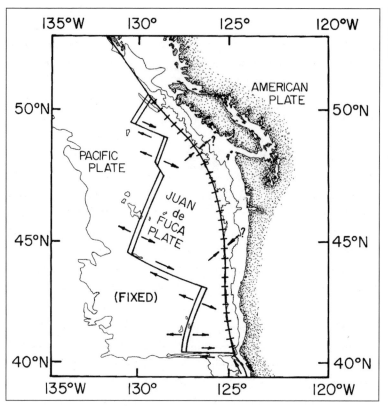

Tectonic plates in the North Pacific.

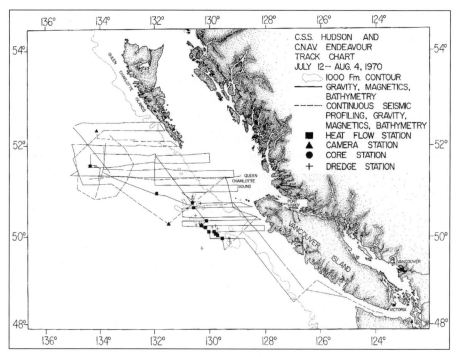

Plan of the Queen Charlottes survey.

extreme complexity where the structures and motions involved cannot be easily determined theoretically, so that direct field measurements must be made.

These measurements would be of several kinds. Firstly, the normal gravity and magnetic survey lines would be run; for instance the pattern of magnetic lineations which is produced when the spreading crust solidifies reveals the direction of spreading. Secondly, seismic reflection profiling would be done with the ship under way, a form of glorified echo sounding using a powerful sound source (an air-gun) to produce echoes from internal layers of sediment and bedrock as well as from the seabed itself. The third technique would be seismic refraction shooting, in which one ship fires off an explosive charge while another records the arrival times of sound pulses that have passed down through the water, through various layers of rock and then up through the water to the surface again. This would tell us the actual thicknesses and compositions of the rock layers under the seabed. By shooting in different directions it would be possible to test for anisotropy, a property which some rocks have of transmitting sound with a different velocity in different directions, because of the stresses in the rock produced by seafloor spreading. Finally, a battery of supporting studies would be done, such as measuring heat flow through the seabed, taking cores, and dredging for bottom rocks.

We sailed on the morning of July 12, initially for sea trials to test the newly repaired engines. I arrived at Esquimalt just in time to catch the ship, and found that in my absence my giant poster of a Tahitian belle, chief source of my fantasy life in the North Pacific, had disappeared from my cabin bulkhead. More ominously, a large diesel compressor had been bolted to the deck immediately above my cabin. The compressor was to run the air-gun for the seismic reflection profiling. The air-gun is a 300 cubic inch cavity pumped full of compressed air which is released every 16 seconds; this gives the loud underwater belching noise needed to penetrate the upper layer of seafloor sediments. Where the sediments are thin it is possible to see bedrock beneath the sedimentary layers, and to trace this to the places where it outcrops as rock pinnacles. Since this type of profiling is carried out with the ship under way, the compressor was clearly going to operate continuously directly above my head. An indication of just how nasty it was going to be came when the system was run up for testing during the day. The results were frightening. The noise in the cabin was like that of a pneumatic drill, while the bulkheads and deckhead were visibly vibrating.

We ran up and down Juan de Fuca Strait during the morning, shuddering and shaking as full power was applied to all four engines. At 3 p.m. we put back to the pilot station at the mouth of Esquimalt Harbour where the Marine Superintendent and other officials were taken off by pilot boat. We had been pronounced seaworthy. Without further ado, or another night in port (for which I had been hoping) we put out to sea.

Charlie Maunsell was chief scientist for this leg, with Dave Ross in charge of the geophysical work, assisted by Charlotte Keen, Shiri Srivastava, Don Barrett, Keith Manchester and other BIO geophysicists. Dave gave me the 12-4 satellite watch, sharing with two students, Mike Purdy and Earl Davis. Earl was a graduate student at the University of Washington, while Mike had just completed his degree at Imperial College, London, and was about to go on to the Geophysics Department at Cambridge to do his doctoral research. Three of the normal faces were absent on leave: the Doctor; the Chief Engineer, who was replaced by a pleasant Scot called Gilmore; and the Captain, who was replaced by Fred Mauger, the Chief Mate.

The first night watch passed quietly. We were still in the Juan de Fuca Strait, the coasts of which showed up clearly on the 24-mile range of the radar, with strong reflections off mountainsides inland. The watchkeeper on the geophysical console was Brian Taylor, a UBC student doing a summer job on board. This was his first time at sea, and although the sea was calm he was as sick as a dog. I felt very sorry for him. But when I went below at 4 a.m. I felt more sorry for myself. The air gun had begun operations, and the noise in my cabin from the compressor was deafening. It was impossible to remain within the cabin, let alone sleep, so I moved my mattress into the photographic darkroom behind the geochemistry laboratory, where I lay down amongst the bottles and chemical odours. Thus poisoned, I slept fitfully, thrashing around in my sleep and smashing the darkroom safelight which I had modified to serve as a bedside lamp.

I awoke feeling ragged and sick. The day was calm, cold and sunny and we had a view of jagged snow-capped mountains in northwest Vancouver Island, 30 miles away; their rugged outline was quite different from the gentle summery countryside around Victoria. We ploughed steadily northwards, and by the morning of July 15 we were 50 miles south of the Queen Charlotte Islands, awaiting our rendezvous with the CNAV (Canadian Navy Auxiliary Vessel) *Endeavour*, which was to be our companion for the seismic refraction work. The technique calls for the two ships to begin close together. One ship then steams away from the other, dropping charges of gradually increasing size as the distance increases. The other ship remains stationary with a floating cable trailing behind, in which an array of hydrophones picks up the sounds of the explosion after transmission through the sedimentary layers.

Endeavour drew alongside early in the afternoon, a handsome white ship operated by the Defence Research Board in Esquimalt, with a high fo'c's'l and a helicopter hangar aft. We streamed our 400 ft long hydrophone cable, supported by red plastic floats. *Endeavour* sailed off, dropping her charges over the stern. In the quiet of our hove-to state each charge sounded as a faint boom through the steel of our hull. She disappeared into the sea mist, and after a few hours we set off to join her for a fresh rendezvous and a second line. The work that she was doing was quite dangerous, for the largest charge that she dropped, at the greatest distance from us, contained 500 pounds of TNT, making it larger than the average depth charge. Today the whole technique has changed; instead of a floating hydrophone cable, the receiving ship places its sensors on the seabed, well away from wave noise, and the shooting ship can use charges as small as a quarter of a pound.

On our way northwards we had marked the second rendezvous spot by mooring a radar transponder buoy there. This buoy had a beacon activated by pulses from our own ship's radar, which would then transmit a signal back to a receiver on board *Hudson* giving range and bearing information, thus allowing us to fix our position more exactly than by satnav alone. Unfortunately this beacon did not work and we finally found the buoy as a faint radar blip when we were almost on top of it. Off went *Endeavour* again, initially in the wrong direction, while we leaned over the stern and tried to snare the evil looking globular jellyfish which abounded in this part of the ocean. So passed the second and then a third seismic line.

At the end of the set of lines we returned to the transponder buoy, which was a red and yellow polystyrene float some seven feet in diameter, hauled it out of the water and replaced it by a spare. The electronics in the ship still picked up nothing, so the fault clearly lay in our receiver rather than the buoy. We also met up with *Endeavour* again, picking up 25 pounds of salt from her and doing a deal whereby our awful movies were exchanged for her good ones.

Now came the important anisotropy experiment. Previous research had shown that the rocks in the Earth's mantle – the 1,500 mile thick layer underlying the crust – must themselves be flowing sluggishly, since they show a difference in properties in different directions. In particular the velocity of compressional P-waves (a type of sound wave) in the mantle varies with direction, with the highest velocity corresponding roughly to the direction of motion of the overlying crust. To measure these velocities in all directions the shooting ship must steam a circle around the receiving ship, and this is what was done. We hove-to with our hydrophones out, while *Endeavour* steamed off for 75 km and then ran a circle of that radius around us, letting off no fewer than 58 charges of up to 500 pounds in weight. When Charlotte Keen and Don Barrett came to analyse the results afterwards, they found that there is an anisotropy of about 8% in velocity, but the direction of maximum velocity is 107° whereas the direction of crustal spreading, inferred from the magnetic pattern, is 90°. The discrepancy suggests that perhaps the crust does not move with the upper part of the mantle, but in a somewhat different direction, like ice floes on the surface of the sea.

On July 19, for a change, we tried a heat flow station. The idea here is to lower a probe into the seabed to measure the vertical flow of heat from the Earth's crust up into the ocean. In the interior of the Earth the decay of radioactive isotopes, especially those of uranium, thorium and potassium, produces the heat which keeps the earth's core molten and which drives convection currents which in turn generate the earth's magnetism. The heat flows radially outwards from the liquid core into the surrounding mantle, believed to be a plastic solid which can be made to flow slowly. The sluggish convection currents in the mantle produce horizontal motion at its surface which drags the overlying crust along with it – although not perfectly, as we had just discovered. We would expect the vertical heat flow through the crust to be greatest over places where the crust is thin, or over spreading centres, since these mark the lines of upward convection from the mantle.

The heat flow measurements were carried out by Clive Lister, an Englishman from the University of Washington. He used an instrument called a Bullard probe after its inventor, the man who got me on to "Hudson-70". The probe is a 7 foot long steel rod with a finned weight at its top end to drive it into the seabed. Along the rod at equal intervals are 27 thermistors (a type of transistor which measures temperature). The probe is driven into the bottom and left there for half an hour to reach equilibrium. Then the 27 temperatures are recorded, giving the temperature gradient in the sediment. This is not enough to determine the heat flow, because we need to know the thermal conductivity of the material in the sediment. This is measured by switching on heaters which warm the central thermistors by a known amount, then measuring the new temperatures of the outermost, unheated thermistors. From these measurements both the conductivity of the sediment and the vertical heat flow are obtained. A typical value is about 2 microcalories per square centimetre per second. On July 19 we found 2.7, but Clive went on to do several more heat flow measurements, including a series of seven stations ten days later over the Explorer Ridge, a spreading centre between the Juan de Fuca Plate and the Pacific Plate, at 50° 21'N, 130° 7' W, where new crust is being created. Here Clive was lucky enough to measure 16.8 microcalories, the greatest heat flow ever recorded from the ocean bed. What he did not realise then was that this is a region with a high density of hydrothermal vents, narrow 'chimneys' only 1-2 metres across through which molten and even vaporous material is vented up to the seabed. Such vents were not discovered until the late 1970s, and it is likely that Clive's extremely high measurement was done only a few metres from an unsuspected vent.

On the first heat flow station we were overhauled by five Japanese whale-catchers, heading northwest at high speed for the whaling grounds in the Bering Sea where they were busy slaughtering the last of the bowhead (right) whales. Our little survey box was full of marine life, although there were no biologists aboard to study it. One day a huge school of over 100 porpoises surrounded the ship, and we saw the occasional right whale. Black-browed albatrosses were also common, and one evening a small black storm petrel came on board, flying as usual into a floodlight. The poor creature spent the night vomiting, and although he was kept in a sink in the laboratory and fed with a pipette, he died within a day. At every station I noticed huge swarms of jellyfish, like small inflated plastic bags, so dense as to be herded together into bunches by the waves.

Two days later we finished the seismic refraction work, which had gone well despite continuous problems with the old, patched hydrophone cable that we were using. *Endeavour* left us, heading for Port Hardy in northern Vancouver Island. We now began a long and tedious series of east-west survey lines, each line terminating near the sodden rainswept coast of the Queen Charlottes. By now I was thoroughly fed up with the tedium of the survey work, made worse by the foul weather, which was like an English November of continuous overcast, chill and rain. The Canadian record for rainfall, over 250 inches per year, is held by a nearby mainland town called Ocean Falls. The only excitement was an attempt at bottom photography of a seamount at 52°10'N, 134°W, again by Clive Lister. We hove-to over the seamount, lowered the camera and moved slowly ahead. The instrument comprised a home-made steel frame contraption carrying the camera, which ran continuously for 15 minutes taking movie film at 5 frames per second, and a thallium iodide light source which emits in the 'green window' of the spectrum, a region where sea water is unusually transparent. The camera worked but the light source did not, so the seamount's appearance remained unknown to science. Later Clive got the camera to work on another seamount, showing ripple marks on the seabed which are evidence of strong bottom currents.

To make matters worse, the compressor above my head started to operate again as we began the seismic reflection profiling. Life was now truly a misery, and I sank rapidly towards being a physical and mental wreck. This period was absolutely the worst of the whole "Hudson-70" expedition. I remember one night coming off watch at 4 a.m. with Brian Taylor, cooking bacon and eggs in the pantry, and finding Bill Shaw the Chief Steward lying face down and totally comatose in the conference room. One of his boots had somehow found its way into the dining room. Normally his drunken stupors seemed rather squalid, but this time I felt a profound fellow feeling for him and his attempt to escape from the realities of life.

I tried to get out of my low state by exercising. I calculated that 160 circuits of the geochemistry laboratory or 48 circuits of the upper deck equalled one mile. The upper deck was inaccessible because of torrential rain, so I tried 80 circuits of the lab. I ended up very bored, very dizzy and rather bruised from knocking against desks and chairs. Another therapeutic project was a ship's newspaper, for which Pat Solowen (a secretary from BIO, on board to keep the survey's paperwork in order) was the editor and typist. I laboured manfully over a lengthy article of high literary quality about the British Club in Punta Arenas. Unfortunately the other contributions were not up to the same standard, and consisted mainly of doggerel, Newfie jokes, and anonymous squibs to let off steam, such as:-

All things bright and beautiful,
All creatures great and small;
All things wise and wonderful
Our Doctor shoots them all.

My hopes of deliverance were raised briefly by a total engine breakdown on July 25, when we lay-to helplessly for three hours. While the engineers scurried to and fro I lay luxuriantly in my bunk, free at last of the compressor noise. A conference was held to discuss putting back into port, but it was decided to carry on. We ran more west-east lines, one of which brought us right into the entrance to Quatsino Inlet in northern Vancouver Island. The inlet was filled with small fishing vessels, with forests rising behind, but the intense rain made the scene utterly dispiriting.

But time passes, even at sea, and by August 4 it was all over. I was so exhausted when the compressor noise finally ceased that I slept right through our early morning arrival in Esquimalt and far into the afternoon. And so ended any interest I might have had in a career in marine geophysics. I felt sure that it was the sea that fascinated me, not the rocks at the bottom of it, and I was grateful for the hard lesson.

What remained? Only one precious week in western Canada before the hard road to the Arctic. On the evening of our arrival there was the normal cocktail party and open house on board. Next morning I set off with Harvey, my friend from the engine room, for a visit to Vancouver in his rental car. The trip showed me a side of Vancouver life that I hadn't seen before. We called on a friend of his, Jim, who lived with his parents in a typical characterless suburb called Port Moody. Jim was an authentic Sixties figure, friendly yet inarticulate, his mind addled by drugs. His pride and joy was his Harley-Davidson chopper, lovingly converted in slavish imitation of the bikes in *Easy Rider*. We set off for a drive around town in which Jim wanted to visit some 'friends'. The friends also lived in normal suburban houses, and each visit lasted only a few minutes, during which a package changed hands. It did not take me long to realise that Jim was a drug pusher, and he openly told me the details of his trade. He dealt in marijuana mainly, he said, although some of it was probably "cut with smack", i.e. mixed with heroin, presumably to turn clients on to a more expensive habit. He got his supplies by going every week to another typical suburban house, where the garage had been converted into a warehouse, presided over by two gangsters who toted guns. "I guess they're Mafia," he said, unconcernedly. He viewed his role in life as providing a social service, helping his clients to achieve heightened consciousness. The fact that the proceeds of his transactions went to help an organised crime empire did not concern him. Jim was a pleasant person to talk to, and had no trace of evil about him, but he had one glaring deficiency found in many west coast dwellers, an inability to comprehend reality as a whole. He lived in a world of his own, with his own few ideas, and was a perfect tool of ruthless men. It was a tremendous relief when the day was over; for one thing, we were being followed around town much of the time by police cars, and I was very happy when we caught the ferry back to the island.

The last few days were a whirl of visits to the Reynells in Deep Cove, to the Copelands and their lovely daughter Anita, and to local sights such as the Oak Bay Marina, with its complement of performing killer whales. One day Pete and I hired a catamaran and sailed out over the blue waters of the Straits of Georgia. It was a precious time, soon to be over. Fate was to bring me back to live and work in Victoria, but never with the carefree happiness of that first visit.

I made one more visit to UBC, and almost decided to go there for my PhD. Fatefully, at the same time I received a telex from the Scott Polar Research Institute in Cambridge, to which I had written from South America. They, too, offered me a PhD place. After a year away, the Cambridge that I had been so happy to leave exerted a temporary, but fatal, nostalgic pull. I decided to go to Scott Polar. With this decision made, I bade farewell to the beauty of life in western Canada and prepared to face the unpleasantness of the Arctic.

CHAPTER 19

NORTH TO THE ARCTIC

It was a virtue not to stay,
To go our headstrong and heroic way
Seeking her out at the volcano's head,
Among pack ice, or where the track had faded
Beyond the cavern of the seven sleepers ...

Robert Graves

IT WAS AUGUST THE thirteenth and a gloriously sunny morning, the air filled as usual with the heady scent of deep pine forests. As I stood on the deck of the *Hudson* in Esquimalt Harbour and watched the familiar ritual of the lines being cast off, I should have been filled with eager anticipation. At last we were sailing to complete the first circumnavigation of the Americas, heading into the icy wastes of the Arctic to venture a Northwest Passage to the eastern sea. Nothing could be more romantic. But instead of joy I felt an aching sense of sadness and loss. I had fallen in love with the west coast of Canada. I loved its sense of space and freedom, the beauty of its scenery, the limitless forests and mountains, the painful loveliness of the luminous islands in the Gulf of Georgia, the friendly and relaxed people, and the warm climate. It was so tempting to stay, and to never leave this place. Only my puritan sense of duty and a perverse desire to see "Hudson-70" through to the end kept me on deck instead of on the sunlit dockside with the two pretty girls who were waving us off.

We slid past frigates and freighters and one of the big red weather ships that maintain Ocean Station Papa in the North Pacific. Our journey ended at the fuelling jetty on the far side of the harbour, where *Hudson* would spend the rest of the day taking on no. 2 diesel oil for the 3,200-mile voyage to Herschel Island in the Beaufort Sea. Anxious to drink in the very last of

British Columbia, Peter Reynell and I took a taxi into Victoria where we had lunch on the waterfront and then wandered up past the Chinese temple and school, buying last-minute items and gazing at the life around us. We were two friends, soon to be parted for ever although we did not know it. Pete was leaving his home, and I was leaving a place that I longed to make my home. Neither of us wanted to get back aboard, but I had to attend a scientists' meeting, so reluctantly we trailed back to the ship where the prison doors clanged shut.

My new companions made up a skeleton crew, on board to run basic survey operations as far as Herschel Island, where a large contingent would join to carry out a month-long geophysical survey of the Beaufort Sea. The senior scientist for this leg would be Bernie Pelletier, a sedimentologist from Bedford Institute. Familiar faces were Kegong Shih, Mike Purdy and Vernon Coady from the west coast survey, and Gus Vilks, a veteran from the Rio to Buenos Aires leg. There were two women, a middle-aged palaeontologist called Frances Wagner and a beautiful geologist from the University of Calgary called Chris Havard. Pelletier explained that we would be doing standard gravity, bathymetry and magnetic profiling along the route, and occasionally stopping for oceanographic stations and cores. The Beaufort Sea survey would be the first one ever carried out there, of especial importance because of the possibility of finding offshore oil, and we would be joined for it by *Baffin*, our near-sister which was sailing around from Halifax through the Panama Canal, and by the smaller *Parizeau* of the Pacific Oceanographic Group. Then would come the Northwest Passage if ice conditions were favourable. The route sounded exciting but the work did not; I knew by now that most marine geophysicists lack the oceanographer's love for the sea and for the natural phenomena of the ocean world, and I longed for the inspiring presence of a von Arx or Pickard.

Meanwhile there were the tasks of watchkeeping on the console and satellite navigator to be assigned. Mike Purdy took charge of a party of navigation watchkeepers, while I was to teach three people (Gus, Chris Havard and a geologist from Calgary called Chris Yorath) how to run the console.

Sailing time arrived too soon. We now had a helicopter on board for use in ice reconnaissance, and it was due to go up on a test flight as soon as we left the jetty. I claimed a seat on board in my role as Official Photographer, so as the lines joining us to British Columbia were finally cast off I was climbing into the front seat of the gleaming Bell Jet Ranger of Highland

Helicopters. Strapping myself in and clutching the movie camera I glanced at the middle-aged pilot who was sitting smiling beside me.

"Hello, I'm Wilfred," he said in a cultured English accent. "Is this your first time in a helicopter?"

As I nodded he took off quite suddenly, like an express lift. The harbour, the ship and my stomach were left far below us. Unlike an aeroplane, a helicopter seems to consist mainly of Perspex. The deep nose and side windows, a window in the roof and an alarming window that opened under my feet, all made it easy to see that this thing had no wings. Wilfred hurled the machine into steep banks and climbs over Victoria. The ship, steaming backwards out of her berth, was a tiny speck cleaving a white rent in the deep blue fabric of the sea. After I had recovered enough to do some filming, Wilfred brought us down to a smooth landing on the helicopter pad, which had been repainted with a bullseye target for the occasion.

Twice more he took off with other sightseers. By the time he and his mechanic had finally deflated the floats and run the craft into the hangar on its trolley, Victoria was far off in the heat haze and Vancouver Island was just a low range of wooded hills in the distance. We were far across the Juan de Fuca Strait, sailing towards the misty Olympic Mountains of Washington State. As we went below, Wilfred remarked casually,

"I used to fly Spitfires during the War. They were more fun than helicopters."

When we reached the centre of the Strait we turned west and headed for the open Pacific. The magnetometer was streamed in the evening, and I settled down to the first console watch, made more pleasant by the company of Chris Havard who was learning how to watchkeep from my example.

The next morning was bright and sunny, with the air still full of forest smells. We were now on a Great Circle course for Unimak Pass, the main shipping passage through the Aleutian Islands into the Bering Sea. The sea was an intense dark blue with scattered whitecaps. I could see the mountainous west coast of Vancouver Island off to starboard, between the competing blues of sea and sky. Through glasses I spotted the break in the mountain chain which marks Nootka Sound, Captain Cook's first landfall on the North American coast during his second voyage of 1772-5, and the place where he paused to fell a tree and fit a new mast to one of his ships. Just north of it was the sharp promontory of Cape Cook, beyond which the island fell away towards its northern tip at Cape Scott. By early afternoon the land had disappeared and we were alone again with the infinite Pacific Ocean.

The first station was done in the afternoon, at 50°N, 130°W. A genial biologist named Dan Faber from the Royal Ontario Museum did a vertical plankton tow, while surface tows were done from the bow. Gus Vilks did a core, finding a heavy glutinous sediment which put a 5,000 pound strain on the line as the coring tube was hauled out. Gus, with his colleague Mike Gorveatt of BIO, began the slow patient analysis of the core by taking samples from it at 20 centimetre intervals. As I watched him at work he let me look at one sample through the microscope. A wonderful cluster of glittering jewels flashed before me, made of jagged glassy crystals of quartz, tiny fragments of volcanic rock, and translucent wind-blown dust particles from shore.

My work very quickly became routine. Apart from watchkeeping I was computing the previous day's gravity and magnetic data, a tedious task. Our surroundings became boring as well. We entered a world of overcast, mist and damp in which our horizon shrank to a hundred yards around the ship. The grey miserable region lay only a little to the west of our Queen Charlotte Islands survey area which had been equally depressing. Occasionally out of the murk would appear a Black-footed Albatross, but the birds seemed too morose to stay airborne, and instead of performing their flying display they would flop down into our wake and root around for food in the turbulence. Life was made bearable by visits to Pete Reynell's cabin to sample his rum and the home-made cookies baked for us by Anita.

Then early in the morning of August 18 we ran into a heavy storm, the worst so far on "Hudson-70". I was woken by a heavy roll which threatened to throw me out of my bunk, and shot all the loose contents of my cabin onto the deck. Few people appeared at breakfast. The ship had to reduce speed to 8 knots in the face of a 60 knot wind which was bringing a steep rolling sea onto our bows. *Hudson* buried her bow in almost every large wave, and it was awe-inspiring to watch from the bridge and see the bow ponderously rear like a great leviathan then plunge down into the sea which engulfed it. The spectacle was made more mysterious by the fact that we were still in dense fog. Sheets of spray crashed with immense force into the windows of the lounge and bridge. I saw green water coming over the bow, which foamed and boiled its way aft over the foredeck. The anchor hawse pipes became geysers, jetting water into the air at every plunge. Water leaked through the lounge windows and into the corridors through the door seals.

Early in the afternoon a massive sea toppled the bottom drill which had been tied down on the foredeck. This very large piece of equipment, the size of a crane and weighted down with a tripod base of railway wheels, was a gas-powered drill designed to bore a 30-foot hole in a rocky bottom and extract a core. It fell onto a cable running from the foredeck winch to the starboard A-frame. The cable held, precariously. The bo'sun called out the crew who lashed themselves to lifelines and staggered out, soaked to the skin, onto the heaving deck. After an hour of effort the drill was safely lashed down, although many of the crew had been swept off their feet. I went up to the crow's nest to photograph the sea, but realised my mistake when the motion almost threw me down the interior of the mast. I retreated to the bridge top, and was rewarded by the sight of a sudden burst of watery sunlight, which pierced the fog and lit up a vast vertical sheet of spray rising from the bow like a cascade of diamonds.

During the storm we crossed the Aleutian Trench, one of the great oceanic deeps, which lies off the edge of the Alaskan continental shelf. The depth increased to 6,500 metres from the 4,500 of the North Pacific, mostly by way of two steep cliffs, one of which descended at a 45° angle for 700 metres. The bottom rose just as quickly on the north side of the trench, and soon we were up to 750 metres, where we stopped for a piston core. Another hour of sailing brought us up to 70 metres, on the shelf at last, the place that we should have reached during von Arx's gravity survey. The sea changed to a confusion of short choppy waves as we crept through the fog towards Unimak Pass. The Aleutians were showing on our radar, but our world was as grey and small as ever.

Miraculously, early in the evening, the fog rolled back like a curtain to reveal Unimak Pass. We were in the centre of it. Five miles to starboard rose Scotch Cap on Unimak Island, a pair of barren dark peaks over 5,000 feet high. Glaciers and snowfields coated their upper flanks and the saddle between them. The slopes swept down steeply to the sea; lower down the bare rock gave way to moss, grass and dwarf bushes. A glacial stream ran down from the snowfield in broad loops cut into the soft volcanic rock. The whole shape of this island was altered in 1964 by a major earthquake, which pushed up new mountains and coastline. Off to our left we could just see the other side of the Pass, where the smaller Ugamak Island was swathed in cloud.

The sea in the Pass was full of life, both natural and man-made. Porpoises played around us, their black and white bodies flashing beneath our keel; the small brown head of a sea otter poked up inquisitively off our quarter; and a large fur seal basked in the water off our beam with his head and shoulders exposed. The air was filled with flocks of geese, Arctic terns and shearwaters. A single tufted puffin kept pace with our bridge front, looking ungainly in the air with his plump dark body and stubby swollen red beak. A strange sight was the large number of kelp rafts that dotted the sea. Each raft, made of closely woven kelp strands, looked like a huge brown doormat several yards across. The larger rafts provided resting places for the Arctic terns. Whence came this extraordinary concentration of life? As usual, the sea bears the answer; we were entering the rich, productive water mass of the Bering Sea shelf, full of nutrients, and leaving behind the relatively barren North Pacific surface water.

The man-made life in the Pass comprises all those ships which seem to be scattered randomly on the face of the world ocean, but which come together in a few vital passages. A Russian freighter, probably bound from Vladivostok to Seattle or Vancouver, passed southward to starboard of us, dwarfed by the mountains of Unimak Island. An old Esso tanker followed us through the Pass, and a stern trawler kept us company, heading north into the rich fishing grounds. As I write these words, I am in fact once again sailing through Unimak Pass, in winter and darkness. The island stands as a dark and shapeless mass in the moonlight, the lights of seven fishing vessels surround us, and the kelp mats drift mysteriously past as they did in 1970.

An hour later the fog closed in again and we lost sight of the Aleutians. We ploughed onwards into the calm grey Bering Sea. Next day, after a morning station, I was in the mess peacefully drinking my lunchtime coffee when the fire alarm sounded. This had happened many times before because of a blown fuse or faulty contact, so I nonchalantly continued drinking and gazed with amusement at the worried looks of the newcomers. But the alarm kept on ringing urgently, and even we old lags felt slightly less confident. Perhaps the ship really was on fire. The certainty hit us all at the same moment and panic set in with a rush for the cabins. Down below I found the passageway filled with smoke. As I passed the engine room hatch there was an acrid smell of burning and a junior engineer rushed past shouting "It's in here!" In my cabin I grabbed my lifejacket and cast about vaguely, wondering what to save from the flames. I had just picked up my diary when the 'All Clear' came over the loudspeakers. With great relief I returned to the mess to join the shamefaced panickers, including Bernie Pelletier who had been the first person to reach the lifeboats. Soon came the explanation. No. 1 generator on the port side had exploded, and was now a molten wreck. Old

Sam Lambert, before leaving the ship in Victoria, had predicted that this would happen soon, but his Jonah-like prophecies had been dismissed as drunken ramblings. Now we were reduced to three engines instead of four to tackle the Northwest Passage. Hurried scientific meetings were held, and the real possibility of putting back to Victoria was discussed. But it was finally decided that we should press on.

Next morning, August 21, we took advantage of the glassy sea to heave to and send divers down to fix a plate over the cavity in the hull which contained the retracted transducer of our echo sounder. This was to protect it from the ice which lay ahead. The two divers were to be Mike Gorveatt and our loud-mouthed Doc. In unguarded moments the Doctor had claimed to have dived with Jacques Cousteau, and he kept a full set of scuba gear in his cabin along with his arsenal of rifles. Now he was to be put to the test, since Mike, a qualified diver, was not allowed to dive alone. The port lifeboat was lowered bearing the aquanauts, and moored alongside the ship. The frogmen disappeared, but surfaced after only a few minutes. The Doc was shaking his head dramatically.

"There's a hidden swell around the hull!" he announced as the whole gang trooped back aboard. "We couldn't get near the goddam transducer - we were getting scraped to pieces by barnacles!"

Mike was silently fuming. In the bar later he confined himself to the comment that the swell was all in the mind of the Doctor.

While diving was in progress the helicopter was hauled out again for joy rides, and I managed a short hop. The fog had cleared, and we were sandwiched between a vast flat grey sea below us and flat grey sheets of Arctic stratus cloud stretching away to the horizon above us. The *Hudson* looked like a small toy below us in a world of grey.

While more joy rides were going on, I wandered to the stern to try out a cod jigger that I had bought in Victoria. I was joined by Case de Frece, the new Third Mate, who had borrowed Pete's jigger. Case was a Dutchman who had moved to Nova Scotia after a long history of seafaring. He told me of his brief career on a Panamanian freighter, where he was offered the berth of Chief Officer. For this he needed a Mate's ticket, foreign-going, which he did not have since his previous career had been in fishing boats. The company advised him to go to the Panamanian Embassy in The Hague, where for five dollars they made out a Mate's ticket on the spot with no questions asked. The high accident rate of Panamanian ships is not surprising. As we chatted we had jigged away without success in a sea filled with large jellyfish, a foot or so across, coloured fetid brown or purple and with long trailing arms. I gave up for a while, but when I returned Case had caught two brown and white fish, each a foot long, of a kind unknown to me. They attracted the nearby Newfie crewmen, who picked them up, fondled them, dropped them, then tried gutting one. After much muttering they triumphantly identified this strange species as 'codfish'. Later I found that they were pollack, one of the main fish caught in the Bering Sea, a favourite food of fur seals and also of the Japanese, who flavour, colour and shape them to make artificial 'crab sticks'.

We had scarcely got under way again when word came that a dead whale was in sight. I rushed up on deck to see a bloated body falling astern. Bumping into the Captain I was inspired to ask, with little hope, if we could come about to investigate further. To my pleasant astonishment he agreed, and we made another close pass of the corpse. The whale was about 50 feet long and was floating high in the water, almost on its back, revealing a light-coloured underside. Something was protruding from its stomach; a flag, perhaps, or a collection of hand harpoons. It was undoubtedly a bowhead whale, the Pacific variety of the right whale – they were called 'right' by the sailing whalers because they swim slowly and float when killed. Bowheads migrate through the Bering Sea into the Chukchi and Beaufort Seas during summer, to feed on plankton near the ice edge. In 1970 they still had to run the gauntlet of the organised Russian and Japanese whaling fleets in the Bering Sea, then further north face the less organised traditional Eskimo hunters of Alaska, who work from small boats and who frequently strike a whale only to lose it. There was no ship within radar range, so we could not tell whether the poor creature had been lost by a whalecatcher or an Eskimo. He was still dead, a useless sacrifice from a species which is close to extinction. Later in the day I was fortunate enough to see two live bowhead whales off the port bow, about a mile away. Their blow was a characteristic cone of spray which hung in the air for several seconds before dispersing. They swam past together, showing their smooth black backs which have no dorsal fin. Today the bowheads are protected from modern whalers, but the Eskimos still have a quota so as to maintain some vestige of their traditional way of life.

In the evening we approached St. Lawrence Island, which lies at the northern end of the Bering Sea where it narrows towards Bering Strait. Another attempt was to be made to fit the plate over the sonar cavity. We came in to anchor in a shallow cove on the south side of the island. The cove swept round to a dark promontory called Kialegak Point on the chart, 1,100 feet high. At the other end of the cove a series of rough hills ended in a long sand spit leading to a similar rocky point called Apavawook Cape. Out to sea behind us lay a few small rock pinnacles called the Panuk Islands. Again, silence and greyness were everywhere.

Out into this bleak landscape flapped the two aquanauts, who descended once again from the ship's lifeboat. Once more the Doc emerged after a few minutes, shaking his head violently. This time he complained that he could not clear his ears and was suffering acute pain from them. Mike prepared to go down alone, but the Mate forbade it. So the plate was left off, and as soon as we entered the ice the sonar transducer was ripped away. Mike was trembling with fury, and the Doctor diplomatically retired to his surgery to oil his guns.

Bernie and the Captain had gone up in the helicopter to investigate the island, and as they returned I lurked on the pad in hopes of a flight. These were rewarded when Bernie set up a flight for Pete, Bill (a BIO technician) and myself. Wilf sent us soaring into the air and headed for the long sand spit. From the air this resolved itself into an arc of sand backed by a network of small shallow lagoons. Geographers call this a Haff-Nehrung type of coast, from a region in the Polish Baltic, and it is created by a coastal current transporting sand along a gently-sloping shoreline. The sand was dark orange, and the pools were tinged red by algae. The land rising behind was bleak and bare, with brownish-green moss and lichen as its only covering.

Suddenly we spotted yet another dead whale. This one was a pink mass lying high up on the long arc of beach, an intensely sad sight. It was lying on its side, slightly curled, and displayed all the features of a humpback whale – stubby body, long mouth, axial grooves running from under the chin down to the breast, and above all the long, strangely scalloped flipper. The humpback is even rarer than the bowhead, with an estimated population of 1,000, and it has been totally protected since 1962. Flocks of seabirds rose from the corpse as we circled low. I eagerly photographed this rare sight, planning to inform Peter Beamish. The vast empty beach was a lonely grave for the poor creature; the Bering Sea seemed to be a fatal place for these great mammals.

As we left the whale Wilf leered evilly at me then flew the craft apparently straight into the hillside, only pulling up at the last moment. At least I could see the terrain from close up, and it was clear that Apavawook Cape is just a mass of loose cinders, probably from a recent volcanic eruption.

Pleased at our terror, Wilf sped back to the ship where we landed at 11:30 p.m., still in broad daylight. This was not because we were in the Arctic but because we had not altered our clocks since Victoria, although local time should be three hours earlier. On Bernie's flight he had seen some huts and some scientists in a tent; in fact the island has permanent Eskimo settlements.

Next morning we approached Bering Strait itself, the narrow gateway to the Arctic Ocean. At 10.30 a.m. a large block of bare rock loomed up and passed a few miles to starboard. This is King Island, only a mile across and 700 feet high. It is an extraordinary place. Through binoculars I could see a mass of small specks clinging to the steep cliff-like side of the island. They were houses, built on pilings and lashed to the rock. These are the abandoned dwellings of the 200-strong King Island Eskimo community, a close-knit group that used the island in winter for seal and walrus hunting, retreating to the mainland in summer. Several decades ago they gave up this uncertain existence and now live year-round near Nome, living mainly by ivory carving, but their former houses remain. As we passed the island I could see, low on the starboard horizon, a hazy line of peaks marking the Seward Peninsula of mainland Alaska. I went below to send a cable to BIO about our whale sighting.

By 2 p.m. we were into the Strait. The peaks on the starboard bow grew larger and resolved themselves into two main promontories, Cape Cook and Cape Woolley. Cape Cook is named after Cook himself, who explored Bering Strait in 1778 during his third voyage. Beyond these capes came a final promontory, Cape Prince of Wales, the westernmost point of the American continent, named by Cook after the dissolute Prince Regent (Cook also discovered and named King Island). Seven months and many thousands of miles ago I had watched Cape Horn, the southernmost tip of America, glide by on just such a calm day. Now I had reached the western limit of this immense continent which I yearned to explore more thoroughly. As we rounded the cape and viewed it from the north side it looked very much like Cape Horn Island, a long black mass rising to a ridged peak over 1,400 feet high with the curious name of Potato Mountain.

We passed close under the cape. Like Unimak, the slopes were covered with brownish-green moss and cut by the channels of streams. Patches of snow and bare ice lingered in crannies that were sheltered from the sun. At the foot of the cape were some scattered huts and the transmitting masts of a radio station.

Meanwhile, on our port side the Diomede Islands were in sight ahead. First we passed a big, square, heavily weathered rock lying right in the middle of the shipping channel. It is called, appropriately, Fairway Rock. Five miles north of it are Big and Little Diomede, the only place in the world where the USA and Russia are less than two miles apart. Little Diomede Island, a low nondescript lump of dark rock, belongs to Alaska. Great Diomede, or Ratmanova Island, a larger lump behind it, belongs to Russia thanks to the geographers who drew up the 1867 Convention line dividing Russia from its newly-sold former province of Alaska. Each of the Diomedes used to have an Eskimo settlement, but in the 1960s the Russians moved their Eskimos to the mainland, afraid that the friendly intercourse between the villages might lead to an influx of dangerous ideas. Today, thanks to the vagaries of politics, the villagers can visit freely again.

The Strait was full of life. Auks skittered across the surface, barely touching the water with their feet and wings until they would jerk their heads suddenly downwards in search of a morsel. Tufted puffins bobbed alongside, while a single pure white ivory gull balanced perfectly in the air above us. Migrating whales were all around. Three kept station with us, all bowheads moving north into the Beaufort Sea for the summer. One broached a mile ahead of the ship, throwing the whole hind part of his body and his flukes high into the air as he dived.

Beyond Cape Prince of Wales the Alaskan coastline subsided into low curving sand spits. Off to the left, however, as the gap between the two Diomedes opened, it revealed, misty and low on the horizon, a glimpse of Siberia. This was Cape Dezhneva (East Cape), the easternmost tip of the Asian mainland. Through glasses the cape resolved itself into a long low promontory rising at each end into two subsidiary capes, Cape Peyak to the south and Cape Uiguen to the north. I was elated at my first sight of Asia, and thought also of the deeper implications of this meeting of ultimate west and ultimate east. But Gus stood beside me gazing at Siberia with more sombre feelings. He was born in Latvia, and when the Russians invaded in 1940 his family were tipped off that they were on a list for immediate arrest and shipment to Siberian labour camps, like all other Latvian intellectuals. They fled to Canada.

After dinner I went to sleep, exhausted by the sights of the day. At 6:30 p.m., as I slumbered, the news was piped that we had just crossed the Arctic Circle, at 66°30'N. At last we were in the true north.

August 23 was our first day in the Arctic Ocean, or rather the Chukchi Sea. Arctic weather took over after the interminable days of greyness, and cold sparkling sunshine lifted our spirits. Far off on the horizon to starboard rose the two hazy jagged peaks of Cape Lisburne and Point Hope on the Alaskan mainland. A small blue-hulled survey vessel approached us. She kept radio silence and told us nothing about herself; we assumed that she was doing a confidential survey for an oil company. We did plankton tows and a core. In the afternoon the sea suddenly became alive with pairs of walruses playing on the surface. They are ungainly brutes with leathery grey hides and enormous whiskery snouts, their tusks hidden underwater. It was faintly embarrassing to watch them making love in the water, rather like observing an elderly uncle in the act.

Then finally the sight that we had been waiting for appeared. Pack ice! At 7 p.m. a long irregular white line spread across the horizon ahead of us. At first glance it looked like a white cliff, but through glasses I could see that this was a mirage. The ice itself lay low down on the horizon, but floating above it was a second white line, joined down to the first in places but elsewhere floating freely with sky visible beneath it. In places there was a third line above these. As I watched, the mirage dissolved and reformed at its ends; it was frighteningly real. This is a 'superior mirage', caused by a thin layer of cold air lying immediately over the ice, with warmer air above it. Light rays coming from the tops of the floes are curved downwards at the boundary between the cold and warm layers, and reach the observer as if they were coming from the sky. Bernie claimed that during a geological field trip in the Arctic he had seen his camp in this way from a distance of 90 miles.

As we approached the ice pack the air temperature fell rapidly. Small cakes which had become separated from the main pack drifted past us and there was the occasional bump as we knocked one. It was time to use the helicopter for its real job of ice reconnaissance. The first flight took Bernie and Roy Gould, the navigator, to search for a way through the pack. The second flight was a joy ride. The third flight was also a joy ride, and I got on it, along with Pete Reynell and Claud, the chief cook.

We took off into a pink evening mist. The ice edge, which had appeared such a solid barrier from deck level, turned into a gentle progression of ice density, from small scattered cakes to larger, closely packed floes, until after 12 miles about 80% of the sea surface was covered with ice. In the outer part of the pack the floes were melting; they were pockmarked with pools and puddles of surface meltwater, and fringed with green where the freeboard of the floe had been eaten away leaving a submerged sill. Deeper inside the pack, sheltered from wave action, floes hundreds of metres across started to appear, with pressure ridges snaking across them. Pressure ridges are a problem both for sledge travellers and for icebreakers. They are long features which can be several metres high and up to 50 metres deep. They are formed in the interior of the Arctic where the ice forms a continuous sheet which can be broken up by wind to form long narrow cracks of open water called leads (or 'polynyas' if they are wider). The leads soon freeze over, but the weak young ice within them is easily crushed by any new compression of the icefield, building up a long heap of rubble which freezes together to form the strong and fearsome barrier called a pressure ridge.

Deep inside the ice Wilf descended to 250 feet and we saw much more detail of the ice. The low sun showed up the ridges in stark relief, and I also saw that the ice pack, far from being a hostile environment, sheltered rich animal life. Within the space of two miles I saw three colonies of seals hauled out on ice floes, safe from predators. Each colony consisted of a couple of dozen chocolate brown bodies, which plunged into the sea as we passed noisily overhead, leaving brown stains behind them. Further on I saw a plume of spray and then the huge body of a bowhead whale, lying stationary just below the surface in a pool among floes.

Soon after, Wilf was called back to the ship. We had received a call for help. Three Eskimos in a boat had disappeared on a seal hunting trip. We were passing the settlement of Wainwright, from which the message had come, so we lay to and awaited the arrival of a boat from the village. Wainwright was the first Arctic village that I had seen, and it is typical of Arctic Alaska and Canada. It was a stark collection of huts, of red and white wood or shiny aluminium, strung out along a low bare shoreline. Behind lay the lights of an airstrip and the huge white dome of a DEW Line (Distant Early Warning) radar station, erected in the 1950s to detect Soviet bombers. The featureless brown tundra of the coastal plain was broken by a wide meandering river which entered the sea west of the village.

At length a boat arrived, bearing two Eskimos with a written message. We all gazed curiously at our first Eskimos, and they gazed back in a faintly amused way. They were very mongoloid in their features, with deep brown skin, wide flat noses and lank black hair. But if we were expecting noble savages we were, of course, mistaken. They spoke with American drawls and wore nylon parkas and rubber thighboots. Their boat was made of aluminium, not sealskin, and was powered by a massive Evinrude outboard. So much for explorers' tales. The Eskimos have always called themselves Inuit, meaning 'men', and today the world follows suit, but in 1970 the white world still called them Eskimos. They sped off, accompanied by several packs of cigarettes from our stores, and Roy Gould followed in the helicopter to discuss the problem with the villagers; eventually he returned to say that four search aircraft were on their way, and that we were not needed any longer. We sailed onwards for our first encounter with the ice.

The Beaufort Sea is the name given to the part of the Arctic Ocean which lies north of Alaska and of the Mackenzie Bay area of the Northwest Territories. The ice in it moves clockwise in a gigantic circulating motion known as the Beaufort Gyre, so that here north of Alaska the ice drifts westward, grinding against exposed headlands of the coast as it goes. During summer the ice retreats a short distance from the coast across most of the Alaskan North Slope. This allows ships to squeeze their way between the ice and the land so as to get into the Canadian part of the Beaufort Sea, which is more open. Just east of Wainwright, however, lies Point Barrow, a choke point where the Alaskan coast has a northward bulge which protrudes into the ice drift even in summer, and usually there is no alternative for a ship but to enter the polar pack here. This is the worst ice of the entire Northwest Passage route, since it is old ice from the Arctic Basin made more formidable by the additional ridging which it has undergone as it grinds against the coast. It was the barrier which now faced us. Fortunately the entire crew, from the Captain downwards, had the virtue of ignorance, since nobody had been in Arctic ice before. Neither had the ship, despite having been built seven years earlier to full icebreaker specifications. So we went straight at it. Initially the shocks were terrifying. It felt as if the ship was sinking. Each collision threw the unwary off their feet. We lurched from side to side, and the crashing noise of each collision would be followed by a horrendous scraping sound as the broken floes passed along the side. It was worst of all for the crew in the foc's'l. None of them got any sleep.

Morning came, and we were in thick fog again. The ice, in so far as we could see it, was a 50% cover with much open water. The floes drifting past seemed to be of two types. One was fresh and blue when overturned, with a thick top dressing of snow; this was ice from the central Arctic Ocean. The other was dirty and slushy, streaked with brown layers like chocolate and vanilla ice cream. This was fast ice which had grown in place against the coast in winter then broken out into the pack in spring, having picked up dirt from the seabed en route. I discovered that, on our first entry into the ice, both of our logs had sheared off as well as the sonar. This made the computer processing of our position more difficult, so I sent a cable to BIO asking for a spare log probe to be sent out.

After breakfast I went up to the bow to watch our progress through the ice. There was enough clear water for us to find leads which ran in approximately the correct direction. Our technique was to build up speed and power in a convenient lead, smashing the small floes within it in a series of juddering shocks. Then, when the lead ended and an area of consolidated ice blocked our passage to the next lead, we would run up onto the heavy floes and ring 'engines amidships'. The motion of the ship, and her cutaway icebreaker bow, would carry her right on top of the floe, where she stopped. For a few seconds nothing would happen. Great cracks then opened across the floe and *Hudson* subsided through the 2-5 metres of ice with a snarling crunching noise. The shattered floe fragments boiled and heaved in a maelstrom of confusion, rearing up like leviathans with water streaming off them, and sometimes turning right over to reveal red algal growth on their undersides. After scraping along the sides of the ship, the big lumps bobbed slowly up and down in our wake, joined by newly created brash and rubble. Sometimes there was a narrow entrance to a new lead which we could not negotiate successfully. We would strike one floe obliquely and cannon off it sideways into the next floe, like a dodgem car. We left wedge shaped dents with flecks of paint on every floe that we treated in this way.

In the absence of a log to give us course and speed we had to stop completely every four hours for a satellite fix. During the morning we found that we had been averaging only two knots towards the east, because of the tortuous course that we were following.

At noon we did a station during our position fixing. We thrust forward and backed off a few times to clear a space, then quickly did the plankton tows and took a Van Veen bottom grab. The clam-shaped grab came up with a big lump of black glop, from which Frances Wagner isolated winkles, limpets, scallops and a tiny bristled whelk shell, all covered in green algae. There were granite pebbles that had been smoothed by rubbing against the bottom while encased in an ice floe, but most of the sample was coarse black sand. For most of the year plankton life is sparse in the Arctic Ocean and the deposition rate of sediment is therefore slow, only one metre per thousand years.

The afternoon satellite fix put us off South Bay, only a little way east of Point Barrow. The ice was thicker, and the shocks began to affect the ship. The satellite antenna broke loose from the vibrating mainmast, and as it was our chief means of navigation Hugh had to climb the mast to replace it. Miraculously, when it seemed that we were about to be stopped for good, causing a humiliating retreat, the ice began to clear to only 10-20% cover. Roy screwed the ship up to 15 knots "while the going is good". Up on the bridge Ben the quartermaster, who had never been in ice before, was steering *Hudson* through the leads like a car, twirling the wheel to avoid large floes.

We stopped that night to give the crew some sleep. Morning found us again in thick ice and thick fog. The meltwater pools on the floes had frozen overnight into transparent black ice. Most of the floes were dirty, as we were now close inshore in an effort to avoid the worst of the pack. At one point our navigation echo sounder (still working) showed only 32 feet of water under the keel, so we moved further offshore. During the worst of the battering I had to go down to the forward hold to fetch some echo sounder paper, my first visit to this part of the ship. It was an Aladdin's cave of buoys, dories, ropes and spare anchors, smelling of pitch and tar. The genie guarding it was the only person aboard who was oblivious to the shocks that resounded through the ship, the storekeeper Archie Birchell. Archie's Newfie accent was so thick that even Newfies could not understand him. His normal expression was a disarming and completely benign smile, like Harpo Marx, which he wore for me as he signed out the rolls. But inexplicable dark forces occasionally stirred inside him. He was sent to sea after attacking his father and a Mountie with a shotgun, and one night at 'Maria Teresa's' in Punta Arenas he tried to strangle Pete Reynell and had to be prised off by several of his shipmates. I escaped unharmed.

Once again it looked as if we were going to be stopped, and once again the ice cleared miraculously and the fog with it. A scene of incredible beauty was revealed. The sea was littered with scattered floes of fantastic shapes, all glinting in a blue sky under a burning sun. The strange gleaming artifacts distributed over the glassy plain of the sea looked like an exhibition of modern sculpture, and I rushed to sketch the scene.

By evening the last floes had disappeared and the sea was clear to the horizon. We had made it. The multi-year ice, freshened by years of partial melting and refreezing, was behind us. So was the heavy pressure ridging. Ahead lay the open southern Beaufort Sea of Mackenzie Bay, awaiting our survey. We were back in Canadian waters, having crossed the Alaskan boundary. The land that lay over the horizon to starboard was the fabled Yukon.

Next morning we moved in towards Herschel Island, our goal for this first leg of the Arctic passage, where we were to pick up more of our party. To my disappointment I learned that the harbour at Herschel was too shallow to enter, and that all transfers would be by helicopter. The island soon appeared in the distance, a low brown streak about 10 miles long, rising gently to the low ridge of Collinson Head at its eastern end, named after the commander of a search expedition for the lost Sir John Franklin. Behind the island lay the distant snow-capped mountains of the British Empire Range, which divide the Yukon from Alaska and which are the furthest extension of the Rockies towards the north.

The new contingent had arrived a few days earlier at Tuktoyaktuk, a large Eskimo village at the mouth of the Mackenzie River, and this morning they had been ferried out to Herschel by the big Bell 212 helicopter of the Polar Continental Shelf Project, a government polar research base at Tuktoyaktuk. Our own small helicopter scurried to and fro, ferrying them aboard. There was Bosco Loncarevic himself; my old friend Bruce Carson; Roger Belanger, a French-Canadian photographer from BIO who was taking over photographic duties from me on this vital Arctic leg; Jim Shearer, also from BIO, to work on the seismic profiling; Tony Harding, a Londoner working for Hunting Surveys who was operating his company's sidescan sonar on charter to BIO; and, inevitably, Roger Smith. The first evidence of his presence was the chaotic state of confusion in which I found my cabin. Then a face with a gigantic smile appeared out of the top bunk.

"Hi, shit face," was his customary welcome.

The Beaufort Sea survey was not going to be so bad after all.

CHAPTER 20

A SUMMER IN THE BEAUFORT SEA

The great sea has set me in motion
Set me adrift,
And I move as a weed in the river.
The arch of sky
And mightiness of storms
Encompass me,
And I am left
Trembling with joy.

Eskimo song.

AND SO WE SETTLED down to a month of survey work in the unknown Beaufort Sea. Today it seems impossible that Canada could have neglected her Arctic waters so much. The Beaufort Sea is now the centre of Canada's search for offshore oil, and in summer is full of drill ships, barges, icebreakers, tugs and dredgers, all ploughing their way among a dozen or so artificial islands constructed in the shallow nearshore waters. None of that existed in 1970. The Beaufort Sea, larger than the Mediterranean and ice-free for up to three months of the year, was almost completely unknown. The only information on its oceanographic structure came from the transit of the Royal Canadian Mounted Police schooner *St. Roch* in 1940 on her way through the Northwest Passage, and a brief survey in 1951. Nothing was known of the seabed, its sediments or its underlying geology. But in 1969 an exploratory oil well at Atkinson Point on the Tuktoyaktuk Peninsula had struck oil, suggesting that oil-bearing structures could exist under the Beaufort Sea itself. That was why, all of a sudden, no fewer than three survey vessels (*Hudson*, *Baffin* and *Parizeau*) were assembled here. And our results were to change the history of the Beaufort Sea irreversibly.

Our survey technique was simple and tedious. We had drawn up a set of parallel survey lines, 15 miles apart, running northward from the coast. We would set out on each line from the southern end, steering at 5 knots and carrying out seismic profiling as well as recording gravity and magnetics and towing the sidescan sonar behind the ship. Every few miles we would stop for an oceanographic station and a core. The line would end when we reached the ice edge, which in this unusually mild year lay over 100 miles off the coast across most of the width of the Canadian Beaufort Sea. The plan was to do the northward line during the night, and then return southward along the same line doing stations during the day. This was soon abandoned because the lines were so much longer than expected. Our positioning was to be closely controlled by a Decca Hi-Fix radio navigation system set up for the summer with a line of transmitting stations along the coast. Unfortunately our Decca receiver didn't work, so we had to continue with our laborious method of stopping for satellite fixes.

My jobs during the survey were to keep a night watch on the geophysical instruments and to spend the day computing the previous night's gravity and magnetic readings. Roger was keeping a watch on the satellite navigator. On the first night I kept the 4-8 watch, nastiest of all watches. The only pleasant thing was the sunrise at 5 a.m. The sky was covered with thin flat plates of Arctic stratus except for a narrow band on the horizon which began to glow, first pink and gentle, then red and powerful, until finally a great orange mass thrust itself from the sea and threw a garish light over the ship and the quiet waters. The next day I managed to change my watch to the more pleasant 12-4, which I could share with Roger on the satnav and Pete Reynell on the bridge.

The first discovery of something completely new about the Beaufort Sea happened on the first survey line. I happened to be down in the after lab at the time and watched it happen. We were starting our northward run and were still in shallow water. The sidescan sonar towfish had just been launched, and Jim Shearer and Tony Harding were manning the recorder in the lab. The towfish, a small streamlined body, sends out acoustic pulses which probe the seabed to either side out to a range of 300 metres. Hydrophones on the fish pick up the reflected pulses and feed them to the recorder to generate a map of seabed features. The map looks like a landscape seen from the air just before sunset, because bumps on the seabed have a 'bright' side nearest the fish, where the sound pulses bounce off it, and a long 'shadow' side where the bump has obstructed the acoustic beam and no reflections are seen. Similarly, a trough has a dark bottom and a bright far edge. We all expected the map of the muddy nearshore zone to be a blank – a great expanse of featureless silt. Instead we saw a complex array of long narrow troughs in the seabed, as if a drunken ploughman had been at work. It was a fascinating pattern of intersecting lines, some straight as a die and others curved round into circles and spirals. We had discovered seabed scouring. I rushed up to the console and found that each scour mark that crossed the ship's track showed up on the ordinary echo sounder as a small indentation in the seabed, only 6-12 feet deep. These scour marks must have been made by pressure ridges embedded in the winter ice cover and dragged over the bottom by the force of wind and current on the pack. They pose a previously unsuspected hazard to any plans for offshore pipelines or wellheads.

The next exciting discovery was that these scour marks did not disappear when the water depth reached the limit for normal pressure ridges – say 30-40 metres. Instead they were still there, though less frequent, down to 60, 70 and even 100 metres. What does this mean? Do pressure ridges exist down to this depth? Or is it that these scour marks in deep water are very old features, relics of the time several thousand years ago when sea level in the Beaufort Sea was lower? We know that the seabed of the Beaufort Sea continental shelf has been sinking since the end of the Ice Age, as the whole Canadian Shield tips over from the release of the great weight of ice sheets on its eastern side. Also, we know that the sedimentation rate in the Beaufort Sea is very slow, because of the small amount of plankton, so that a scour mark could take thousands of years to fill in. Today, the questions that we discussed so eagerly in the *Hudson's* after lab are still not properly answered. Nobody has found a good way to date scour marks. Down to 60 metres we can reasonably imagine present-day pressure ridges doing the job. But at 100 metres we are not sure. In my later career measuring ice thickness from submarines I have found ridges as much as 55 m deep but no deeper. For the oil companies a lot depends on the answer, because they need to know how far out to sea they must bury their pipelines to avoid being damaged by ice.

From the seabed I lifted my eyes to the heavens, and on the second night watch saw my first Aurora Borealis. Pete phoned me from the bridge at 1:30 a.m. and I rushed outside to see a flickering green curtain lying in a great low arc across the sky. In its central part the curtain was faint and hazy, but at its ends the individual trails were bright enough to cast a reflection on the sea. Each trail is a charged particle from the sun that is trapped in the

Earth's magnetic field and which makes the upper atmosphere glow as it passes through it. The particles are at least 20 miles up in the air, yet many people have reported a whispering sound from the aurora. I heard nothing above the sound of the ship's engines, but I could see how such an impression could be given by the flickering folds which danced about and dipped down towards the distant black coast. How could something like that be silent? Gradually the vision faded as a fog bank rolled up.

At the end of our next southern line I got my chance to visit Herschel Island. Frances Wagner wanted to collect some fossil shell samples on shore, and I managed to get aboard the helicopter, along with Roger Belanger. We took off after lunch and soared through a clear blue sky for 15 minutes until the low brown streak of Herschel showed ahead. We crossed the coast on the north-west side of the island, a line of low earth cliffs that were shattered and eroded by great wedges of solid ice which protruded from them. These 'ice wedges' are formed when water from the sea or from streams enters a fissure in the cliff and freezes; the expansion forces the wedge open at the expense of the cliff. The island is also underlain by permafrost, permanently frozen soil which begins only a few feet down. In summer, when the snow melts and the rain falls, the water cannot soak away downwards, so it stands around in a network of shallow boggy lakes or else runs off in temporary rivulets and streams. Here on Herschel the run-off from streams and the erosive effect of ice wedges are both carrying enormous amounts of soil out to sea; the island was surrounded by a halo of muddy water. Geologically the island is of very recent formation, and at this rate of destruction it will last for only a few thousand more years.

We came down low over the flat surface of the island, which nowhere rises above 400 feet. This was my first taste of muskeg, the typical terrain of the Great Barrens and the Arctic coast. There is a coarse soil which supports a summer vegetation of moss, lichens, grass and fragile but beautiful Arctic flowers such as bog cotton and saxifrage, with the occasional dwarf willow bush in sheltered spots. This plant cover is saturated with water, which lies everywhere in ponds and lakes or else rushes along in streams. Among the ponds are small hummocks of dry soil, raised by alternate freezing and thawing of the 'active' near-surface permafrost; these hummocks are riven by patterns of polygonal cracks.

At the eastern end of the island we came to a low sand spit, littered with logs and driftwood, which loops round to enclose the small sheltered harbour of Pauline Cove, Herschel's only anchorage. At its head there was a random collection of huts, shacks and oil drums, and a small wooden fishing boat rode at anchor in the choppy bay. We landed on the beach and were greeted by a couple of young men who emerged from the largest of the huts.

"Welcome to Decca Green," they shouted. "Come and have some coffee!"

They escorted us into a freshly painted white hut, with two large radio masts sprouting from the roof. Decca Green was one of the three Decca radio navigation stations that were maintaining the Hi-Fix chain for the summer survey work; the others were at Atkinson Point and Hooper Island. The crew were here for six months, and were anxious to talk to anyone about anything. Inside the hut all was quiet comfort, with easy chairs, coffee tables, a fully equipped kitchen and separate sleeping quarters. One whole wall of the main room was taken up with the Decca and radio communications equipment. What did they do for enjoyment?

"Well, we water ski," they replied, seriously. "In wet suits, of course."

They pulled out a 'Tourist Map of Herschel Island' that they had carefully drawn, featuring 'Madame Fifi's High Class Cathouse', movies, nightspots and water skiing. Then the leader mentioned a trading arrangement that he had organised between the local Eskimos - who use Herschel as a fishing base in summer – and the captain of *Parizeau*, to provide the ship with fresh Arctic char in exchange for groceries. He suggested that we did the same. I promised to ask, knowing that the Chief Steward would refuse, as indeed he did.

As we talked, a 40 knot wind began whipping past the windows. Wilf said that he would probably have to fly back to the ship instead of taking us around the muskeg to sample, so I went out into the gale to have a quick look around the settlement. On the beach I came upon the bodies of several skinned seals, each about five feet long. Only the eyes and mouths remained; even the flippers had been removed. The bodies were covered with rolls of grey blubber, looking like old woolly sweaters. The skins were hanging up on racks to dry. The Eskimos who use Herschel as a summer hunting ground sell their seal pelts to the Hudson's Bay Company store in Tuktoyaktuk, where in 1970 the going price for a pelt was 25 dollars, continuing a noble tradition of rapacious exploitation. Next to the seals I saw the sad lonely body of a baby beluga whale, about five feet long. The technicians said that the mother had been caught in a gill net a few days earlier, but had been completely cut up; beluga blubber, or 'muktuk', is an Eskimo delicacy. The baby had followed its mother inshore and died. Adult belugas, or white whales, exceed 18 feet in length and are almost pure white; this baby was a leathery brown-grey, perhaps because of putrefaction.

The rest of the settlement comprised a white hut flying a Canadian flag (the former RCMP base), wooden storehouses for boats and fishing gear, and three or four living huts for the transient Eskimo fishermen and sealers. 'Huts' was too good a word for the latter. They were in fact miserable shacks, made out of driftwood, unpainted, and full of gaping holes. The windows were of plastic sheeting, and they were surrounded by mounds of garbage cans, plastic bottles and other non-destructible detritus of the white man's world. Herschel has a sorry history. Most of these huts date from the whaling period of 1880-1910, when Yankee sailing whalers followed the bowhead whale from the Bering Sea into the Beaufort Sea and used Herschel Island as a summer base. Eskimos were attracted to this centre of activity, and were used – for pitiful or non-existent wages – as harpooners and crewmen on the whalers, or to help melt down the blubber. Their womenfolk, liberally supplied with booze, were used as whores. Finally the RCMP was forced to set up a post to restore order. By 1970 this era was long vanished, and Herschel was once again a deserted backwater. But history has a way of repeating itself. Just a few years after our visit, in 1976, the offshore oil industry came to Herschel, to use it as a wintering port for the fleet of drilling ships and icebreaking supply vessels that are busy every summer in the Beaufort Sea. For a while Herschel was a boom port again, until a new wintering spot was dredged out of shallow water further to the east in Mackenzie Bay. The last time that I saw Herschel, in 1992, it was once again the little lonely settlement that I saw in 1970, with the difference that it has been made a National Park and the buildings have been restored to better than their original splendour.

Wilf was now anxious to be off, so I could not stay to meet the Eskimo hunters that I spotted coming home around the head of the cove. We took off just in time to avoid a fog bank that was sweeping across from the mainland. As we soared upwards the fog moved in to envelop Herschel Island, and continued to advance rapidly in great wide billows. We finally overtook it when we were half way to the *Hudson*, which glinted in the clear water ahead. Soon after we landed on board the sky became obscured and the weather closed in, with rising seas. It was a lesson in how fast conditions can change in the Arctic.

The latest report from the ice patrol aircraft of the Atmospheric Environment Service was that the ice edge had retreated to 150 miles from the coast, so we began a long northward survey line to explore these hitherto uncharted waters. Our route took us across the shelf edge and into the deep basin of the Arctic Ocean, also into a storm with waves of a height that we had not seen since the Bering Sea. The Captain, roused to a sudden flurry of efficiency, held a fire and lifeboat drill followed by a Captain's inspection. The drill was the first since the tropical Atlantic, but since we all had warning things proceeded in an orderly fashion. I grabbed my lifejacket and went up to the port lifeboat where everything was being filmed by Roger Belanger. Pete was in charge of the boat, armed with a chronically outdated list of personnel. We stood around joking, while Wilf revealed that his great-uncle had been bandmaster on the *Titanic*. Far from playing *Nearer, my God, to Thee*, it appears that the band played ragtime to keep the passengers calm, and then headed for the lifeboats; his uncle survived until 1949. The Captain's inspection was a solemn farce. It was preceded by a visit from the useless cabin steward, Dennis. He was supposed to clean our cabin every day, but had never done so before. Next came a deputation composed of the Captain, Chief Steward and other disreputable characters in cinema commissionaires' uniforms, who checked on the neatness and tidiness of each cabin. Roger and I made up some mildly satirical slogans which we plastered on our cabin door to greet them. The contingent stopped outside, muttered to itself and passed by without entering. We had gone too far, however, for we were summoned to Bernie's cabin for a solemn ticking-off.

At the end of the northward line the ice came into sight without a mirage but with 'ice blink' to warn us of its nearness. The sky just above the horizon appeared brightened and whitened due to the reflection of light from the ice surface onto the bottom of the cloudy overcast. The return line, parallel and further west, brought us near Herschel Island again by the evening of the 30th, and again I begged a ride in the helicopter which was taking mail ashore and picking up equipment.

Cruising at 1,000 feet we crossed 30 miles of grey, silent ocean. Thin broken cloud was above us, while rain squalls swept around the horizon with the low sun reflecting off the falling sheets. Again we passed over the eroded cliffs and sodden green and yellow muskeg of Herschel, and landed in the cove. The cove was full of screaming kittiwakes, while little auks bobbed on the water. Eskimos' gill nets, with wide gauge to catch Arctic char, were laid out to dry on the beach. Two friendly huskies came running up and sniffed and nuzzled me as I walked. I struck across the spit, wading in my duffel-lined rubber Arctic boots through the ponds and rivulets in which a lush grass grew. Eventually I reached one of the more solid Eskimo huts, which had a line of washing outside. A little shy Eskimo boy with a chubby face, wrapped up in a brightly coloured nylon parka, gazed at me from a distance with a big smile on his face. No adults were around. Back on the beach a row of ringed seals were awaiting skinning, with beautiful grey pelts spattered with patches of darker grey-blue. A box of freshly-caught char showed that the Eskimos had been busy; the fish looked good eating, a foot or more long with brown body and silvery underside. At the water's edge I found a quite different fish, puffing away and slowly expiring. He was nine inches long, greenish brown, flat and with both eyes on top of his head. His belly was bloated and four little spikes stuck out behind each eye. I carried him off as a specimen.

Wilf was now ready to go, but offered to provide more sightseeing on the way back. I suggested that we fly round the southern shores of the island. We followed the broad sweep of Thetis Bay, passing more ice-wedged cliffs hanging over short beaches of coarse sand littered with driftwood from the Mackenzie River. The southern end of this bay forms a long sand spit called Osborne Point, and here we saw the trim fishing boat of our earlier visit riding at anchor. Wilf pulled off a spectacular landing on a small sandbank beside the boat. A high-speed outboard quickly appeared and disgorged three friendly Eskimos in fur-fringed duffel parkas. They explained that this was the research boat *Nana II* of the Fisheries Research Board's Northern Research Laboratory in Inuvik. They had been setting seal nets on the mainland coast and trying to measure the salmon runs at the mouths of the Firth and Malcolm Rivers nearby.

We took off again, catching sight of *Parizeau* making her way in to Pauline Cove, then we were soon back aboard *Hudson*. Dan Faber pronounced my fish to be a sculpin, a bottom-dwelling scavenger and a pest to the fishermen because its spiky body rips their nets. He thought that its bloated belly and location implied that it had swallowed something too large for it and had swum ashore to die. He kept it for dissection. Next day we came up alongside *Parizeau* in Babbage Bight, west of Herschel Island, to exchange equipment. She was spick and span, and lowered a gleaming sounding launch in an efficient manner. Pete Reynell, who had served aboard her, praised her Captain, Colin McAngus, as a man who was interested in all aspects of oceanography and who was an inspiration to his crew.

Unfortunately we were condemned to the less inspiring *Hudson*, and as the days of the survey rolled on I began to feel for the first time in

"Hudson-70" a quite unpleasant atmosphere developing aboard the ship. The three leading scientific figures – Bernie, Bosco and Chris Yorath – were continually and publicly quarrelling over plans and priorities in data collection, and this was affecting the atmosphere of our small community. Disagreements are inevitable among ambitious scientists who are entering a virgin environment and are seeking to carve out new knowledge in their particular spheres. But in this case it went further, and a personal note began to creep in. Somehow the Arctic does this to people – the history of Arctic exploration is studded with arguments, mutinies, murder (Charles Francis Hall was poisoned by his men in northwest Greenland) and plain fraud (Peary, Cook, Byrd and their claims to have reached, or flown over, the North Pole). Perhaps it is the way in which the unattractive environment – for us, an endless succession of days of bitter damp chill, grey cloud or fog – turns people in on themselves and on each other. In my later career as a polar oceanographer I have learned to prefer the late winter (March-May), with its crisp dry cold and clear skies, as the best season to work in the Arctic, while the summer is the worst.

One example among many occurred on September 7. I was on watch at the geophysical console in the afternoon when Roger Belanger came up with his tripods and floodlights to film the action. When he had set everything up and focused his camera, Bosco Loncarevic appeared and ejected me from my seat. He then had himself filmed performing scientific-looking but fictitious work at the console, pretending to write notes on charts and twiddle knobs. This took a long time, as Roger was a perfectionist. When he had finished, I was allowed back to repair the damage. We had lost a great deal of gravity and magnetic data because a paper tape punch had run out during the filming. Of course, the photos were excellent. Belanger next moved to the satellite navigator where Roger Smith was on watch. This time Bernie Pelletier intervened and said that Rog must not be filmed because he was not a member of the expedition. Brave Bruce Carson did his best, as always, to improve the atmosphere and keep people cheerful. One night watch he sidled furtively up to the console room with the news that he had found a secret route into the ship's food store and had swiped three steaks. We cooked them in the Engineers' Mess and had an early breakfast of steak, eggs, bacon and toast in the console room. Further secret night feasts followed.

Despite all this, science was still being done and important discoveries being made in this unexplored frigid sea. By September 9 we had done 72 oceanographic stations, and Dan Faber and Gus Vilks had managed a large number of plankton tows and bottom trawls. Dan had found a 'fish nursery' area with a very high concentration of young Arctic cod and borrowed a nylon mesh shopping bag from me to concoct a plankton net to catch them. Frances had found her first mollusc in the upper sediments, a small clam. And one of the bottom cores set a new length record for the Arctic Ocean of 30 feet, the previous best being 12 feet. Most interesting of all was the discovery of underwater pingos. Pingos on land are a well-known feature of the Mackenzie Delta region, and are basically mounds of earth-covered ice. They look like small conical volcanoes, rising starkly from the flat muskeg landscape to a height of 200 feet or more. They are formed when a lake drains because of a change in the course of the streams that feed it. The deeper lakes on the muskeg do not freeze to the bottom during the winter, and their deep parts contain water at 4°C, its temperature of maximum density. This 'warm' water melts the permafrost below and around the lake. When the lake disappears, the permafrost compensates for this sudden removal of heat by rising again, pushing up the soil above it in a ceaseless quest to find an equilibrium position. Within a few years a conical mound rises out of the old lake bed. A reverse process can occur if a new lake forms, when it may sink into a depression of its own creation; this is called, appropriately, an 'ognip'. So far, so good. But this explanation cannot account for a pingo forming underwater. Their origin is still obscure, although their shape on the echo sounder resembles exactly that of pingos on land. One theory is that they date from the time several thousand years ago when the present Beaufort shelf was dry land, and are preserved by the fact that underwater permafrost can continue to exist several tens of kilometres out from the coast.

A close investigation was made of one of these underwater pingos on September 10. It was 40 feet high, a perfect cone with a crater in the middle. Firstly we positioned ourselves over it and did a core, which missed the crater but caught the outer flank of the pingo. Then we lowered the underwater TV camera. The equipment consisted of a pyramidal metal frame on which were mounted floodlights, a stills camera pointing downwards which could be triggered from the surface, and a TV camera which could be tracked in two planes from the surface. The control equipment was in the forward lab, and I watched as we lowered away. First came a huge cloud of mud as we hit bottom. Then the camera was raised a few feet and gave an excellent view of the bottom drifting slowly past. It consisted mainly of featureless mud, with a few molluscs embedded in it and with the occasional shadow of a fish flashing by. The camera was hauled in with the video still running. We saw the bubbles and turbidity as it broke surface and then a view of the deck and the approaching boots of the bo'sun.

Scours and pingos were not the only underwater features discovered during the survey. There were diapirs, or mud volcanoes, which looked like pingos on the echo sounder but which lacked the tell-tale inner echoes of an ice core; their origin is unknown, but they later became very important when they were found to be the sites of the Beaufort Sea's oil deposits. There were conical depressions in the seabed, like ognips on land, which looked like the ruins of collapsed pingos. Some of the cores were found to contain lenses of freshwater ice, direct evidence for the first time that permafrost extends out under the sea. And the sediments themselves told a story. Near the mouth of the Mackenzie the bottom was silt-covered, deposited by the outflow of the mighty river, while further out to sea clay and sand took over. The extent of the silt showed that the river outflow turns east and runs along the coast of the Tuktoyaktuk Peninsula before turning out to sea and merging with the great westward drift of the Beaufort Gyre.

A welcome break in our work came on September 11 when it was time to refuel off Tuktoyaktuk. So shallow is the water off the Mackenzie Delta that we had to anchor 20 miles out and take on the fuel from an oil barge. When we arrived we found *Parizeau* still fuelling, so we hauled off and spent five hours surveying a nearby magnetic anomaly region. This caused a blazing row between Pelletier and Loncarevic over who had the power to order the ship to do what. Later in the afternoon we edged in again towards the barge over a glassy sea. All that could be seen of the distant land was the peak of the tallest pingo on the Delta. We dropped anchor, and the barge was disengaged from *Parizeau* by a tug called the *Kelly Hall* and dragged slowly over to us. Meanwhile the helicopter began ferrying people ashore for various purposes, including the collection of data from the magnetic station on Atkinson Point. Pelletier had offered me the chance of a flight to Tuktoyaktuk, but he then proceeded to change his mind. I was therefore hopping mad, so I went to the bar with Pete to drown my anger in drink. After a while we decided to try to have a look over the *Kelly Hall*, so we went down to the quarterdeck where she was moored alongside.

We found one of her deckhands negotiating with our crew for the purchase of a bottle of booze. He offered to be our guide, and revealed that he was an engineering student from Queen's University working during the summer vacation. The *Kelly Hall*, he said, was one of 27 ships of the government-owned Northern Transportation Co. She spent six months per year, the navigable Arctic season, on a single tour of duty involving towage and supply work throughout the western Arctic, including the Mackenzie and the North Slope of Alaska. She had to be virtually self-contained, so her quarters and facilities were even more spacious that those of *Hudson*. She also had a very shallow draft – less than six feet – so that she could work close inshore. Her main deck contained cabins and a large spotless dining room and galley. The cook was a well-built, jolly woman who spoke with a heavy East European accent. Aft of this was the engine room, set in the superstructure at deck level because of the shallow draft. The twin diesels were as spotlessly clean as the galley stove. On the deck there were more cabins, topped by a panoramic bridge.

Seeing the Second Mate's cabin door ajar, Pete decided to call on his opposite number. We found the mate, a bushy-bearded character, engaged in drinking rum with a colleague. A drink was pressed into our hands. The rum came from *Parizeau*, which had been very hospitable in providing booze; in fact, her captain had invited people at random into his cabin for drinks. Since *Kelly Hall* was a dry ship, this had produced some noticeable effects quite rapidly. Firstly the Captain of the tug had got dead drunk, and the only sober officer when she came alongside *Hudson* had been the Second Mate himself. Secondly, they expected the *Hudson* to provide similar hospitality. This had not been forthcoming. Our Chief Steward had rudely refused all offers to buy booze. Then when the *Kelly Hall's* captain had staggered on board for a fraternal visit he had been received by Roy Gould as if he were some slippery dago in a tropical port. This angered him, and he demanded to see our Captain, who was in bed allegedly sick. On being refused he stormed out, ordering the pipes to be disconnected. There was an hour's standoff before tempers were smoothed and pumping could begin.

Pete and I headed back to our own lounge where we found the Captain and purser of *Kelly Hall* ensconced. The purser was a long-faced Scot while the Captain, who was now only moderately drunk, looked like a music hall parody of a fighter pilot. He had a round chubby face with enormous rosy cheeks and an uptwirled handlebar moustache. Dan Faber was dispensing beer and sympathy, and had calmed him enough to let pumping begin. Shortly afterwards *Kelly Hall's* Chief Engineer came in, looking like an old Northern comedian. He was a real Geordie from South Shields, with a genuine cloth cap and a line of patter to match.

The makings of a party were developing, so Pete got his accordion and I my guitar. Soon a fine sing-song was in progress, with everybody joining in except the participants in a rowdy dice game at the other end of the lounge. Frances was singing lustily, and Chris Havard came and sat on the arm of a chair and sang all the verses of the songs, clean and otherwise, in a pretty voice. Bernie was visibly fuming and went and sat by himself. When pumping was complete he was the first to tell the *Kelly Hall* people to leave. The Chief Engineer did a tap dance out of the door and ended up with a grand flourish by peeing on the quarterdeck.

Next day Bernie called me into his cabin for an extraordinary interview. He declared that playing the guitar in the lounge "can lead to drinking or worse", that it "will turn the girls into sluts" and that "other people in the lounge have complained to me". I was informed to my surprise that "there are several people on board who came from Puritan families and have never heard swearing", that "the crew of the barge were just scum" and that my guitar playing should be kept "where it belongs, in your cabin or the crew's mess". I was astonished to realise that Bernie was genuinely upset by what seemed to me an innocent and happy party. Yet nastier episodes left him unmoved, such as the previous night when the Doctor, drunk in a dice game, plunged his sheath knife (with which he claimed to have killed 53 Germans while in the Dutch Resistance) into the beautiful wood veneer of the card table. I simply could not fathom Bernie's reasoning, but it was clear that I was in the doghouse again.

Matters seemed to calm down a few days later when Bernie actually joined in a sing-song, bringing his own accordion out of his cabin to accompany us.

The days dragged on, as we ploughed across the Beaufort Sea from the ice edge to the nearshore shallows. Roger and I tried to keep sane in our own way. One day a freak snowstorm descended on us, preceded by a sudden swell which sent the ship rolling 27° to starboard and catapulted everything off the drafting laboratory tables. Soon an inch or two of snow lay over the decks. Frances, Roger Belanger, Rog Smith and I clasped 'carol sheets' and stood outside the bridge wing door singing *Good King Wenceslas*. With snow in our hair and eyebrows we banged on the door after each verse. Pete Reynell, who was on watch, opened up and handed us each a biscuit, for which we doffed our forelocks and wished the Young Squire a Merry Christmas. We moved on to the door of Hugh's electronics workshop. Hugh was more Scrooge-like and gave us a rude sign. Another night Rog and I, bored with our console watch, devised a tap dancing routine around the geophysical laboratory, with me doing the percussion accompaniment on the console instruments. This caused an irate phone call from the awakened giant Roy Gould in the cabin below. Finally there was the ship's newspaper, the *Hudson Chronically Horrid*, based loosely on the awful *Halifax Chronicle Herald*. This project was suggested by Dan, and Frances offered to do the typing. We drew up a poster asking for contributions (anonymous or otherwise) and left boxes around the ship. In the end we had to twist arms and write much of the paper ourselves. I wrote a short story entitled 'I was a sex-change priest on CSS *Hudson*'. The result was a creditable improvement on the newspaper produced during the West Coast survey, with reports on work done, advertisements, poems, articles and games.

Finally, on September 21 came the last day of the survey and a sense of tremendous relief. A big party was held in the lounge which I had to leave at midnight for my console watch. Loncarevic, anxious to squeeze the last ounce out of the cruise, had us running a gravity calibration line all night, up and down a previously surveyed gravity line north of Atkinson Point. When I came down again at 4 a.m. the party was still in progress, but I went off to bed since I had been promised a run ashore at Tuktoyaktuk the next day when personnel were to be exchanged for the run through the Northwest Passage.

I was up with the dawn, but the promised 8 a.m. flight did not materialise. The weather was poor, and it was decided that people with the most urgent needs (those leaving the ship and with planes to catch from Inuvik) should go first. After much tedious waiting, I finally managed to jump into a helicopter with Frances and Pete Reynell about 10 a.m. As a final shot the Captain sent Pete word that he could not go ashore, but such was his own desperation to escape from *Hudson* that he pretended not to have received the message.

I felt physical joy flood over me at leaving the *Hudson* after such a long confinement and I happily watched her disappear astern. We cruised off towards the coast. Purple rolls of cloud rushed past just above us, while the horizon was dotted with the white curtains of snow squalls. The sediment-laden water below us was grey-brown and speckled with whitecaps; wherever the sun broke through the surface glinted with a cold yellow.

Soon we crossed Atkinson Point and spotted the famous oil well which had started the Beaufort oil rush. It had been partially dismantled for winter; the derrick was lying on its side and there were several aluminium prefabricated huts scattered around it. We turned and followed the coast of the Tuktoyaktuk Peninsula to the southwest. The landscape was of low muskeg, covered with thousands of lakes. Many of them were circular, making the terrain look like the Western Front on a rainy day. Areas of slightly higher bare ground were broken up by frost action into polygons bordered by long open cracks. The shore itself was fringed by an offshore sandspit, littered with logs and driftwood, which created a sheltered coastal lagoon. Winter was on its way, and most of the lakes were partially frozen. The first stage is frazil ice, a milky suspension of small crystals which gives the surface a dull greasy sheen. Many lakes had progressed beyond this to a coherent sheet of ice which varied from dark and thin in the centre of the lake to white and thick around the edges. The wind direction during freeze-up was preserved in great striations of frozen bubbles across the ice surface.

Some way down the peninsula we saw the first pingos. Most of them were so low as to be little more than hummocks, but one magnificent specimen rose like the breast of a submerged mermaid from the water of the coastal lagoon. Others were more irregular and distorted by partial collapse and earth slides. None was more than 100 feet high.

At length we reached Tuktoyaktuk and flew over the village. Its dominant feature was the big DEW-Line radar station, with a large spherical radome and several fixed parabolic reflectors. The village is built on several interconnected patches of lowland, cut up by lakes and inlets, with the outermost patch being the exposed coast itself. Gravel roads connected the pieces of the village, and led to an airstrip further inland. Further inspection would have to wait, as we flew on a few miles to visit the two largest pingos in the region, which stand together as a pair. We landed at the base of the larger, on a bed of sodden grass.

Wilf stayed in the helicopter while Frances, Pete and I set out to climb the pingo. It resembled a giant slag heap; the sides were very steep and led up to a broken flattish summit. We splashed through a shallow river which wound round its base, then scrambled up the soft earthy slopes. Halfway up Frances found an outcropping of the tiny brown mollusc shells which she was seeking. This was evidence that the soil of which the pingo is composed was under the sea only a few thousand years ago. The pingo sides were clad in dwarf willows, a wiry scrub only a few inches high, with leaves that were brown and dying as autumn rushed on. Frances found the skull of a small rodent, and in two places we saw the entrances to burrows. These could be home for several possible species, including the lemming, ground squirrel (*siksik*) or Arctic hare. The earth at the top of the pingo was soft, showing that the permafrost core had not erupted at the peak. There was a surveying mark and some film wrapping discarded by Roger Belanger. There was also a blizzard raging, with a cutting wind whipping hard nodules of snow at us. We decided that it was time to depart. We slid down the soft sides of the pingo and regained our machine, to various comments from Wilf about being a taxi driver.

Wilf flew back to Tuktoyaktuk, circled the hamlet and brought us down by the beach at one end of the village. He landed between two Eskimo huts, rousing the inhabitants. These were perhaps the two oldest and most tumble-down shacks in town. One was thrown together from odd bits of wood; the other was built out of logs. Two very shy and pretty little Eskimo children, clad in colourful parkas with big furry hoods, came running out of one hut but were too timid to come close to us. They were called back by their mother, a very beautiful young woman with long black hair.

Next to these huts was the Anglican mission, a rather shabby old wooden building whose roof was adorned with a white wooden cross and a white-painted bell. Beside it was the Catholic church and mission, a far more elaborate green-painted wooden clapboard building looking like a Byzantine basilica. Over the altar was an octagonal wooden dome, and the transepts had stained glass windows. High and dry by the church lay a wooden boat called *Our Lady of Lourdes.* She was the former Catholic mission boat, now a 'boatel' providing accommodation for visitors. She was a stout 50 ft vessel, with a stern deckhouse carrying the ship's wheel on its roof, to aid ice navigation. The single mast had a barrel lookout for ice working. Beside the boat lay a great pile of lumber, presumably for a new mission building, but suggestive of an old-fashioned mechanism for disposing of heretics.

In this part of the village several modern homes were going up, with cheerful Eskimos pausing from their hammering to wave at us. A few were dressed in traditional summer parkas of caribou skin, with the fur side inside, but more had switched to modern store-bought parkas of nylon lined with down or artificial fibre. We wandered on past the village's four oil storage tanks to a second patch of buildings, all modern and gaily painted. They were roomy clapboard and varnished pine dwellings, raised on piles to avoid melting the permafrost. Some seemed too roomy, built in southern Canadian style with large picture windows, and all were heated by oil furnaces with fuel tanks outside. The heating costs must have been enormous, for Eskimos who were mostly living on welfare. There were many motor vehicles around, although driving possibilities seemed somewhat limited. Laid up until winter were skidoos, the occasional traditional dog sledge, and even a four-seater sled powered by an airscrew.

Along the shoreline we saw a team of huskies chained up, powerful wolf-like dogs with thick coats of various colours. They seemed friendly until I took my camera out, at which their hackles rose. Behind them were shacks used to store fishing equipment and some small aluminium outboards. We rounded the bend of the shore and came to a long building housing the Tuktoyaktuk Fur Garment Project. This was a new co-operative venture where the Eskimo workers bring in their own furs to make into parkas, mukluks (fur boots), mitts and tourist-trap toy animals called Tukpiks, all for sale in the adjoining store. We found the store closed, and set off to find someone who might be able to open it. Behind the store we spotted a pile of peat sods enclosing the entrance to the Tuktoyaktuk community freezer. This is simply a large shaft sunk into the permafrost and enlarged into chambers at the bottom. Meat kept here is preserved indefinitely and is used communally by the residents of the town. Eskimo tradition leans towards community endeavour, although this is tragically dying under the impact of self-centred Anglo-Saxon society.

Finally we spotted the Government hut, from which flew the flags of Canada and the Northwest Territories. The young official inside, called Tom, said that the fur store was closed because of a heating failure but would reopen in the afternoon. The office was decorated with press cuttings of the recent visit of the Queen, Prince Philip, Prince Charles and Princess Anne to Tuk (the locals prefer to shorten the name of their town), with photographs of them striding down the main street. Outside the office a signpost pointed to such destinations as 'Moscow 10,000 miles; North Pole 1400 miles; Whales 12 miles; Edmonton 1800 miles; Inuvik 85 miles'. Wilf suggested that we eat lunch at the Polar Base, so Tom phoned the cook and asked her to cater for four more people.

Our helicopter taxi flew us to Polar Base, which lay some way back from the village. It is the headquarters of the Polar Continental Shelf Project, a government body which offers logistical support to research projects in the offshore Arctic. The base was a long L-shaped building which included a restaurant, accommodation and recreation rooms for visiting personnel as well as an equipment stockpile. As we landed a larger helicopter circled and landed beside us. This was Polar Base's own helicopter, which was evacuating the departing personnel from the *Hudson*. The two Chrises, Tony

Harding, Jim Shearer and Roger Smith piled out, Rog being resplendent in a red muskrat-lined parka that he had hired an Eskimo lady to make for him. We headed for the crowded cafeteria, where gamey-tasting pork chops were on the menu. The cook, a pleasant Eskimo woman, asked me it I wanted two, and did not bat an eyelid when I accepted. It turned out afterwards that by doing so I had denied her a lunch – they always brought the exact number of chops required out of the meat store. It showed to what excessive lengths Eskimos go to be friendly and obliging, an aspect of their nature which has been ruthlessly exploited by the white man.

I sat down near Bruce Carson, who introduced me to 'Five Star Walt'. a local character who was living proof that the hippy culture had reached beyond the Arctic Circle. He looked like a Hindu mystic, with long straggly hair and beard and an embroidered headband. He worked as a technician on the Decca chain and was also a ham radio enthusiast who had managed to pick up Fred Muise's broadcasts from the South Atlantic. His principal sideline, and the origin of his name, was distilling hooch liquor. Tuk was a dry town, and the only liquor around had to be brought in privately from Inuvik or made on the spot. 'Walt's Five Star' was liquor which was aged for all of five days before sale, with a descending order of stars for less mature brews. Walt had been forced to suspend operations temporarily because a heavy storm of a few days before had contaminated the town water supply (it also carried away the RCMP post from the end of the sand spit). Walt's unofficial home whilst in Tuk was Polar Base, where he slept stretched out on the pool table. When the Queen visited Tuk, Walt presented himself to her with the words "Hi, I'm Walt." Sitting beside Walt was his antithesis, a sprucely uniformed pilot who captained an SRN-6 hovercraft used for summer survey work around the Delta. In this impossibly boggy terrain it is an ideal form of surface transport.

After lunch Wilf stayed at Polar Base while Frances, Pete and I set off again for the fur store. The road was full of happy children in coloured parkas heading for the federal school, an airy modern building down by the shore. We found the fur store still closed, and again enlisted Tom to help us. He drove us in his minibus to the home of the lady who ran the store, then, having found that it would be open soon, he offered to drive us round the village.

As he drove he told us something of Tuk, where he had lived for two years. Tuk was founded in 1837 as a trading post by the Hudson's Bay Company. It remained a tiny settlement until the recent opening up of this area in the search for oil, but was now growing fast. In the past year 51 new houses had been built, all by Eskimo labour, although the contractor and electricians came from the south. Tom said that Tuk was the best settlement in the Northwest Territories, but was evasive when we asked him what the families in the shining new houses did for a living. Some worked on construction and survey projects during the summer, he said. Others went hunting and fishing although only five families now had regular trap lines. Most of them he implied, live off welfare, a demeaning life for a people who have always lived off the land. Down by the shore we passed two wrecked fishing boats and a great pile of driftwood deposited by the recent storm; Tom said that for the Queen's visit the entire beach had been cleared of driftwood and every house in the town repainted. Tom showed us the curling rink, the lending library, the power generating plant which was being expanded to 600 kw, and the fire station. Four house fires had occurred that year, all due to drunken Eskimos smoking in bed.

Finally Tom showed us the Hudson's Bay store, which sold all of the necessities and many of the luxuries of life at inflated prices. It incorporates a trading post which bids for raw furs and is a social centre for Eskimos, full of old toothless ladies smoking like chimneys and chewing gum. The scandal of the Bay has always been the low prices that it gives the Eskimo for his furs and the high prices that it charges for groceries and consumer goods, hooking the Eskimo into an endless cycle of debt. Tom had a mandate to break this cycle, by running a revolving account to buy furs. He would offer a certain amount on account, and then send the furs to auction in Edmonton. When the payment came he subtracted his advance and gave the rest to the Eskimo. He quoted the case of a hunter to whom he advanced 1,800 dollars for a set of pelts; they fetched 5,800 dollars at auction. Another hunter sold a similar set to the Bay which gave him only 1,800 dollars as a final price.

Outside the store Tom left us and we watched an Otter seaplane of Northward Aviation circle the village and land in the lagoon. It taxied up to the jetty behind the Bay store, where a crowd of Eskimos were waiting. This was the thrice-weekly flight to Inuvik which kept Tuk in touch with the outside world. The plane disgorged ten passengers and a mountain of freight, then a truck drew up carrying our departing *Hudson* gang. I helped them load their bags then bade farewell to my friends of the Beaufort Sea survey, especially to my cabinmate Rog for whom "Hudson-70" had now ended. I knew that we would meet again.

We turned back to the fur store, which was now open, and gazed in envy at the beautiful parkas of muskrat, ringed seal or wolf. My purse was too slim to buy anything except some muskrat slippers and a pair of wolf mitts. Eskimo ladies, some of them the toothless gossips of the Bay store, wandered in and started stitching away, creating works of wonderful craftmanship in a casual way.

It was now very late. Wilf whisked us back to the ship where we arrived at 3:45 p.m. There was a large reception committee on the flight pad and we feared the worst, as apparently the *Hudson* had been frantically trying to find out where we were. I escaped before anyone could speak to me. Pete was in a worse situation because he had missed a watch and left without the Captain's permission. He was left in no doubt that official wrath would follow. We both felt that the trip was worth the consequences, since Tuk is one of those critical places that are in transition between two utterly different concepts of society and of living. The Eskimo has always gained his livelihood from the living world of the Arctic; the white man now seeks its non-living resources for a profit. Which society will ultimately succeed is still unknown. As I write, the assault on Tuk has continued. The village still exists, more or less unchanged, but a little way along the coast from it sits 'Tuk Base', a gigantic self-contained oil industry logistics base, full of workers who are flown in and who spend a few weeks here at a time, completely cut off from the Eskimo village just a few miles away.

Our survey of the Beaufort Sea was now over. Our voyage through the Northwest Passage was ready to begin.

CHAPTER 21

THE NORTHWEST PASSAGE

Westward from the Davis Strait, 'tis there 'twas said to lie;
The sea route to the Orient for which so many died;
Seeking gold and glory, leaving weathered broken bones,
And a long forgotten lonely cairn of stones.

The Northwest Passage
Stan Rogers

HERE ARE TWO POSSIBLE routes for a ship attempting the Northwest
Passage. The more direct takes her through the narrow Prince of
Wales Strait between Banks Island and Victoria Island, and thence
into the wide straight thoroughfare discovered by William Edward Parry in
1819 and named Parry Channel after him. Parry Channel is made up of three
connected links – Viscount Melville Sound, Barrow Strait and Lancaster
Sound – but together they form the main marine highway through the
Canadian Arctic Archipelago. This was the route taken by the icebreaking
tanker *Manhattan* in 1968, and earlier by the icebreaker HMCS *Labrador* in
1954 (which sailed both ways through the Passage in a single season) and by
the RCMP schooner *St. Roch* on her returning voyage from east to west in
1944. In a good summer much of Parry Channel is free of ice, but a serious
blockage often occurs at the northern end of Prince of Wales Strait, where
Polar ice which has drifted in from the Arctic Ocean via M'Clure Strait
blocks the exit from the narrow channel with an impassable plug of heavily
ridged multi-year ice.

The second route is more southerly and takes a ship among the shallows
and islands of Coronation and Queen Maud Gulfs. This was the route used
by Amundsen on the first successful voyage through the Passage in 1903-6,
and was the route that Franklin was exploring when he came to grief in 1846

through becoming trapped in the pack ice. It is a good route for small vessels that can negotiate the shoals and intricate channels but it is not suitable for large ships. So *Hudson* was bound through Prince of Wales Strait.

We raised anchor on the evening of September 22 and set off to the northeast on our dangerous quest. We hit our first ice during the night watch, at 3 a.m. Fortunately it consisted of just a few strips of brash ice fragments, and as we were experiencing a powerful swell it was safe to assume that it was not the beginning of heavy pack. We ploughed on through the autumn darkness, cheered by a report from *Baffin* ahead of us that she was in open water. We even kept our delicate gravimeter running. It was an eerie feeling to stand in the wheelhouse and watch us passing between the scattered floes that loomed as white ghosts in the searchlight beam.

By daylight we were in Amundsen Gulf, which was ice-free. We did three oceanographic stations during the day, followed by a seismic line running northwards towards the coast of Banks Island. By late afternoon a spectacular rugged coastline of snow-covered sea cliffs and crags appeared in the distance, and at 8 p.m. in the last of the autumn daylight, we came up right underneath the great vertical cliffs of Cape Lambton. Sheer rock walls loomed to 2,000 feet all around us; we lay in a little bay only half a mile from land, yet the echo sounder showed 240 metres of water. Heaps of scree lay at the bottom of the shattered cliffs, broken off by the harsh action of frost on the rock. This grim but impressive scenery occupies only a few miles of coastline, between Cape Lambton and Nelson's Head, where the cliffs pile up into a great edifice which does indeed look like a human head; the rest of Banks Island is a gently rolling tundra lowland like most of the south islands of the Arctic Archipelago.

It was a great surprise to run into this isolated piece of mountainous coastal geology after the flat boggy tundra of the Alaskan coast and the Mackenzie Delta. We were also beginning to run into another phenomenon of the Northwest Passage, the multiplicity of place names, mostly of Royal Navy origin. During the 19th Century many Royal Naval expeditions explored parts of the Northwest Passage, led by men like Ross (John and his nephew James Clark), Parry, Franklin, McClintock, M'Clure, Collinson and Kellett. Each commander gave out names with gay abandon, sometimes to quite minor features, trying to flatter those in England (such as Admiralty high-ups) who were in a position to offer or withhold promotion and honours. Nelson's Head, for instance, was named Lord Nelson's Head by its discoverer, Commander Robert M'Clure of HMS *Investigator*, who landed on it on

Peter Wadhams

August 7 1850 (the first landing on Banks Island by a white man) and raised the British flag. Banks Island itself had been seen in the distance by Parry's expedition of 1819 from their furthest west point on Melville Island, and was named by Parry after Sir Joseph Banks, then President of the Royal Society and in his youth the naturalist on Cook's first voyage.

That night we entered Prince of Wales Strait (named by M'Clure) and began the most difficult part of the Passage. *Baffin* reported that she was hove-to off the Princess Royal Islands, a group of islets lying a third of the way up the Strait, with heavy pack ice ahead of her. We felt our way slowly along the Strait all that night and all the next foggy day, navigating by radar fixes from the land on either side. We met with no ice. In the afternoon the fog lifted enough for us to catch a glimpse of the low hills of Victoria Island to starboard, then it set in again, cold and clammy. The bo'sun had made a plaque commemorating "Hudson-70" which was to have been deposited on the Princess Royal Islands, but fog grounded the helicopter.

The blow fell on Pete that day. He received a written reprimand from the Captain for not standing his watch off Tuktoyaktuk. The Captain had added some quite unjustified remarks regarding Pete's behaviour in general. This was a serious blow to Pete's career, since such documents go into his record, and it was doubly painful coming as it did from a man like Captain Butler whose own behaviour left so much to be desired. Pete vowed grimly that he and the Canadian Government would soon part company.

Towards evening the fog was as thick as ever, when quite suddenly concentrated pack ice seemed to materialise around us in complete silence. It was a total cover (ten tenths, in meteorological parlance) of first-year ice, with floes about four feet thick. This was thin enough to push through, but there were worrying signs of worse ahead. The open leads which we had always found between the floes earlier in the summer were now frozen over with young transparent black ice (called 'nilas', a Russian term), and the constraints of the narrow Strait had produced occasional ramparts of pressure ridging several feet high. We kept going through the night in a fierce blizzard, using our searchlight to probe the ice ahead of us, and shivering as we watched the driving snow sluice horizontally across the beams. *Baffin* reported even worse ahead, and we learned that the Department of Transport was sending the heavy icebreaker CCGS *John A. Macdonald* from Resolute to our assistance. The unspoken question in all our minds was, had we left it too late in the year to get through the Passage? The ice north of Alaska was now hard against the coast, and there was no way out to the west. Would we be trapped?

Next morning it was bitterly cold. I went out on the foredeck, slipping and sliding over the snowdrifts which covered it. There, just taking shape in the mist, was our salvation. The *John A. Macdonald* had arrived! She was a proud-looking vessel, smartly painted with a red hull and red maple leaf on her funnel. She was much bigger than *Hudson* – 9,000 tons, with triple screw diesels giving 14,000 HP, more than double our power. Two years earlier she had saved *Manhattan* from humiliation by breaking her out of impossibly heavy ice on several occasions. Her main work, apart from escorting ships, is to supply the scientific and military bases in the Arctic, so her long foredeck was given over to hatches for her cargo holds. Her superstructure lay well aft, where she also carried her helicopter pad. The *Baffin,* which we had not seen for days, appeared out of the mist behind her and we set off in a convoy, with *Hudson* bringing up the rear.

We were now at the crucial north end of Prince of Wales Strait, where the ice is heaviest. In all directions solid ice stretched to the misty horizon, mostly smooth and snow-covered but in places crumpled into long snaking ridges, heaps of white rubble that barred our path. We stopped from time to time for stations, carried out with difficulty in the mess of broken blocks and brash ice left in the wake of *John A. Macdonald.* We had run a line of stations from Amundsen Gulf, including five in Prince of Wales Strait itself. The stations were done by none other than Ced Mann, who had rejoined at Tuktoyaktuk. We found that the surface water was below 0°C and remained below zero to the bottom at about 200 metres, although the salinity steadily increased with depth. The first stations in Parry Channel showed the same. We could draw some important conclusions from this. In the Arctic Ocean proper, as shown by our deeper stations in the Beaufort Sea, there are three layers of water: a surface layer of cold, low-salinity polar water, diluted by the run-off from Arctic rivers; a layer of warmer water, extending from about 200 metres to 900 metres depth and reaching a maximum temperature of about 3°C; and a cold bottom layer. The warm layer is called Atlantic Water, as it originates far away in the North Atlantic where the warm West Spitsbergen Current (an extension of the Gulf Stream) sinks underneath the polar water at the ice edge north of Spitsbergen and then spreads out through the Arctic at mid-depths. Our results showed that the Northwest Passage is too shallow to allow Atlantic water from the Beaufort Sea to mix with the deeper water in Baffin Bay; only the surface waters can mix, which they do by means of a slow current from west to east. In terms of life forms, the result ought to be that surface plankton from the Beaufort Sea may also be found in Baffin Bay, but creatures from deeper layers will not. This was exactly what Gus Vilks was beginning to find in his plankton tows.

Each station was done as quickly as possible, as we found that the wake of the vessels ahead of us slowly closed up because of pressure in the ice. I went up to the crow's nest and watched seals pop up and hunt for fish among the overturned floes that were bucking and rearing behind us. Suddenly I saw a line of footprints, stretching out across a large snowy floe to starboard of the ship. Foolishly I thought that one of the ships ahead of us had arranged an excursion on the ice, but when I climbed down I was met with:

"Did you see the polar bear?"

"What polar bear?"

"The one on the port side!"

Of course, when I looked it had already vanished into the mist.

This perilous northern end of Prince of Wales Strait marks the furthest limit of the search for the Northwest Passage from the westward in the 19th Century. In 1845 Sir John Franklin was sent out by the Admiralty with two ships, the *Erebus* and *Terror,* on what was expected to be a triumphant voyage through the Northwest Passage. He disappeared, and during the next few years no fewer than 24 search expeditions set out to seek him; in the process they explored the Canadian Arctic islands more thoroughly than in the whole previous century. One such expedition was sent out in 1850 by the Admiralty under the command of Captain Collinson in the *Enterprise*, with the *Investigator* as his second ship under the command of Robert M'Clure. Their task was to round Cape Horn and enter the Arctic from the west, seeking Franklin in the waters east of the Beaufort Sea. M'Clure was hungry for personal fame and for the £10,000 reward offered by the Admiralty to the first man through the Northwest Passage; these things interested him far more than the fate of Franklin. He sneaked past his commander in the Bering Sea and went off ahead by himself in search of glory, exploring up Prince of Wales Strait (which he named) past the Princess Royal Islands (which he also named) until he got hopelessly stuck at the northern end of the strait, exactly where we now were. He had to winter here in the middle of the pack ice in an exposed position during 1850-1 and was almost wrecked. He then sailed back southwards and around the outside of Banks Island, trying to enter the Passage again by M'Clure Strait, which he discovered. Again he was trapped and, forced to abandon his ship, he and his men were fortunately rescued by another expedition searching from the east. By accident therefore, he became the first man to pass through the Northwest Passage, and he laid claim successfully to the £10,000 reward, to the fury of Franklin's widow.

The power of *John A. Macdonald* led us safely through this critical spot, and we triumphantly exited from the mouth of Prince of Wales Strait late on September 25. Our escort led us across to the north side of Viscount Melville Sound, searching for a shore lead that she hoped might have been created by the northerly wind. But she hoped in vain; the ice was thicker than ever, with many heavy pressure ridges. We hit a large one obliquely at speed, and the ship canted over so that the port rail was only a foot above water. From my cabin I saw my porthole submerge, so that I could look up at the ice from underwater. It stayed that way for what seemed an age. As I prepared to evacuate the cabin we slowly slid off the ridge and daylight returned. Later in the day we damaged a propeller. In ice a ship needs steel propellers to avoid damage; we still had our bronze propellers, as the steel replacements had not reached Victoria during the drydock period. With a piece out of one of the blades we now started juddering and shaking whenever we reached a critical speed of 7 knots.

After a hair-raising day of slow progress we hove-to for the night so that the crew could sleep. In the lounge the unfamiliar figure of Roy Gould shambled in; normally he did not drink and thus did not frequent this abode.

"Say, chaps, I've been adding up our mileage so far. We're over 48,000! You realise that by the end of this voyage we'll have done 55,000 miles. Fifty – Five – Thousand – Miles. Jesus!"

He blundered out again, exhausted by the burden of ice navigation.

Next morning the convoy set off once more. *Baffin* kept getting stuck, and *John A. Macdonald*, like a faithful sheepdog, had to return and run rings round her to break her out. Near-whiteout conditions prevailed all day; the sky was overcast and the mist closed in around us, blending with the almost featureless snow and ice surface. The only contrast in this claustrophobic world came from the rubble walls of the pressure ridges, dividing up the floes like stone walls dividing fields in the West Country of England.

By the following day, September 27, the ice was finally beginning to thin and it looked as if the worst was over. Stretches of open water began to appear, although freezing was taking place in these. Some had only the first skim of frazil ice on them, while in others this had grown thicker and congealed into small plates with raised edges, called pancake ice. In a few cases the pancakes themselves had frozen together to produce the first stages of a coherent ice sheet. The Arctic winter was beginning.

Baffin sent a message back to us that she had polar bears in sight. We all crowded to the rail and peered into the gloom; we were ploughing through yet another expanse of featureless snow-covered ice. After about ten minutes we saw a set of footprints disappearing away to starboard but no bear; he must have been frightened off by the ships in front. However, later in the afternoon the fog cleared and we entered a region with much open water. There, standing on an ice floe about 100 yards to port, and staring at us curiously, was a family of three polar bears. Two were adults and one a cub. Their shaggy coats were a dirty canary-yellow in colour, against which their black snouts and eyes stood out in sharp relief. They stood gazing proudly at us, with no sign of fear, and even followed us for some way along the floe, moving deliberately to give a sense of immense power under perfect control. They seemed fully aware that they are the true masters of the Arctic.

Ice conditions now became very variable. In the midst of solid pack large areas of open water would appear – these are known as polynyas, another word borrowed from the Russian. Some of them had clear water in them, but most were covered in whole or part by slicks of grease ice. These slicks were not coherent, but were easily broken up by the wind into long streaks, looking like oil films when they reflected the sun. Then we would cruise into large areas of very new but more solid ice, only an inch or two thick, grey and translucent, a type of nilas. We scarcely felt it as we crunched through it, and our bow wave propagating out to either side would bend the thin flexible sheets and shatter them into small pieces. Then thicker ice would appear again, and so it went on all day. We were making quite rapid progress past Melville, Byam Martin and Bathurst Islands, following in reverse the pioneering (and lucky) voyage of Lieutenant Parry in 1819, who in a single season explored along this channel as far west as Melville Island.

By the morning of the next day, September 29, we were within helicopter range of Resolute on Cornwallis Island, the main supply base and communications centre for the Arctic Archipelago. Here our journalists left us. A party of three journalists had joined us at Tuktoyaktuk for the Passage transit, and had been a quiet but civilising presence for the past few days. They comprised Dave Spurgeon of the *Toronto Globe and Mail*, Ken Palka of Canadian Television, and Kurt, a Viennese-born photographer. After the shambles at

Valparaiso I was expecting the worst, but found to my surprise that they were intelligent and interesting company in the lounge, where they spent most of their time. Now they had to fly out to file their stories, and were taken by helicopter into Resolute from which there is a regular air service to Montreal.

We followed more slowly. Dawn had found us entering Intrepid Passage, the channel which leads towards Resolute, with Bathurst Island to port and the small Lowther Island to starboard. The rising sun shone rosily on the snow-covered slopes of this hummocky isle, while Bathurst was swathed in overcast. Other small islands lined the passage: Griffith Island, a high snowy plateau; and Browne Island, which was just a large black mass of rock. The latter was named by Parry after a young lady friend whom he had entertained before sailing and had thoughts of marrying. He wrote in his diary:-

> *I amused my party yesterday very much by putting my life-preserver on Miss Browne, and making her blow it up, or inflate it, herself!*

At last we reached Resolute Bay itself and dropped anchor. The Northwest Passage was now effectively completed. The goal for which several hundred sailors and explorers had laid down their lives had been accomplished in air-conditioned luxury in only one week, thanks to the power of the diesel engine. It was always madness to attempt to navigate these narrow ice-choked channels in sailing ships, and the sad thing is that the enormous courage of the Victorian sailors could have been used in a better cause.

The bay was filled with young ice, and Cornwallis Island rose behind in shallow hills, smoothly rounded and snow covered. The 'town' consists of several enclaves around the bay. Nearest to us was the Inuit village, an artificial settlement established by the Canadian Government in 1953 to provide Inuit labour for the Resolute base. The Inuits were lured to this bleak site by false promises that it was a good hunting ground, and were now engaged in litigation with the government to get some kind of compensation. The village had a neat layout of 40 gaily painted wooden huts, regimented in rows down by the shore, with street lighting and a central building flying the Canadian flag. Lines of huskies were staked out down by the shore. A mile or two behind the village, and only just visible, was the military and scientific base complex, which includes an airport and a hotel. The hotel at that time charged 25 dollars a night, which was blatantly extortionate, but of course it was the only place in town.

The *John A. Macdonald* anchored near us, and *Baffin* steamed up on our port side, looking battered after her ordeal. All the paint was gone from her bow up to the anchor chute. A theatrical pause ensued until our helicopter returned with the news that the party of geophysicists that were to join for the Baffin Bay leg had not come in on today's plane. To avoid wasting time we steamed eastward into Barrow Strait to do some station work.

The final station before Resolute had been no. 284, completing a line of seven done in Parry Channel. We now steamed eastward to 90°W, off the shores of Devon Island, and ran southward across the Parry Channel doing five evenly spaced stations. This was a quick process, because the maximum water depth was only 300 metres. The whole water mass in the Channel was colder than -1°C (freezing point for salt water is -1.8°C), with a salinity which rose steadily from 31 parts per thousand at the surface to 34 at the bottom.

Late afternoon brought us to the end of the station line off Prince Leopold Island, a small island with gigantic vertical cliffs which rise 1,000 feet sheer from the sea. The top of the island was swathed in the low cloud base, and the cliffs which filled the gap between sea and cloud were of ancient rock, deeply eroded, with the horizontal strata emphasised by a light dusting of snow. Roger Belanger took off in the helicopter to try to film us from the top of the cliffs, but could not reach them in the cloud and so came down to sea level and had us break ice in order to get some impressive footage. Southward of these looming cliffs lay the northeast corner of Somerset Island, with hills which glowed pink in a random patch of evening sunlight, rising up towards a 1,000-foot high plateau. These islands were discovered and named by the busy Parry in 1819; he named Somerset Island after his home county, although the resemblance is difficult to see.

We now learned that the geophysical party had arrived after all and had embarked on *Baffin* which was bringing them out to us. We had no space on board, because we still had people aboard who were due to disembark at Resolute, so we sent *Baffin* back again to drop off her passengers at the Resolute hotel. She did transfer to us Dave Ross, who was due to take over as Senior Scientist again for the final leg in Baffin Bay.

The night was spent in throwing a party in the lounge for those about to leave. Next morning we anchored in Resolute Bay and ferried them ashore by helicopter. They included Bosco, Gus, Dan Faber, Frances Wagner, Roger

Belanger and Mike Gorveatt, who was about to be married. The joining party appeared, and proved to be almost the same gang as for the West Coast survey: Charlotte Keen, Don Barrett, Tom Courtenay and Pat Solowen. Then there was 'P.J.', an Indian research student from Dalhousie with an unpronounceable name; and Mike Eaton, a middle-aged Englishman who had gone to University after retiring from the Royal Navy Hydrographic Service and was now a hydrographer in Halifax.

I was not allowed ashore by Bernie Pelletier as a punishment for outstaying my time in Tuktoytaktuk. Bernie himself, however, went ashore with Joe Avery the bo'sun, and with Roger Belanger, to plant a plaque there in commemoration of "Hudson-70". The plaque had been lovingly made of wood by the bo'sun in the Antarctic, with riveted metal letters spelling out 'CSS *Hudson* Expdt'n 70 Capt D.W. Butler'. Anything made by Joe was solid. He had wanted to leave it in the Antarctic, but there was no opportunity; then he could not get ashore on the Princess Royal Islands. Finally he set it up two miles from Resolute on a rock, using a pneumatic drill to make three holes into which he cemented three metal posts to which he riveted the plaque. It was meant to last; perhaps he was thinking of the destructive skills of the looters in the Antarctic.

Finally, with loading complete, we set off eastwards in late afternoon, bound for Baffin Bay and home. We were turning the final corner in our lap of the world.

CHAPTER 22

HOME IS THE SAILOR

In Baffin Bay where the whalefish blow,
The fate of Franklin no man may know;
The fate of Franklin no man may guess,
For Franklin with his crew doth rest.

Lady Franklin's Lament
(broadside ballad)

ITH HALIFAX SO CLOSE, and with the circumnavigation almost complete, it seemed impossible that yet another survey had to be done, let alone a geophysical one with the same unpleasant attributes as the West Coast survey. But so it was. This time Baffin Bay was the scene of operations, our companion ship for seismic shooting was to be the U.S. Coastguard icebreaker *Edisto,* and the aim was to test whether the rocks underlying Baffin Bay are continental or oceanic - in other words, is Baffin Bay an ocean?

We got down to business immediately. The gravimeter was run up and the magnetometer streamed. I was put on the geophysical watchkeeping rota with the familiar 12-4 watch; Mike Purdy had the 4-8 and P.J. the 8-12. The month of October began as I sat down at midnight for my first watch. Before the end of this month "Hudson-70" would be over and I would be back in Cambridge. The idea didn't seem possible; this ship had become my only home, and the limitless ocean was my place of work. I dismissed the thought from my mind.

At 4 a.m. I retired as usual to the lounge for a nightcap and conversation with Pete Reynell, and then to bed. The noise began at 7 a.m. I knew that it was coming, that we would be running continuous seismic reflection lines while on passage, but this did not make the noise any easier to bear. I fled to cabin 141, an empty one near the stern on the port side. It was still noisy there, with a further contribution from the screws and steering engine. It was also unheated and dank, but it was bearable, and I slept fitfully until noon.

Our seismic line took us eastward through the rest of the Northwest Passage and by afternoon we were at the entrance to Lancaster Sound. We were over on its southern side, and to starboard and ahead of us loomed the rugged snowy mountains of Baffin and Bylot Islands, rising to 6,000 feet. I could see a huge outflow glacier on Bylot Island coming down between mountains and emptying into the sea. This was a peculiarly appropriate place for the *Hudson* to be, for Robert Bylot was one of the gang of mutineers who cast Henry Hudson adrift in 1611 in the bay which was later to receive his name, ending the life of one of the greatest of polar explorers. Miraculously, Bylot managed to argue his way out of his deserved punishment, and was allowed to take part in two more Arctic expeditions with William Baffin during which Baffin Bay was explored for the first time.

The sea ice around us now consisted only of scattered rotted floes, but we still had to weave between them to avoid damage to our towed hydrophone array. As we entered Baffin Bay, however, we started to see our first Arctic icebergs. The first ones to appear were small low bergs, perhaps 40-50 feet high and 200 feet long, but when we came on to station 291 in late afternoon we hove-to beside a big one. It was between 100 and 200 feet high, in the shape of an almost perfect pyramid with a slightly irregular apex. The ice was not translucent, but looked like hard-packed snow, with some tilted layer structure visible. Unlike Antarctic icebergs which calve from floating shelf ice, Arctic bergs break off from the narrow steep glaciers which tumble down from the mountains of Greenland and Baffin Island into the fjords. They are therefore of irregular shape when they calve, and become more irregular through repeated capsizes during their long lives. Some of the bergs around us may have been of local origin, but most would have calved from the glaciers of east or west Greenland (mainly west), from which over 10,000 bergs are born per year. The bergs drift northward along the Greenland coast in the West Greenland Current, swing around the northern end of Baffin Bay, and then drift southward in the Baffin Island Current. They end their lives off Labrador or Newfoundland, or threatening shipping on the Grand Banks, after perhaps two or three years of voyaging. My late colleague Dick Brown from the Chilean fjord survey wrote an excellent book on the life history of Arctic icebergs, entitled *Voyage of the Iceberg*.

When I went on watch that night P.J. told me that the magnetometer fish had just been neatly sheared off from its cable by an ice floe. Luckily we had a spare, which was fitted the next day. Meanwhile, when I crawled into cabin 141 again I had to share it with another refugee, Ernie Poitier the Chief Electrician, whose cabin was normally next door to my own.

Next day the new fish was streamed but did not work. We were not totally lost for magnetic profiling, because *Baffin* was co-operating with us and running an independent set of gravity and magnetic lines in Baffin Bay for a few days. We crawled onwards at 6 knots, our maximum speed during seismic reflection work, and reached the centre of Baffin Bay, surrounded by dozens of large and small icebergs. Exiled as I was from my cabin by noise, I decided to start packing up my gear. In the North Pacific the carpenter had made for me a gigantic sea chest, which weighed a ton even when empty. At Resolute, when the forward hold was opened, I had it brought out and hauled it into the hangar. Now I settled down to paint it and fix hinges on the lid. The bare wood thirstily absorbed coat after coat of grey marine paint, until the paint alone must have doubled the box's weight. Then I started wrapping up all my precious rock, shell and plankton samples from the seven seas and packed them away.

That night, as Pete and I were having our customary 4 a.m. tipple in the deserted lounge, we were joined by Tom Courtenay of the geophysical team. "When will the noise end?" I asked. "Soon," said Tom dejectedly, since everything was wrong with the equipment. Concealing my delight, I asked him to expand. Firstly there is the hydrophone array, known by the geophysicists as the 'eel'. It is a 400-foot long, oil-filled floating tube with a hydrophone every 25 feet. To minimise water noise the eel should be stationary in the water at the instant that it receives the echo from the air-gun. To achieve this with the ship in motion, a slacking winch is used. This slowly hauls in a bight of cable, then just as the gun is detonated it releases the bight at a speed of 6 knots, so that the eel sits stationary in the water for a few seconds. Well, said Tom, the eel is leaking, some of the hydrophones are out of action, the slacking winch is dodgy and the compressor is faulty. It was a comprehensive list. And indeed, at 8 a.m. the compressor gave up; sea water had leaked into the fuel tank and stopped the engine. We were very near the end of the seismic line in any case, far over to the east of the Bay with Greenland not far over the horizon. The peace was like paradise.

With our seismic line prematurely ended we set off to make our rendez-vous with *Edisto* for the seismic refraction shooting. We reached the general position in the evening, which turned out to be a belt of quite heavy ice. Here in the centre of Baffin Bay lies the 'middle ice', a large conglomeration of sea ice which remains throughout the summer in the stagnant region between the West Greenland Current to the east and the Baffin Island Current to the west. Like the weed in the Sargasso Sea it is herded into the centre of the gyre where it remains drifting around. The ice was not compact, but consisted of a wreckage of semi-melted brash and blocks which were herded by the wind into a series of long narrow bands.

That night the ship ran deliberately into a region of denser ice to damp down the wave motion, and occupied a night station, number 292. First Bernie Pelletier did a vertical plankton tow, carrying on Gus's programme in the absence of Gus, who had to leave at Tuktoyaktuk because of family illness. Then Ced did the bottles. I prevailed on Ced to let me help him for therapeutic reasons; he scarcely needed help, since he was only doing 6 bottles down to 200 metres. Nevertheless it was a real tonic; Old Stan was on the controls of the winch as usual, with Merle to help him, and the scene brought to mind all the many happy days in the distant southern seas. The sky was clear and bright with stars, and the ice floes glinted attractively as they heaved up and down in the swell.

The cast was followed by the luxury of a full night's sleep, since the console instruments were also closed down. In the morning *Edisto* appeared out of the mist, having found us on radar. She looked decrepit and ungainly, with a white hull which needed a coat of paint and a helicopter hangar which seemed to take up half of her length. Nevertheless she was a vintage vessel of a famous class, the 'Winds'. During the war the Germans established clandestine weather stations on the east coast of Greenland, from which they broadcast information for use by U-boats. To clear these out an attack from the sea was mooted, for which an icebreaker was needed. Unfortunately, no suitable icebreaker existed. Very well, said the Americans, we will build six of them. And so they did; by the time they were completed the Germans had long gone, but the 'Wind' class survived to form the backbone of the US icebreaker fleet. They escorted convoys to Alaska and the Antarctic, and one was even lent to the Russians for several years. In 1973 two super-icebreakers were built to replace them, but proved unreliable, so the last of the 'Winds' soldiered on until the late 1980s.

Hudson and *Edisto* set off together to get out of the ice and find a clear space for a seismic run. On board *Edisto* were Keith Manchester of BIO and 20 tons of explosives. Early in the afternoon we found a likely region, hove-to and put out our eel. *Edisto* set off and threw her first charge when she was about a mile away. At first it looked as if a disaster had occurred, for a great spout of steam came out of her foredeck at the time of the explosion, but this must have been a coincidence. The first and smallest charge was 30 pounds; she steamed away from us for nine hours and dropped 54 charges of increasing size at ten minute intervals with a final charge of 500 pounds. Down in my cabin the explosions sounded loudly through the hull, followed in each case by three or four fainter echoes a few seconds later, from the sound waves which had passed through different layers of the crust or mantle.

I stood a night watch on the console, then in the following afternoon we did a second seismic line with *Edisto* steaming in the opposite direction, to eliminate any anisotropy effect. The direction was not quite opposite, since some ice had drifted across the planned track line, but it was near enough. Without further ado, *Edisto* jettisoned ten tons of unused explosives over the side, transferred three people to *Hudson* and then headed for home. The three were Keith Manchester; his technician Larry Johnson; and the seismic shooter himself, a bulky American called Bob Parker who was given the spare bunk in my cabin.

When the records of this experiment were eventually analysed, the results were absolutely conclusive. Baffin Bay is an ocean. The arrival times of the sound waves from the explosions showed that below the seabed there is first a 2 kilometre layer of unconsolidated sediment (the normal clay or silt), then 2 kilometres of more closely packed consolidated sediment, then 4 kilometres of crustal rocks in two distinct layers, then the very sharp discontinuity in sound velocity (called the Mohorovicic Discontinuity) which marks the transition from the crust to the mantle. In other words, the total depth from the seabed to the mantle is only 8 kilometres, which is characteristic of oceanic crust; the crust under the continents is more than twice as thick. Many questions remain. If it is an ocean, how did it form? Normally we would expect to see a mid-ocean ridge which acts, or has acted, as a spreading centre to cause Greenland to separate from North America. But there was no evidence of such a ridge in the seismic reflection data, even of a ridge buried under sediment. So the mystery of Baffin Bay's nature has been solved, to be replaced by a new mystery of its origin.

That evening we came onto another station and again I helped with the bottle cast, which was good therapy despite the driving sleet. Ced was only running bottles down to 200 or 400 m despite the fact that the centre of Baffin Bay is 2,400 metres deep. He said that this was simply to provide data to support the plankton tows, but it seemed a shame that the line of stations which we had carried around the entire circumference of the Americas should now be completed in a less than perfect way.

After the station the horror of seismic reflection began again, since the compressor had been mended. I stood my 12-4 watch while my new cabin-mate spent the night in the lounge absorbing no fewer than 14 doses of Navy rum. The *Edisto*, like all US Government ships, was dry, and Bob Parker was definitely wet, although a pleasant humorous character. His effort to compensate for days of deprivation ended in a sudden call from nature which resulted in him urinating over the floor of the deck officers' toilet, making him instantly unpopular in those quarters. He had to be helped below to my cabin, where I found him at 4 a.m. snoring away in an atmosphere of pure ethyl alcohol vapour. The anaesthetic effect of this actually allowed me to sleep fitfully despite the inhuman noise and vibration.

After another 24 hours of hell the compressor fell silent for ever. The final seismic reflection line had been done and we set off on the magical course of 180° for home. My work was reduced to one watch a day and help with bottle casts. The oceanographic stations traced our emergence into warmer water. At 71°N the sea surface temperature was 0.4°C with a subsurface minimum temperature of -1.3°C; at 69°N it was 0.6°C with a minimum of -0.4°C. After this station we actually entered a final band of pack ice, about 7 miles long but only 200 metres wide. This was the last of the sea ice; from here on the sea was cold but clear, cluttered only with the now-familiar icebergs.

October 10 found us at the southern end of Davis Strait with the Atlantic Ocean before us, a friend that I had not seen for many months. We crossed the Arctic Circle and did station number 299 at 65°N, finding the sea surface temperature up to a tropical 1°C. The morning was fresh, fine and exhilarating. Icebergs had disappeared, the air was warmer, and the ocean looked indefinably oceanic; something about its smell, colour and shape told me that we had stopped being polar explorers and started being oceanographers again. A flurry of gulls joined the ship, swooping and skimming over the surface as if to welcome us back to the open sea.

Our final station was number 301 at 58°N, opposite the coast of Labrador. It was a solemn moment when the last Knudsen bottle of "Hudson-70" came off the wire. The closing days of the voyage were a time of reflection. We sailed very slowly, so as not to arrive in Halifax too early. After a minor revolt by the crew, the Captain agreed to sail around the outside of Newfoundland rather than through the Strait of Belle Isle, so that Newfoundland too would be part of the America that we had circumnavigated. I finished packing my trunk with the treasures of the voyage, and spent many hours gazing out over our wake as we ploughed through the gentle swell over the misty Grand Banks, thinking of the experience that was over and how I could possibly reconcile it with my future life. I knew that I would never again be happy in an ordinary environment; I would be an outsider for the rest of my life.

On October 15, despite our slow pace, we came in sight of the familiar wooded shores of Nova Scotia. We crept up to the oil terminal in the outer wastes of Halifax Harbour and moored alongside a tanker for the night. Our grand arrival was scheduled for the next day, so officially we were not here. But "Hudson-70" was over. It was a difficult time for everyone; most people were almost within sight of their homes yet could not reach them, while for us old lags there was little feeling of celebration at our circumnavigation of the Americas, only sadness at parting and nostalgia for the adventure that seemed to have no end and was now ending. What we needed was a good drunken party, but nobody felt like starting one.

The morning of October 16 was sunny and warm. At the appointed hour we slipped our mooring and headed towards the razzmatazz, trailing behind *Baffin* which was allowed to dock first. The crew were, of course, all in uniform. And it was quite a welcome. As we approached the Narrows, a tug foamed into view and took station ahead of us, spraying fountains of water from its fire hoses. A helicopter swooped low over us, circling and dipping as the camera crew (including the untiring Roger Belanger) filmed us. We felt like royalty. We proceeded up to the Narrows and under the two bridges. A solid mass of humanity waited on the dock at Bedford Institute. Ministers and dignitaries, including Joe Greene himself, waited with speeches in hand in a roped-off area heavily guarded by Mounties; we were not to know that the country was in a state of siege, and that only that morning the War Measures Act had been invoked in response to the kidnapping of two politicians by Quebec extremists. Around the guarded area surged a colourful throng of friends and relatives. We slowly approached the dock, and the deck crew in their unfamiliar uniforms hurled heaving lines, freshly adorned with monkey's fist knots, at the stevedores. I was down on the quarterdeck, and as soon as the gap between ship and quay narrowed, I leapt ashore. I was the first man to circumnavigate the Americas.

The night after we arrived, I drove with Harvey, another engine room mechanic and his girlfriend, to a cottage that they used in a small fishing village near Halifax called Three Fathom Harbour. After we had cooked the steaks, drunk the wine and talked the evening away, Harvey and I lay in our bunks in one bedroom, gritting our teeth with envy while sounds of struggling came from the other bedroom, terminated by the joyous cry,

"I've made it! I've come! Hey, Harvey, I've come!"

But then I gazed out of the window and saw a sight of unbelievable beauty. The harbour bar lay under the cold pure light of a full moon while a long swell from the open Atlantic beat upon the breakwater, sending moonlit spray sweeping over the tiny huddled houses of the village.

My voyage had ended as it had begun, with the great ocean of truth.

CHAPTER 23

POSTSCRIPT TO AN EXPEDITION

*You here - you all had something out of life; money, love,
whatever one gets ashore - and tell me, wasn't that the best
time when we were young at sea; young and had nothing, on
the sea that gives nothing, except hard knocks - and sometimes
a chance to feel your strength...?*

Joseph Conrad

THE "HUDSON-70" EXPEDITION IS part of history now, and oceanography has grown into an older science. Year-long expeditions no longer sail forth to explore the unknown oceans; "Hudson-70" was the last of that great series of long voyages of ocean discovery begun by HMS *Challenger* in 1872. Today ships manned by small groups of specialists set out for voyages of one or two months to study a particular aspect of a small piece of the ocean, to test the predictions of the increasingly sophisticated mathematical models which describe the oceans's behaviour. Tomorrow the oceans will be monitored almost entirely by satellites, unmanned underwater vehicles and automatic drifting buoys, while oceanographers will stay at home with their computers. It was an immense privilege, at the very start of my career, to be able to take part in the last of the great oceanographic voyages.

On that climactic day of October 16 1970 when we sailed triumphantly into Halifax to complete the first circumnavigation of the Americas, life did not end for any of the men of "Hudson-70", nor for the ship herself. Life goes on, and unlike a romantic novel where everyone lives happily ever after, real life has a way of slipping past, giving few people the chance to practise or repeat the momentous lessons that they learn during its most intense periods.

My own story is perhaps a typical one. I flew straight back to England to begin my graduate work in Cambridge, plunging into a project to study the interaction of ocean waves with sea ice in the Arctic. The project took me to sea again in a submarine and to the sky in a remote sensing aircraft, but to work for three years on a single topic was a frustrating experience after the breadth of vision that "Hudson-70" had given me. In 1974, after gaining the Ph.D. which is the passport to a scientific career, I left Cambridge and went to Victoria BC again to try to recapture some of the dreams of "Hudson-70". But life had gone rushing on and all had changed. I returned to Cambridge in 1976 to run a research group at Scott Polar Research Institute concerned with polar oceanography and sea ice research. On one level my life has been successful; I have risen to a respectable position in the scientific world, have been on many research cruises, written many papers, and have a reputation in my 'chosen' field (a field which, like so many people, I 'chose' by accident and remained in by default). But on another level, my life has been an unsuccessful quest to recapture the insight and the awareness of reality which "Hudson-70" gave. The voyage, although it ended 39 years ago, and although I have been to sea again in almost every one of those years, was the central formative influence in my life.

Many human beings have an inner awareness that the Universe is a living entity, of which the part which we can see or measure with our scientific instruments may form the least important component. This awareness can come from religious faith or from the experience of love. For fortunate people, the awareness is reinforced by flashes of insight, brief mystical experiences of being in contact with, and part of, something greater than themselves. Freud called this, with unknowing appropriateness, the 'oceanic feeling'. On "Hudson-70" the oceanic feeling was present for me, not in brief flashes, but for much of the time. It gave me a vision of the meaning of my own existence, and of human life itself, which was equivalent to a sense of spiritual certainty, despite being inexpressible in words and inaccessible to the rational part of my mind. On my return to civilisation this inner awareness of truth was snatched away and has not been offered again. Since "Hudson-70" I have been trying to regain a grail which I once possessed, but then lost. Meanwhile the years pass ever faster, like water rushing under the keel of a rudderless ship.

Time has treated my fellow voyagers with differing amounts of cruelty. The most tragic case was my old friend Pete Reynell. Angry at the Captain's reprimand, and inspired by the repeated showings of *The World of Suzie*

Peter Wadhams

Wong aboard the ship (our only good film), he resigned from the oceanographic fleet and went to a maritime college in Hong Kong to study for his Master's certificate. In 1972, with his ticket obtained, he shipped as mate on a Hong Kong ferry being towed to India for scrapping. To avoid a storm they put in to Cam Ranh Bay in Vietnam, where during the night several of the ships in the harbour had limpet mines attached to them by Viet Cong frogmen. Pete's ship sailed next morning and was never seen again; it is probable that it blew up and sank with all hands. The terrible news drove his father to a paroxysm of despair, leading to a refusal to accept that Pete was dead and a desperate personal search through South East Asia for evidence of his survival. The happy, closely knit family life at Deep Cove could not have been more cruelly destroyed.

My other close friend, Roger Smith, had a happier history. He married his beautiful girlfriend Lorna whose picture had adorned our bulkhead, completed his studies at Queen's University, and went on to a successful career as a petroleum geologist in Calgary. He is completely unchanged, as open and outgoing as ever. Also unchanged, though a little balder, is the hero of "Hudson-70", Bruce Carson. We all received bronze medals from the Canadian Government after the voyage, but Bruce deserved a gold for his ability to maintain morale under the worst possible conditions. Some Hudsonians are still at Bedford Institute, which has grown greatly in size since 1970, but many have now retired and some, sadly, have died. Ced Mann moved to Vancouver Island to run the newly-built Institute of Ocean Sciences. Hugh Henderson married his lovely Chilean girl. Roy Gould, after being captain of *Baffin* for a while, retired to England to run a country pub in Kent. Pancho Rey, my old friend from the Chilean fjords, fled the country after the 1973 coup and is now an oceanographer in Bergen, Norway, still living amongst fjords. Jan Piechura is a senior scientist at the Polish Institute of Oceanology at Sopot.

Hudson herself still sails the seas at the time of writing (2009). She is elderly now as oceanographic ships go, but is still the flagship of the BIO fleet. She is now operated by the Canadian Coast Guard and so is known as CCGS *Hudson*, and her hull is painted red. She has received a facelift in which the graceful flying bridge with its teak rail has been removed and a larger wheelhouse with big windows put in its place. This makes room for the vastly increased amount of electronic navigational equipment that is now necessary in oceanographic ships. She has done no more long voyages, keeping to the North Atlantic and Eastern Arctic. Captain Butler left her,

352

after being awarded an honorary Doctor of Laws degree at Brock University, Ontario, for his work on "Hudson-70". Fred Mauger, who was her First Mate on "Hudson-70", became her next Captain. When I last visited her in 1986 the silent but totally competent Joe Avery remained her Bo'sun, but no other members of her original crew then remained except the storekeeper Archie Birchell. The Doctor was fired soon after "Hudson-70" for striking a crewman, and was replaced by two female nurses. Some years later he shot himself.

Our understanding of the oceans is deeper now than at the time of "Hudson-70" but narrower. Some important discoveries have been made, for instance the realisation that a large percentage of the energy of motion in the sea is contained not in the steady currents that produce the nice straight arrows in oceanographic atlases, but in the turbulent eddies, tens of kilometres across, which are the ocean's equivalent to storm centres in the atmosphere. We have learned that the ocean has a 'weather' as well as a 'climate'. But as oceanography has matured its practitioners have become more specialised, and few can appreciate the whole picture any more, the complex interactions of currents, water masses, nutrients and food chains that produce the varied splendour of life in the sea and which determine the ocean's role in global climate. The young oceanographers now being trained have no opportunity to acquire the breadth of vision of a von Arx, in the absence of the old-fashioned long multidisciplinary cruise in which the physics and biology of the ocean are explored together. We need more "Hudson-70" expeditions.

Villefranche-sur-Mer 2009

APPENDIX A

SHIPBOARD SCIENTIFIC PARTY
for
"HUDSON-70" EXPEDITION

Atlantic Oceanographic Laboratory,
Bedford Institute, Dartmouth, N.S., Canada.

Barrett, D.L.

Belanger, J.R.

Bruce, J.

Cameron, W.M.

Carson, B.O.

Coady, V.

Coote, A.R.

Corbett, T.J.

Corkum, P.L.

Courtney, T.F.

Duedall, I.W.

Druhan, D.

Eaton, R.M.

Foote, T.R.

Garner, D.M.

Gorveatt, M.

Grant, A.B.

Greifeneder, W.B.

Haworth, R.T.

Henderson, H.

Hiltz, R.S.

Hughes, M.

Johnston, B.L.

Keen, C.E.

Lewis, E.A.

Loncarevic, B.D.

Manchester, K.S.

Mann, C.R.

Maunsell, C.D.

McHughen, S.B.

Melanson, R.C.

Muise, F.

Murray, J.G.

Nielsen, J.A.

Pelletier, B.R.

Piechura, J.

Pilote, J.M.R.

Purdy, G.M.

Reiniger, R.F.

Ross, D.I.

Schafer, C.T.

Shearer, J.M.

Shih, K.G.

Solowen, P.A.

Srivastava, S.P.

Steele, J.P.

Taylor, B.

Thomlinson, A.

Tiffin, D.

Toom, H.

Vilks, G.

Wadhams, P.

Wagner, F.J.E.

Whiteway, W.J.

Winters, D.

Woodside, J.M.

Marine Ecology Laboratory, Bedford Institute, Dartmouth, N.S., Canada.

Beamish, P.C.

Conover, R.J.

Freeman, K.F.

Paranjape, M.A.

Prakash, A.

Sheldon, R.W.

Sutcliffe, W.H.

Canadian Wildlife Service, Bedford Institute, Dartmouth, N.S., Canada.

Brown, R.G.B.

Defence Research Establishment Atlantic, Dartmouth, N.S., Canada.

Bluy, O.

Gill, J.G.

MacPherson, H.A.

Institute of Oceanography, Dalhousie University, Halifax, N.S., Canada.

Atkinson, L.P.

Bhattacharyya, P.J.

Choi, C.I.

Cook, R.C.

Deevey, G.B.

Hyndman, R.

MacLean, A.

Michael, A.D.

Mills, E.L.

Rankin, D.

Sharpe, J.H.

Wangersky, P.J.

Watt, W.

Yoshinari, T.

Geological Survey of Canada, Ottawa, Ontario, Canada.

Bertrand, W.

Havard, C.

Parker, R.

Yorath, C.

National Museum of Natural Sciences, Ottawa, Ontario, Canada.

Bousfield, E.L.

National Research Council of Canada, Ottawa, Ontario, Canada.

Faber, D.J.

Markham, J.W.

Queen's University, Kingston, Ontario, Canada.
Cooke, F.
Smith, R.

Trent University, Peterborough, Ontario, Canada.
Edwards, R.L..

University of Toronto, Toronto, Ontario, Canada.
Beamish, R.J.
Zurbrigg, R.E

McGill University, Montreal, Quebec, Canada.
Lalli, C.M.

Institute of Oceanography, University of British Columbia, Vancouver, B.C., Canada.
Bary, B. Mck.
Chase, K.L.
Davidson, R.
English, D.
MacDonald, R.
Pickard, G.L.
Storm, M.P.

Highland Helicopter Ltd., Vancouver, B.C., Canada.
Pinner, W.
Strad, J.

Pacific Oceanographic Group, Nanaimo, B.C., Canada.
Belleguay, R.
Landry, L.P.
Wong, C.S.

Wood's Hole Oceanographic Institution, Wood's Hole, Massachusetts, U.S.A.
Brewer, P.G.
Dean, J.P.
Densmore, C.D.
Sachs, P.L.
Von Arx, W.

Peter Wadhams

University of Washington, Seattle, Wa., U.S.A.
Davis, E.
Lister, C.R.B.

Oregon State University, U.S.A.
Burt, W.V.
Pond, G.S.

Scripps Institution of Oceanography, La Jolla, California, U.S.A.
Hessler, R.R.

Hydrographic Department, Argentine Navy, Buenos Aires, Argentina.
Rebaudi, R.S.

University of Concepción, Chile.
Ahumada, R.
Chuecas, L.A.
Inostroza, H.M.
Rey, F.R.

Catholic University, Valparaiso, Chile.
Silva, N.

Hydrographic Institute, Valparaiso, Chile.
Montaner, R.E.
Uccelletti, B.D.

Hunting Surveys Ltd., UK.
Harding, A.

Affiliations not known.
Probert, P.
Rock, M.R.
Rogers, G

APPENDIX B

"HUDSON 70": A NOTE ON MARINE SCIENCE PAPERS AND TECHNICAL REPORTS PUBLISHED FOLLOWING THE COMPLETION OF THE EXPEDITION

by
CHARLES SCHAFER
(Bedford Institute of Oceanography)

THE YEARS FOLLOWING THE completion of the "Hudson-70" expedition witnessed the publication of scientific findings and preliminary results of a diverse suite of marine sciences investigations. These reports appeared in peer-reviewed journals, as technical papers in government publications, and as graduate student theses. They can be categorized generally as either baseline studies, specific (targeted) investigations or as methodological experiments and trials.

The baseline studies category is represented by the largest number of publications. It can be broken down further into oceanographic, biological and marine geological subcategories. The oceanographic subcategory includes papers that offer new information on subjects such as:-

- Dissolved oxygen distribution in Atlantic and Pacific Ocean water masses;
- The nature of ocean currents in the Drake Passage;
- The north to south distribution of silicate in water masses of the western Atlantic;
- The physical oceanographic features of Chilean inlets and fjords;
- The size distribution of particles in the ocean;
- The nature and distribution of particulate organic carbon in the Atlantic and Pacific oceans and;
- A comprehensive atlas of physical oceanographic data (temperature, salinity, oxygen, nutrients) for the South Atlantic, Drake Passage, the Pacific Ocean and the Canadian Arctic.

Biologically-focused baseline publications cover a wide range of topics ranging from organisms that spend their entire life in the ocean to sea birds that
make their living by harvesting food from the sea. Within this subcategory
can be found papers that:-

- Reveal the distributions of seabirds in Drake Passage and off the coast
  of Argentina;
- Document the distribution of South Atlantic pelagic ostracods between
  the equator and 55 degrees south latitude.

In addition, there are a respectable number of publications that are essentially
a mixture of biological and marine geological sciences. Many of these report
findings aimed at documenting the distribution and morphological characteristics of species whose skeletons are preserved in marine sediments where
they create a proxy record of water mass and environmental changes that are
driven by both natural climate variability and man-made activities. Scientific
outputs in this multidisciplinary subcategory include studies that have:-

- Established planktonic foraminifera – water mass relationships in
  equatorial and North Pacific waters;
- Determined relationships between living planktonic foraminifera
  species versus the distribution of their skeletal remains in the
  sediments of Canadian Arctic basins and:
- Documented morphological characteristics of Arctic planktonic
  foraminifera environmental indicator species using scanning electron
  microscope technology.

Marine geology baseline surveys carried out during various legs of the
expedition have yielded new information on:-

- The submarine geology of Baffin Bay, the N.W. Pacific Ocean and the
  Bering Sea.

Each of the broad categories of the "Hudson-70" baseline studies described
above is complemented by publications that speak to more narrowly-defined
scientific objectives. Publications of targeted scientific issues in the oceanographic field describe:-

- New information on the effect of air bubble solution on air sea gas exchange and:
- The definition of deep zonal water masses in the equatorial Pacific inferred from anomalous oceanographic properties.

Among the suite of relatively specific biological publications can be found:-

- Studies of the post-larva stage of certain stomatopod crustacean species and:
- The description of a new species of lantern fish from the South Atlantic that has been named Diaphus hudsoni.

Marine geology papers describing specific features and phenomena are represented in comparatively large numbers. Their subjects include:-

- The evaluation of a single geophysical profile recorded in the S.W Pacific;
- A study of the thermal balance of a mid-ocean ridge;
- Observations of the effects of seafloor ice scouring in the Beaufort Sea;
- A survey of submarine pingos (sediment mounds with an ice core) in the Beaufort Sea;
- New information from geophysical measurements made to the north of the Juan de Fuca Ridge;
- Gravity observations along the 150 west meridian (Pacific Ocean);
- A study of S.E Beaufort Sea mollusc assemblages and their potential as indicators of the area's late Pleistocene history and:
- Evaluations of gravity and magnetic data collected in the N.W. Pacific Ocean, the Bering Sea, Baffin Bay, and off British Columbia.

Methodological studies comprise another fundamental category of "Hudson-70" research activity. Although many of these have given rise to the publication of allied scientific and technical publications, they also denote a general and ongoing marine sciences mission aimed at adapting land-based laboratory techniques to a shipboard setting that facilitates the direct and rapid measurement of parameters of interest. Among the category of "Hudson-70" methodological reports are papers that describe:-

- Automated analysis at sea;
- Laboratory experiments on brood protection in an epipelagic pteropod and;
- The evaluation of a dispenser for Winkler's dissolved oxygen reagents.

Among the non-scientific publications that were produced following the expedition, there are at least two that were presented at various conferences and two others that were published in a science news magazine and as a Canadian government report. Last but not least, in 1973 a popularized version of the expedition appeared as a book entitled *Voyage to the Edge of the World*. It describes the day-to-day challenges and tribulations faced by scientists, technical staff and the ship's outstanding crew.

New publications that rely on "Hudson-70" data and archived samples can be expected from time to time for many years to come. We note that both the 'Challenger Reports' series based on scientific results from the HMS *Challenger* expedition of 1872-6, and the "Discovery Reports" series based on results from cruises of RRS *Discovery* in the Southern Ocean, mostly between the Wars, are still active and new papers are still occasionally added based on further analysis of results and biological samples. There is no "Hudson-70 Reports" series, but if interested readers would like to contact p.wadhams@damtp.cam.ac.uk they will be sent a complete list of publications so far arising from "Hudson-70" operations.

INDEX

B

E

H

I

M

T

U

V

W